Sturges W. Bailey

Page 58

MOUNT EVEREST, THE SUPREME CHALLENGE!

A Textbook of

Geomorphology

By

PHILIP G. WORCESTER

Professor of Geology, University of Colorado
Boulder, Colorado

NEW YORK
D. VAN NOSTRAND COMPANY, Inc.
250 FOURTH AVENUE
1939

PREFACE

The contents of this book represent the work covered by the author's classes at the University of Colorado which meet five times a week for eleven weeks. Although field and laboratory work are an important part of any course in geomorphology, laboratory exercises have not been included, for each instructor can best prepare the exercises that will be most valuable for his particular situation. At the University of Colorado each student spends seven three-hour periods in the field. This is supplemented with intensive study of topographic and structure maps.

The book has been planned for an introductory course in geomorphology and assumes little or no previous knowledge of geology on the part of the student. It may be used for more advanced students by making use of the references at the end of each chapter.

It is the author's firm belief that the cultural value of geomorphology has been underestimated by most people. While only an occasional student will ever become a professional physiographer, thousands may become interested in the subject and gain enduring pleasure from continued studies of their physical environment, wherever they may be. This is very much worthwhile!

Many friends and institutions have helped with the illustrations which are credited in appropriate places in the text. The McKinley Publishing Company furnished the necessary base maps; Doctors L. O. Quam, W. O. Thompson, W. C. Toepelman and Professor H. A. Hoffmeister have read and criticized various parts of the text. Particular thanks are due Mr. Julian W. Low, who made the sketches and diagrams, and Miss Geraldine Lee, who aided in countless ways in compiling the manuscript. To all who have helped in the preparation of the book, the author is extremely grateful.

P. G. W.

January, 1939

CONTENTS

CHAPTER   PAGE

I.   INTRODUCTION   1

II.   RELIEF OF THE EARTH   12

III.   RELATIONS OF EARTH AND SUN   35

IV.   MATERIALS OF THE LITHOSPHERE. ELEMENTS AND MINERALS   50

V.   MATERIALS OF THE LITHOSPHERE. ROCKS   62

VI.   EARTH MOVEMENTS AND STRUCTURES   89

VII.   PREPARING THE LAND FOR EROSION—ROCK WEATHERING .   119

VIII.   TOPOGRAPHY PRODUCED BY STREAMS OF HUMID REGIONS .   147

IX.   TOPOGRAPHY OF SEMI-ARID AND DESERT REGIONS   220

X.   GLACIERS AND GLACIAL TOPOGRAPHY   264

XI.   LAKES AND SWAMPS   335

XII.   SHORE FORMS AND SHORE PROCESSES OF SEAS AND LAKES .   372

XIII.   TOPOGRAPHY DUE TO GROUND-WATER   416

XIV.   VOLCANISM AND VOLCANOES   454

XV.   ISLANDS AND CORAL REEFS   479

XVI.   PLAINS, PLATEAUS AND MOUNTAINS   495

INDEX   555

To the Student who uses this Textbook:

This textbook represents many years of learning and experience on the part of the author. It does not treat of an ephemeral subject, but one which, since you are studying it in college, you must feel will have a use to you in your future life.

Unquestionably you will many times in later life wish to refer to specific details and facts about the subject which this book covers and which you may forget. How better could you find this information than in the textbook which you have studied from cover to cover?

Retain it for your reference library. You will use it many times in the future.

The Publishers.

CHAPTER I

INTRODUCTION

The earth is composed of three essential parts, (1) *the litho-sphere*, (2) *the hydrosphere*, and (3) *the atmosphere*. The lithosphere (lithos, a Greek word meaning rock) is the solid part of the earth, and is composed, in so far as our definite knowledge goes, of rocks and minerals. The hydrosphere is the liquid (excluding molten lava) part of the earth. It includes all the waters of the earth that are on or in the lithosphere. The atmosphere, or air sphere, is the gaseous, hollow sphere which surrounds and, to a slight extent, penetrates both the lithosphere and hydrosphere.

EARTH SCIENCES

The sciences which deal with the whole earth, or with one or more of its parts, are the earth sciences. With our expanding knowledge there has been a tendency to subdivide the three main parts of the earth into smaller and smaller units and to study them more intensively. Naturally, this has resulted in increasing the number of earth sciences over that of a few generations ago. The principal earth sciences, as generally accepted at the present time, are geology, geophysics, hydrology, meteorology, geography and physiography, or geomorphology.

Geology. — Geology really means the science of the earth; therefore, a complete study of geology must include the lithosphere, atmosphere and hydrosphere. However, the science, as now understood, has to do primarily with the origin, composition, structure and history of the lithosphere. The investigations of the hydrosphere and atmosphere are only incidental to a complete understanding of the solid part of the earth.

As our knowledge of geology has grown, we have been com-

1

pelled to subdivide the science. Among its important branches are *historical geology*, which deals with the complete history of the earth from its origin to the present; *dynamic geology*, which has to do with the geologic processes that are active on or in the lithosphere; *structural geology*, which is the study of the arrangement of the rocks of the earth; *economic geology*, the origin, occurrence and uses of geologic materials, such as petroleum, metals, clays, etc.; *petrology*, which is the complete study of the origin, occurrence and classification of rocks; *mineralogy*, the study of minerals; *engineering geology*, which deals with the relations of geology to engineering operations; *paleontology*, the science of ancient life as disclosed in the rocks of the earth.

Geophysics. — Some dictionaries define geophysics as *the science that deals with the external physical features of the earth, physiography or physical geography*. Modern practice gives quite a different interpretation to the subject. Not only are the *external* features studied, but much attention is given to the *internal* structure and composition of the earth. Following modern usage, geophysics may be defined as *the science that studies by physical methods the whole planet on which we live.* Like some of the other earth sciences, its limits are not clearly defined; it merges in one direction or another into physics, astronomy, geology, meteorology and hydrology. The systematic use of geophysical methods as an auxiliary to geological research is a relatively modern thing, but great strides are now being made in this field, and we may expect to learn much more about the interior of the earth as better methods of investigation are developed.

Hydrology. — The science of the waters of the earth is hydrology. In its broader aspects it has to do with oceans, lakes, streams and underground waters. Like geology, it is now subdivided into various branches, oceanography, etc., in order to recognize specialization in various parts of the field.

Meteorology. — Meteorology is the science of the atmosphere. Based on physical, chemical and mathematical laws, it seeks to explain the origin, physical condition, heating, cooling and movements of the air. All scientific discussions of weather and climate are based on our knowledge of the physics of the atmosphere.

Geography. — There are groups of geographers who differ greatly in their ideas concerning the subject matter of geography. Some people do not regard geography as an earth science, preferring to consider it a social science. However, nearly all will agree that geography seeks to determine the relations of the physical environment of plants and animals, including man, on the earth to their location, growth and, in the case of man, activities. Like geology, geography has been divided into various parts, such as *political geography*, *historical geography*, *economic geography* and *physical geography*. Some writers regard all these subjects as divisions of *human geography*.

Geomorphology and Physiography

The brief analysis that has just been made of the principal earth sciences should help us to determine the nature and scope of geomorphology or physiography. For a long time there was a tendency to regard physiography as a substitute word for physical geography and to divide the subject into the study of the earth as a globe, the atmosphere, the oceans and the lands. However, as the subjects have expanded, *mathematical geography* has been introduced to treat the earth as a globe. *Meteorology* and *climatology* cover the atmosphere, and *oceanography* describes the oceans. In recent years *physiography*, particularly in America, has come to be regarded as the science of land forms. This usage probably is unfortunate, for evidently the original meaning of the word has been restricted, but both the word physiography and the ideas that it conveys are firmly entrenched in American scientific literature.

Definitions. — In order to avoid a term that must be used in a restricted sense, many geologists and geographers prefer to set aside the word *physiography* and in its place use the more accurate word *geomorphology*, which, strictly defined, is *the science of the form of the earth*, but through common usage is defined as the *science of land forms*. Another somewhat broader definition, preferred by the author, is: *geomorphology is the interpretative description of the relief features of the earth.*

On account of the closely associated ideas represented by geomorphology and physiography these terms, as well as *geomorpholo-*

gist and *physiographer*, will be used interchangeably in the following pages.

Scope. — The scope and limits of the field of geomorphology are not sharply defined. On the one hand, it is closely related to dynamic geology, but this subject is primarily concerned with the structure and composition of earth materials, forces and processes; while geomorphology, although not neglecting these things, particularly emphasizes the *resulting land forms*. On the other hand, geomorphology is closely related to geography, but the geographer uses land forms in a more or less static sense. He is not primarily interested in the *origin* of plains, lakes, ocean basins, and countless other relief features, but takes them as they are and uses them as important features of man's physical environment. This overlapping of various fields is one reason why geomorphology is such an interesting subject. It enters into our daily lives in countless ways. Most students of the subject never become professional geomorphologists; but whether they do or not, it is hoped that the study of this subject will lead to straight thinking and to more interest in and enjoyment of one of the most important factors in our natural environment.

As we shall see continually while studying the subject, geomorphology draws freely on the great earth sciences, geology, hydrology and meteorology. The land surface is, of course, the meeting zone of the lithosphere, the hydrosphere and the atmosphere. Both the air and water react in many ways on the solid part of the earth to change the shape of the land. Examples of these reactions are running water, which carves great canyons or deposits deltas; sea waves caused by wind which wear away shorelines; glaciers which scrape the floor and sides of the valleys in which they move!

Geomorphic Processes. — As we study the surface of the land, we see evidence of two distinct kinds of processes or activities that have in the past changed, or are now changing, the surface of the earth. They are (a) internal processes and (b) external processes. These activities and especially the *results* of these activities constitute the chief subject matter of geomorphology.

Internal Processes. — Many of the most important changes that have taken place in the surface of the earth are due to activities that originate within the earth itself. These may be called internal processes. They are such phenomena as (1) *diastrophism,* which includes the growth of mountains, the rise or subsidence of shore-lines, movements upward or downward of continents, in fact, all

FIG. 1. — A section through the earth at the 40th parallel north latitude showing lithosphere, hydrosphere and atmosphere. The seas are shown in solid black. Vertical scale greatly exaggerated.

the movements of the earth; (2) *vulcanism,* which includes all phenomena connected with the movement of heated material either to or toward the surface of the lithosphere.

External Processes. — Every agency or activity of any sort which operates directly on the surface of the earth may be included in the external processes. Examples are (1) *running water*, (2) *wind*, (3) *chemicals in the air* which decompose rocks, (4) *waves and shore currents*, (5) *glaciers*, (6) *avalanches*, (7) *plants*, and

D. F. Higgins.

FIG. 2. — Man-made terraces in the middle ground, terraces made by nature back of them, China.

E. G. Fine.

FIG. 3. — Mine dumps, man-made hills and ridges, Victor, Colo.

(8) *animals, including man.* Ever since man has inhabited the earth, but especially in modern times, he has profoundly altered the surface of the land. He develops mines and leaves great piles

of waste rock on the land surface; he builds great dams and creates lakes, such as *Lake Mead* which is more than 100 miles long, where formerly there were only valleys or canyons. In numerous other ways which the reader will readily recall, he changes the surface of the lithosphere.

The Earth Is Not Static. — Many people used to believe, and a few still believe, that the earth is in a static condition, and that everything connected with it is just as it always has been since the

U. S. War Department.

Fig. 4. — Fort Peck Dam, Montana. When completed the dam, the largest earth dam on earth, will be 242 feet high and 9,000 feet long between the bluffs, and will contain 105,000,000 cubic yards of earth, gravel and stone. It will create a lake more than 180 miles long with a shoreline of 1,600 miles.

beginning. Nothing could be farther from the truth! The earth is constantly changing; while this sentence is being read, some change has occurred on the land surface. Through a detailed study of present earth processes, we are able to understand better the past history of the earth. In other words, *we interpret the past through a study of the present conditions of the earth.*

Most Changes Take Place Slowly. — Even as recently as one hundred years ago, as a result of their observations in regions where great volcanoes or earthquakes occur, some people believed that most activities of the earth occurred suddenly and with great violence. This idea is called *the doctrine of catastrophe.* We now

know that although there are some catastrophes, _most earth processes act very slowly._ The development of the present Rocky

D. F. Higgins.

FIG. 5. — A valley worn out of a plain by the feet of unnumbered animals and people, China.

W. O. Thompson.

FIG. 6. — The work of ceaseless waves, near Laguna Beach, California.

Mountains has taken sixty or more million years. The Colorado River has been engaged for millions of years in cutting the Grand Canyon, and its work is not yet completed. Volcanoes have built their cones higher and higher through countless centuries. Waves have beaten upon shorelines for unnumbered ages.

It is suggested that the readers of this volume will find it interesting and profitable to try to evaluate the length of *geologic time* through the study of the processes outlined in the following pages.

THE AGE OF THE EARTH

It is beyond the province of this book to discuss in detail the age of the earth. However, in order to get a perspective that will help us to evaluate the time necessary to develop the land forms with which we are familiar, it is desirable to inquire into the entire age of the earth. Students of ancient life (paleontologists) who through *the study of fossils* have traced the development of plant and animal life from the most ancient very simple forms to the present types insist that the earth must be very old. Stratigraphers have determined with considerable exactness the thickness of sediments (shales, sandstones, limestones, coal, etc.) that have been deposited during certain geologic periods. By multiplying the estimated time required to deposit one foot of sediment by the total thickness of the sediments that have been deposited during these ages, they arrive at an estimate of the time required to complete this sedimentary record.

The most accurate and complete method so far known for determining the *minimum* age of the earth is through the study of radioactive minerals. The methods are based on the fact that certain radioactive elements, such as uranium, radium and thorium, disintegrate at a rate which is constant and determinable. Knowing, as physicists do, this rate of disintegration, it is possible to determine the ages of rocks which contain these partially disintegrated elements. Considering the sedimentary and radioactivity data together, Schuchert[1] finds close agreement in the indicated lengths of the last three geologic eras. The sedimentary records of the Proterozoic and Archeozoic eras are not well known and cannot be used; hence, we have at present only the incomplete

---

[1] Chas. Schuchert, *Physics of the Earth*, Vol. IV, *The Age of the Earth*, p. 53. Published by the National Research Council.

radioactive data for determining the time represented by these very ancient eras.

For convenience all geologic time is divided into eras, periods, epochs and ages. Only the periods of the three younger eras are shown in the following table; those of the Proterozoic and Archeo-

GEOLOGIC TIME TABLE

(Based on the radioactivity record)

Eras	Minimum Length of each Era	Periods
Cenozoic (Recent life)	55,000,000 years	Quaternary Tertiary
Mesozoic (Middle life)	135,000,000 years	Cretaceous Jurassic Triassic
Paleozoic (Early life)	360,000,000 years	Permian Pennsylvanian Mississippian Devonian Silurian Ordovician Cambrian
Proterozoic (Very old life)	550,000,000 years	
Archeozoic (Oldest life)	Unknown, but at least one billion years	

zoic eras have not yet been recognized on a world-wide basis. Throughout this text repeated references will be made to these divisions of geologic time; therefore, they should be learned at the outset.

REFERENCES

Note: The references at the end of each chapter represent easily available authoritative books and articles that supplement the text. No attempt has been made to give complete bibliographies.

1. Adolph Knopf, E. W. Brown, Arthur Holmes, A. F. Kovarik, A. C. Lane,

Charles Schuchert: *Physics of the Earth,* Vol. IV, *Age of the Earth.* National Research Council, 1931.

2. W. J. Miller: *Introduction to Historical Geology.* D. Van Nostrand Co., 1937.

3. Raymond C. Moore: *Historical Geology.* McGraw-Hill Book Co., 1933.

4. Charles Schuchert and Carl O. Dunbar: *Outline of Historical Geology.* John Wiley and Sons, 1937.

CHAPTER II

RELIEF OF THE EARTH

In order to use a shorter word in this and later chapters, the *earth* will be used interchangeably with the *lithosphere* to designate *the solid part of the earth*. This usage is not strictly correct, but custom permits it.

As we have already learned, geomorphology has to do with the origin, description and classification of the relief features of the earth. It is appropriate now to classify and to describe briefly the more important relief features.

Shape of the Lithosphere

The lithosphere and oceans together form an imperfect sphere or geoid slightly flattened near the poles and slightly bulged at the equator. The equatorial diameter of this geoid is 7,926.6 miles, while the polar diameter is about 27 miles less; its circumference is about 25,000 miles, and its volume is about 260,000,000 cubic miles.

Every observing person knows that the surface of the earth is not smooth like that of an ordinary class room globe. On the contrary, locally, as at the base of a high range of mountains or on the rim of a deep canyon, the irregularities of the land surface may seem to be extremely great. However, if we could look at the earth from some great distance, say from the surface of the moon, the irregularities of the whole surface would seem small when compared with the great size of the earth. Clearly then the matter of perspective is important in any consideration of the relief of the earth.

12

CLASSIFICATION OF RELIEF FEATURES

In order to get a correct idea of the surface of the lithosphere, we should try to imagine it with all the water, snow and ice re-

U. S. Geol. Survey.

FIG. 7. — Relief map of the United States.

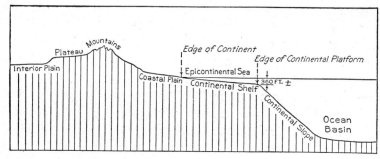

FIG. 8. — Diagram showing parts of a continental platform, ocean basin and related relief features. The depth of water at the outer edge of the continental shelf varies widely, but according to Shepard 360 feet is an approximate figure.

moved. Also, for convenience, let us remove all vegetation. Then, disregarding thin coverings here and there of rock fragments and soil, the bare face of the lithosphere would be exposed to view.

With the lithosphere in this condition, its relief features may be divided into three great groups or orders. They are first order features, *continental platforms* and *ocean basins*; second order features, *mountains, plateaus* and *plains*; third order features, *hills, valleys, buttes, mesas*, etc.,—in short, all the relatively minor topographic forms that occur on the second order features.

R. L. Ives, Courtesy Am. Phil. Society.

FIG. 9.—Part of Middle Park, Colorado. Never Summer Range in the extreme left background, Front Range on the right. Second and third order relief features.

RELIEF OF THE FIRST ORDER

The total area of the surface of the land and water of the earth is about 197,000,000 square miles. The universal ocean, which for convenience is divided into the Atlantic, Pacific, Indian and Arctic oceans, covers some 141,000,000 square miles of the lithosphere. There is so much water in the present oceans that they not only fill their basins, but overflow onto the continental platforms, covering an area of about 10,000,000 square miles.

Ocean Basins. — These are the depressed parts of the surface of the lithosphere. They lie between the much smaller continental platforms and have a total area of about 131,000,000 square miles. Thus, they are about 10,000,000 square miles smaller than the surface of the present oceans.

Depth. — The average depth of the floor of the ocean basins is about 2.5 miles below sea level. However, the ocean floor is very uneven in its surface topography. There are many great irregular depressions known as "deeps" or "troughs," whose depths are far below the average for all the ocean basins. In contrast with these enormous deeps, there are other parts of the ocean floor which rise either gradually or abruptly to, or nearly to, sea level. Careful study of a large-scale, physical map of the oceans will help one to appreciate just how irregular the surface of the ocean floor really is. Due to the tremendous area of the oceans and to the expense of conducting surveys, our knowledge of the relief of the ocean basins is very incomplete; however, with modern methods of depth soundings, we may expect to learn much more about it as time goes on.

Ocean Troughs. — A few of the many ocean troughs (really depressions in the ocean floor, see Fig. 1) are here listed, together with the greatest known depth of each:

	Ocean Troughs (Deeps)	Depth in feet below mean sea level
Philippine Trough	Pacific Ocean	35,432
Guam Trough	Pacific Ocean	31,614
Samoan Trough	Pacific Ocean	30,928
Japanese Trough	Pacific Ocean	27,934
Aleutian Trough	Pacific Ocean	24,228
Porto Rican Trough	Atlantic Ocean	27,972
Javan Trough	Indian Ocean	23,294

Continental Platforms. — The continental platforms of North and South America, Eurasia, Africa, Australia and Antarctica are *the great elevated portions of the surface of the lithosphere.* The area of the continental platforms is about 66,000,000 square miles. However, as has just been stated, the ocean has overflowed its basins and has covered the lower margins of the continental platforms. The area so covered amounts to about 10,000,000 square miles. This represents the difference in the area of the continental platforms, 66,000,000 square miles, and that of the continents, 56,000,000 square miles.

The *continental shelves* are portions of the continental platforms that lie beneath the ocean. They extend out from the continents varying distances, depending upon their slope, until their general surfaces are about 360 feet below sea level. On glaciated shelves the depth of water may be more than 600 feet. From the outer limit of the continental shelves, in most places, the descent to the deep ocean basins is relatively rapid.

The slopes connecting the continental platforms and ocean basins, either steep or gradual, are called the *continental slopes*. Off the coasts of Yucatan, Newfoundland and much of Eastern United States, these slopes are relatively gentle, while off the coasts of Peru, California and Japan, they are much steeper.

Continents. — From what has been said in the preceding paragraphs, it is evident that the *continents are the parts of the continental platforms* that stand above the oceans. If this definition is adopted in a strict sense, many islands, such as those on the north side of North America and even the British Isles, belong definitely to the continents with which they are associated, for they are parts of the respective continental platforms. However, many other islands, such as the Hawaiian Islands, rise abruptly from the ocean floor; while others, for example, the Azores, represent high points on great plateaus that stand high above the surrounding ocean floors but well below the surface of the ocean.

The surfaces of the continents will be discussed in detail later. Here we pause only to note that they are very irregular, probably even more so than are those of the ocean basins. Diastrophism, vulcanism and, particularly, erosion have in the past changed and are now constantly changing the form of the land. The highest known point on any continent is Mount Everest (elevation 29,002 feet) in the Himalaya Mountains. The lowest place is the floor of the Dead Sea, in Palestine, about 2,500 feet below sea level.

If all the mountains and plains of the continents were smoothed down and the material spread over the plains, the average height of the continents would be about 2,500 feet above sea level. Thus, we see, referring to a preceding paragraph, that on the average the continents stand some three miles above the ocean basins. Carrying our smoothing processes still farther, if all the material of the continental platforms were scraped down and spread over the ocean basins, thus making a perfectly smooth surface of the lithosphere, the oceans would stand more than two miles deep over the whole lithosphere.

Continental Shelves. — These are extremely interesting and important parts of the continental platforms. Their varying widths have already been suggested. On their shallower parts, waves, tides, and shore currents are constantly distributing silt, sand and other rock fragments that have been broken by waves from the shore lines or carried to the seas by streams from the land. In general, these processes tend to make the surfaces of the shelves rather uniform, although, locally, deposits of sand and silt make an irregular topography. Some parts of the shelves are great plains extending far out beneath the oceans. However, *the surface topography of the continental shelves is much more irregular than was once supposed.* Shepard and others have shown that there are canyons 2,500 to 4,000 feet in depth on the continental shelf off the coast of New England. World-wide surveys indicate canyons of similar size on nearly all continental shelves and on many continental slopes. On continental shelves in low latitudes corals build fringing and barrier reefs, thus increasing the irregularities of their surfaces.

The Origin of First Order Relief Features

The question of how continental platforms and ocean basins were formed cannot yet be answered. The problem is closely related to that of the origin of the earth. It involves theoretical geology, astronomy, physics and mathematics beyond the scope of this book. Although detailed discussions of the various theories of earth origin are out of order in this book, brief statements will be made to suggest some of the possibilities.

Planetesimal Hypothesis. — According to this hypothesis, which was developed by T. C. Chamberlin and F. R. Moulton, the earth, the other planets, satellites and asteroids of our solar system all came originally from the sun. The earth in an early formative stage was very much smaller than it is now. It grew to a larger and larger size through the incoming to the earth nucleus of billions of tiny solid particles of cooled sun material called _planetesimals_.

When the earth had reached about the size of the planet Mars, it had primitive continental platforms and ocean basins. These initial relief features are believed to have been formed largely through the irregular distribution of the planetesimals incorporated in the growing earth. The hypothesis further holds that the earth, when as large as Mars, may have had an initial hydrosphere and atmosphere. Continuing from this stage, as the earth grew to its present size, the air and ocean water were factors in distributing the incoming planetesimals, so that both continental platforms and ocean basins were perpetuated. The earth finally became considerably larger in volume (not mass) than it is now. At the maximum, its diameter is believed to have been more than 9,000 miles. Since reaching this size it has been shrinking, due to physical and chemical readjustments of its highly heated and compressed internal materials.

The planetesimal hypothesis holds that ever since the formative stages of the earth, _the continental platforms and ocean basins have been essentially in their present positions_. Fluctuations of the borders doubtless have occurred, and geologic evidence also shows clearly that upward and downward movements of the continents have occurred many times. Wrinkling of portions of both continents and ocean floors by mountain-producing forces have taken place repeatedly during earth history, but these movements do not violate the general principle of the permanency of these major relief features of the first order.

Liquid Earth Theories. — Without going into details, it may be said that several theories of earth origin hold that at some time in its formative stage, the earth was in a liquid condition. This liquid earth was very hot and of greater volume than that of the present lithosphere. As it slowly cooled, an outer "crust" was formed. Due to cooling and consolidation of internal material the earth began to shrink. The cool outer crust thus was forced to adapt itself to a shrinking interior. Because of inequalities in the composition of the earth, some parts would shrink more than others, thus leaving elevated portions of the crust as continental platforms and depressed portions as ocean basins. The adjustments may have been brought about through folding (warping) downward of the crust or through faulting (breaking apart and slipping) of the crust. In either case, sharp folds or faults (see Chapter VI) would probably occur on what are now the continental slopes.

Continental Drift. — A relatively new hypothesis of the origin of *present* continental platforms and ocean basins is based on the supposition that the continents may move laterally from one place to another.

It is an observed fact that the rocks of the continents are somewhat less dense than are those which underlie the ocean basins. The theory assumes (1) that at one time this lighter rock of the continents made a thin but complete crust over the whole earth; later, the crust was broken, and, in some unexplained way, the fragments were "rafted together" to make one universal continent which existed from an undated early stage in earth history until comparatively recent times (Fig. 10). Finally, this universal continent which by some people is supposed to have centered around Africa was broken up, and large fragments drifted in different directions to make the continental platforms as we know them today.

There are perplexing problems of geology, paleontology and climatology that yield rather readily to the hypothesis of continental drift. However, the hypothesis violates many geologic principles that have been established during the past century. No adequate forces are known which could either raft together the original light earth's crust, or, more especially, which could break apart a universal continent and move its constituent parts to their present positions. The hypothesis has been widely adopted by European scientists, but so far has found little favor among American geologists.

Continental Foundering. — Many geologists, from time to time, have argued that at one time a large land area connected South America with Africa and extended on east to India and Australia. Another land area is supposed to have connected northeastern North America and northern Europe. These lands are supposed to have foundered, so that they now constitute important parts of the floors of the North and South Atlantic and Indian

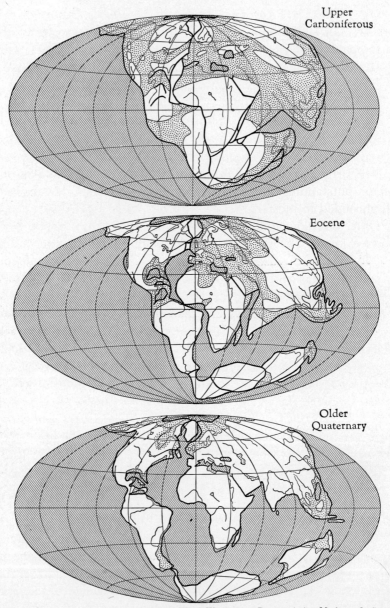

Upper
Carboniferous

Eocene

Older
Quaternary

(After Alfred Wegener). *By permission Methuen & Co., Ltd.*

FIG. 10. — The map of the world, according to the theory of continental drift, for the three periods indicated.

oceans. There are certain geologic data which support this hypothesis, but so far no one has satisfactorily explained the forces which could cause the foundering of such large land masses. Both this and the continental drift hypothesis are directly opposed to the doctrine of permanence of continental platforms and ocean basins.

Conclusions. — It should be emphasized, at this point, that the hypotheses just outlined are not products of wild imagination, but rather are the sober conclusions of eminent scientists who have studied the problems from many angles.

The origin of continental platforms and ocean basins is a question of outstanding interest to the physiographer. Its answer is still shrouded in mystery.

Other questions of similar importance are: (1) Why are North America, South America and Africa roughly triangular in outline? (2) What is the reason for the antipodal arrangement of continental platforms and ocean basins? (3) Why are the continents so largely grouped around the Arctic Ocean, while the oceans are so much greater in the southern than in the northern hemisphere?

These questions are not raised to confuse the reader, but rather to suggest certain interesting unsolved problems that await further investigation. In considering these questions the reader should not draw the conclusion that *all* geomorphic problems are *unsolved*. As a matter of fact, *the origin of second and third order relief features which are described in later chapters are much better understood.* There are many other problems connected with the condition of the earth's interior, its composition and movements which with our present knowledge defy solution. These will be referred to in their appropriate places.

RELIEF OF THE SECOND ORDER

Both continental platforms and ocean basins may be divided into second order relief features, which are *mountains, plateaus and plains*. The plains of the ocean basins, doubtless, are larger than are those of the continents, although our knowledge of the ocean basins is still too incomplete to allow definite statements. It is probable also that greater and more numerous plateaus occur there than on the continents.

The presence of submerged mountains on the floors of the ocean basins has been determined by soundings.   In addition, many mountains whose bases are on the ocean floor rise to or even high above sea level. Mauna Loa, an Hawaiian volcano (elevation 13,675 feet *above* sea level) stands on the ocean floor, which is 16,000 feet *below* sea level. Therefore, Mauna Loa is actually about 700 feet higher than Mount Everest when the former is measured from its sea-floor base and the latter from sea level.

It is interesting to note here certain similarities of location of mountains, plateaus and plains on the different continents. In general, most mountains occur near continental borders. Plateaus, as a rule, are situated on the flanks of or between great mountain ranges. Great plains occur in the *interior* of several of the continents as well as near many coasts.

Mountains. — *A mountain is a conspicuous highland with small summit area.* The question at once will be asked, "What is the difference between a hill and a mountain?" Perhaps no better answer can be given than that of Mill, who used the following quotation: "a mountain is an elevation higher than a hill," while " a hill is an elevation lower than a mountain." In other words, the terms, like so many others used in physiography, are entirely relative. We shall see, as we continue this study, that many physiographic subjects and definitions cannot be confined in water-tight compartments. Overlapping of ideas or lack of sharp distinctions are sometimes necessary because of the nature of the subject.

Mountains are classified according to their geographic arrangement in cordillera, systems, ranges, chains, groups, or as isolated individual units.

Cordillera. — A *cordillera* is a general highland region composed of several mountain systems which may differ greatly in origin and age. The cordillera of northwestern United States and British Columbia is a good illustration of this type.

System. — A mountain system consists of many ranges and groups, all somewhat related with respect to age and mode of origin. The Appalachian system of eastern United States is a good example.

Range. — A range consists of mountains arranged in a long

narrow belt. Such mountains are closely associated in age and origin. The Wasatch Range of Utah is an example. Although great differences in the composition of the rocks and local differences in the structure may be found, the whole range has had essentially the same physiographic history.

Group. — In many places one may find highlands composed of a large number of mountains without definite arrangement. The

Courtesy French Government Tourist Bureau.
FIG. 11. — Mountains in the French Alps.

term *mountain group* applies well to such regions. A good example is the San Juan Mountain group of southwestern Colorado. Here is a region several thousand square miles in area which contains hundreds of high mountains lacking definite arrangement. Long ago the region was uplifted into a broad, high dome; then the dome was covered by extrusive volcanic rocks to a depth of several thousand feet; finally, streams and glaciers cut deeply into the highland, leaving a great, very irregularly distributed group of mountains.

Chain. — Where mountains more or less independent in age and

origin occur in a relatively long narrow band, they may be called a
mountain chain. The term applies with particular emphasis to a
series of volcanoes, such as those of the Hawaiian, Aleutian or
Japanese islands.

Individual Mountains. — In rather exceptional cases, single isolated mountains may be found. Usually they are the result either
of extensive erosion of a region or of volcanic activity.

Summary. — Discussion of the origin of mountains is deferred
to later chapters. It is worthwhile noting here, however, that
mountains are among the most interesting of all great relief features. Through their detailed study one can learn much about the
results of great earth movements, vulcanism, and many types of
erosion. In some respects mountains are like people. There may
be one hundred people in a class room, yet no two are exactly alike.
So it is with mountains! Differences in rock composition, in arrangement of the rocks, in the forces that have sculptured them —
all give different results!

Plateaus.—*Plateaus are highlands with broad, flattish surfaces,
or summits.* In many places there is an abrupt change in altitude
from the surface of the plateau to that of the adjacent mountains
or plains.

In attempting to define plateaus, we again have trouble, unless
we agree *that the term highland is to be used only in a relative
sense!* For example, the Allegheny Plateau, which lies on the west
flank of the Appalachian Mountains, has a surface elevation (near
the mountains) of about 1,500 feet above sea level; while parts of
the Great Plains, which lie on the east side of the Rocky Mountains,
rise to heights of 6,000 feet above the sea. That plateaus may be
even higher than mountains is illustrated by the fact that the highest mountain in the United States, Mount Whitney, is 14,501 feet
high, while much of the Plateau of Tibet in central Asia is more
than 15,000 feet high.

Most plateaus are situated on the flanks of or between mountain ranges, and are definitely related to such ranges in their origin.
Both represent regions that have been greatly uplifted by earth
movements. Usually these forces reached their greatest intensity
in the formation of the mountains.

Some plateaus are unrelated to mountains, having been formed through the piling up of thick sheets of lava, one layer over another, until the height of the lava is greater than that of the surrounding country. The Columbia Plateau of Idaho, Washington, Oregon and British Columbia is an excellent example of this type.

Plateaus, as well as mountains, may be found in all stages of dissection by streams and other erosive agents. If little dissected, their

Richard Ragle.

FIG. 12. — Eroded plains near Manhattan, Kansas. Note the terraces due to resistant layers of sedimentary rocks.

broad flattish surfaces are like plains in surface topography. If greatly dissected, the characteristic plateau surfaces may have been largely removed, leaving narrow ridges, deep canyons, or even mountains and valleys in their place.

Plains. — *Plains are the relatively low lands of the earth.* Their surfaces have low relief. That is to say, their surface irregularities are comparatively small. Since plains are lowlands, they are likely to occur on continental borders only slightly above sea level, where they are called *coastal plains*. If they are situated in

the interior of a continent, naturally they are called *interior plains*.
If parts of continents have been raised by widespread earth movements without much wrinkling or breaking of the rocks, so that the
surface of the land still maintains its low relief, the resulting plains
may be designated as *high plains*. The high plains of Colorado,
Wyoming and New Mexico attain a greater altitude than do most
of the mountains of New England; yet these plains are relatively
low, when compared with the heights of the adjacent Rocky
Mountains.

Practically all the large cities of the world are situated on plains.
The great majority of the people of the earth live on plains. In

R. L. Heaton.

FIG. 13.— Roan Cliffs carved out of a plateau, sandstone above, shale below, western
Colorado.

view of these facts, it is evident that plains are one of the most important factors in man's physical environment. This being true,
the reader will follow with particular interest the discussions in
later chapters which deal with the origin of plains of different types
and with the forces that are now changing them.

RELIEF FEATURES OF THE THIRD ORDER

*Minor irregularities of the land surface, many of which are
common to both mountains, plateaus and plains, constitute the relief of the third order.* Thus, hills, ridges, buttes, ravines, valleys,

lake basins, and a host of other subordinate topographic forms may be found in regions of plains or plateaus or mountains. Some features of this order, such as very deep canyons or very high ridges, may be found only in mountainous or plateau areas. Other features, such as sea caves, stacks and wave-cut terraces, are characteristic only of present or past shore-lines. In general, because physiographic processes on land and beneath the oceans are different, most of the third order relief features of the continental platforms are believed *not* to exist in the ocean basins.

FIG. 14.—Burns Monument, Barre, Vermont.

These minor irregularities of land surfaces add detail to the more general views of mountains, plateaus and plains. Just as a sculptor, starting with a rough block of granite or marble, slowly and patiently carves a beautiful statue, so also does *nature,* with infinite patience and care, carve a magnificent landscape on the surface of what was originally a huge formless block of lithosphere.

METHODS OF SHOWING RELIEF

Many methods have been devised to show relief. Models, photographs, sketches, diagrams, physical maps in colors, topographic (contour) maps and combinations of these are now in common use, and all show relief with varying degrees of success.

Relief Models. — Perhaps the most satisfactory way to show the relief of small areas is through the use of models. These may be seen in many National Park and geologic museums. When properly constructed, based on accurate surveys with adequate attention given to horizontal and vertical scales, models are very useful in showing the salient features of any landscape. They are, however, bulky and expensive to make. Unless the models are very large, it is difficult and often impossible to show minor but important relief features.

Photographs. — Good photographs always will be used to show relief. However, unless supplemented with data based on accurate surveys which give distances and elevations, they can be used only for general purposes. Modern photography, however, has made great strides, and airplane photographs are extensively used in the preparation of topographic maps. Through their use

Model by J. W. Low.

FIG. 15. — A relief model of part of the Front Range, Colorado, from the eastern foot-hills to the Continental Divide. Longs Peak on the extreme right.

many land surfaces can be mapped with less expense and greater accuracy than by older surface methods.

Diagrams and Sketches. — These are used principally for two purposes. They may show the bold general outlines of relief, as in Fig. 16; or they may be used to illustrate details not easily shown by any other method (Fig. 8). They are an important part of every physiographer's equipment.

Colored or Shaded Wall Maps. — These are most useful to show the broad relief features of large areas. Physical maps of continents, the oceans and the world are now prepared by many map companies. In the preparation of such maps, great care should be taken to choose the proper projection, scale and combinations of colors or shades, in order that the proper shape of the various continents and their relief may be shown with greatest possible accuracy.

Projection. — Since the earth's surface is curved, it is evident that it can be correctly represented only by use of a globe. But maps are much more convenient for most purposes; therefore, many ingenious methods have been devised to project the *curved* surface of the earth on the flat *plane* of a map. This cannot be done without distortion of size or area, although for small areas it is not appreciable. For all large areas *projection* becomes a matter of great importance.

Several well-known projections are used for maps of the whole world. The *Mercator* projection, first published in 1569, is a rectangular projection still widely used. It is particularly useful in

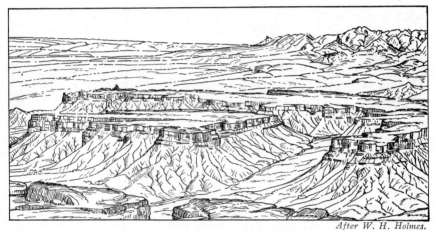

After W. H. Holmes.

Fig. 16. — A copy of part of Holmes's sketch of Mesa Verde, Colo. The sketch brings out clearly the relations of the rocks to the topographic development of the region.

navigation, but inasmuch as areas are correctly shown only at the equator with constantly increasing exaggeration in size with distance away from the equator, it gives a wholly incorrect idea of relative sizes of different parts of the earth. For example, on this map Greenland appears to be as large as South America, yet actually it is only about one-eighth as large. The much-used oval projections of Mollweide and Aitoff show both areas and shapes with considerable fidelity near the centers of the maps, but shapes are distorted toward the margins. Other projections sacrifice continuity for greater accuracy in size and shape.

The mapping of a single continent is much simpler than that of the whole world. Alber's equal-area projection, Bonne's modified conical projection and Lambert's equal-area projection are much used with only moderate distortion.

For still smaller areas a polyconic projection generally is used. This is the standard projection for the United States Geological Survey topographic maps. The central meridian is a straight line; all others are curved and converge to the north in the northern and to the south in the southern hemisphere. The parallels are arcs of circles. While distortion exists, it is comparatively slight.

Topographic (Contour) Maps. — These maps, which are published by the United States Geological Survey and by similar organizations in other countries, are prepared according to definite specifications. They show, through appropriate conventions, relief, all water features and the works of man.

Scale. — The scale of a map indicates the size of the map in comparison with the size of the area which it represents. If the scale of a map is one inch to the mile, it means that two points exactly one inch apart on the map are exactly one mile apart on the land surface. Scales usually are indicated by bars showing miles and kilometers and also by some fraction, such as 1/62,500 or 1/125,000. The former fraction means that one unit of distance on the map represents 62,500 of the same units on the land surface. A scale 1/63,360 is exactly 1 inch to the mile.

The map maker chooses his scale with reference to the detail that will be shown on the finished map. An engineer may need a scale of one inch to ten feet if he wishes to show many details of topography or culture. Reconnaissance maps intended to show only the outstanding facts of relief and drainage may be prepared with a scale of only one inch to five miles. The scales most commonly used on standard United States Geological Survey maps are 1/62,500 and 1/125,000.

Contour Lines. — Elevations and shapes of land forms are shown by contour lines. These lines (in *brown* color on standard maps) are drawn through points of equal elevation. Therefore, a single contour line connects points of the same altitude. All elevations, unless otherwise stated, are based on mean sea level,

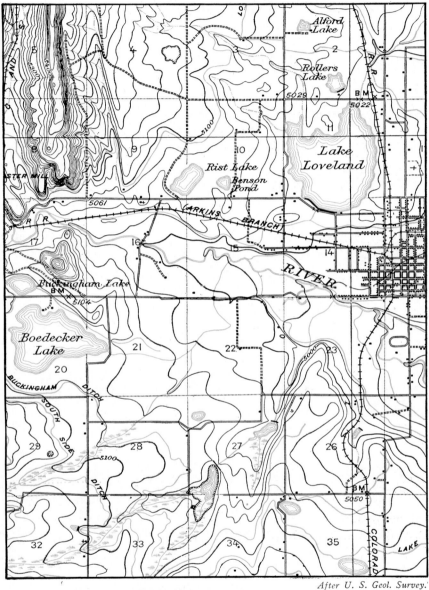

Fig. 17. — A portion of the Loveland, Colorado, topographic map. Scale 1/62,500, contour interval 20 feet. Note the great variety of relief, drainage and cultural (man-made) features shown on the map. Special note: On this and all other sections of topographic maps reproduced in this book the contour lines are shown in black color instead of the conventional brown.

and are determined for any map area by measuring the altitude of
the land from the sea to that locality through precise surveys.

The *vertical* distance between two successive contour lines is the
contour interval. It is always stated on the map. If the relief of
the land is low, as, for instance, on the plains of eastern Kansas,

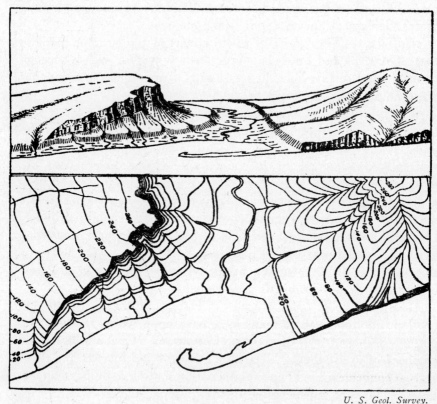

U. S. Geol. Survey.

Fig. 18. — A conventional diagram to show the relations of a topographic map and the
land surface that it represents.

the map maker will choose a small contour interval, ten or twenty
feet. If the relief is high, as in the Rocky Mountains, the interval
used may be fifty or a hundred feet, or even more. Also, the contour interval is chosen with reference to the scale of the map. If
the scale is large, the contour interval may be small, thus permitting
greater details of relief to be shown. The spacing of contour lines

indicates the slope. If the lines are far apart, the slope is gentle; if close together, the slope is steep. Contour lines which run together indicate vertical cliffs.

Water Features. — All features connected with water, snow and ice are shown in blue color. Special symbols are used to indicate such features as salt water, marshes, intermittent streams, etc., etc. All conventions are indicated on the backs of standard United States Geological Survey topographic maps.

Culture. — The works of man appear on topographic maps in black color. Land lines that have been surveyed, such as range, township and section lines, houses, roads, dams, mines and quarries are examples of these features.

Orientation. — Standard maps are so arranged that the top of the map is north; therefore, the right side is toward the east as one looks at the face of the map. Latitude and longitude are shown with proper correction for the convergence of meridians. Also, the magnetic declination is indicated. The earth's magnetic and geographic poles do not coincide; moreover, the intensity of the earth's magnetic field varies from time to time and from place to place. Hence, the north-pointing end of a compass needle, at most places, does not point toward the geographic north pole. Knowledge of the variation of the compass needle in any region is of practical importance to all who use this instrument.

Use of Topographic Maps. — Geologists, almost without exception, use topographic maps as a base upon which to show the outlines and structures of geologic formations. Civil and hydraulic engineers also use them. Mountain climbers and tourists find them a great convenience. They are necessities in modern military operations. They are indispensable to the physiographer. When properly interpreted, the reader not only learns the nature of the topography, but in many cases is able to state with confidence its origin. Streams, wind, glaciers and ground-water — all leave unmistakable evidence of their work on the relief of the land. In many cases even the composition and structures of the underlying rocks are indicated by the topography. Everything considered, *no other method of showing relief is so valuable to the physiographer!*

REFERENCES

1. T. C. Chamberlin: *The Origin of the Earth*. Univ. Chicago Press, 1916.
2. ——: *The Two Solar Families*. Univ. Chicago Press, 1928.
3. —— and R. D. Salisbury: *Geology*, Vols. I and II. Henry Holt and Co., 1907.
4. R. A. Daly: *Our Mobile Earth*. Chas. Scribner's Sons, 1926.
5. Alex. L. DuToit: *Our Wandering Continents*. Oliver and Boyd (Edinburgh), 1937.
6. N. M. Fenneman: *Physiographic Divisions of the United States*. Annals Assoc. Am. Geog., Vol. XVIII, No. 4, pp. 261–353, 1928.
7. ——: *Physiography of Western United States*. McGraw-Hill Book Co., 1931.
8. ——: *Physiography of Eastern United States*. McGraw-Hill Book Co., 1938.
9. N. H. Heck, Chairman, and Committee: *Oceanography, Physics of the Earth* V, Nat. Research Council, 1932.
10. Harold Jeffreys: *The Earth*. Cambridge Univ. Press, 1924.
11. Willis E. Johnson: *Mathematical Geography*. American Book Co., 1907.
12. John Joly: *The Surface History of the Earth*. Oxford Univ. Press, 1925.
13. John Murray: *The Depths of the Ocean*. Macmillan and Co. (London), 1912.
14. *Continental Drift, A Symposium*. Am. Assn. Pet. Geol., 1928.

CHAPTER III

RELATIONS OF EARTH AND SUN

The purpose of this chapter is to point out the responsibility of the sun in causing many of the changes that take place on the surface of the earth. It is a well-known fact that the sun is the chief source of the earth's light and external heat. It may not be so generally recognized that the sun, through the heat that it sends to the earth, controls very definitely many other phases of our physical environment.

THE SOLAR SYSTEM

The members of the solar system are the sun, the nine planets, satellites, minor planets or asteroids, comets (probably not all comets belong to the solar system), meteors and, possibly, gaseous particles which reflect light known as zodiacal light.

The sun, which is the dominant body of the whole system, is believed to be the parent of all the other members. The questions of when and how the solar system was evolved are beyond the province of this volume. They are, however, of primary interest to geologists and astronomers.

The Place of the Earth in the Solar System

The earth occupies an intermediate place in the solar family. It is a relatively small planet, yet not the smallest. It is relatively close to the sun, yet not the closest. The earth revolves around the sun once in 365.25 days, while the planet Mercury moves around the sun once in 88 days, and Neptune's period of revolution is 165 years. The diameter of the earth, 7,926.6 miles, is more than twice as great as that of Mercury, 3,030 miles, yet it is less than one-tenth that of Jupiter, 86,500 miles, and less than one-hundredth that of the sun, 865,000 miles. The mean distance from the earth to the sun is 92,900,000 miles, which is nearly three times as great as that of Mercury, 36,000,000 miles, but only one-thirtieth that of Neptune, 2,791,600,000 miles.

The density (water = 1) of the earth is 5.5, which is only slightly greater than that of Venus, 4.9, and Mars, 4.4, but is much greater than that of the sun, 1.4, or of Saturn, 0.7.

The Earth Is a Unique Planet

The three divisions of the earth, lithosphere, hydrosphere and atmosphere, are not known to exist in similar fashion on any other planet. It is probable that Venus has an atmosphere, but its composition is not known. A hydrosphere also may exist on Venus; however, if it is present, its extent is unknown. It has long been believed that Mars has both atmosphere and hydrosphere; yet no positive evidence of a hydrosphere has been presented, and the evidence that exists of an atmosphere indicates that it is quite different from that of the earth. Our very limited knowledge of the other planets does not indicate that their physical structure and composition are at all comparable to that of the earth. It appears, then, that the earth is a unique member of the solar system, in that it alone is capable of supporting a luxuriant and varied plant and animal life, and of permitting the physiographic processes which induce and accompany our ever-changing physical environment. These features, and others that are more or less peculiar to the earth, are worthy of special consideration.

Movements of the Earth. — The earth has three principal motions. It moves with the rest of the solar system through space; it revolves around the sun once in 365.25 days, and it rotates on its axis once in twenty-four hours. Only the last two movements need be considered here.

The earth's rotation gives us day and night. If the axis of rotation were perpendicular to the plane of the orbit in which the earth revolves around the sun, day and night would be of equal length (12 hours each) at all places and at all seasons. Also, the seasons at any latitude would be essentially the same throughout the year. But the earth's axis is not perpendicular to the plane of its orbit.

Instead, it departs from that position by an angle of 23½ degrees. As the earth revolves around the sun, the north and south poles always point in the same astronomic direction. During the northern hemisphere summer, the north half of the earth is turned toward the sun, while in the winter it is turned away from the sun. As a result of the inclined position of the earth's axis, mid-latitudes have the well-known seasons, spring, summer, autumn and winter; while the north and south poles have six months of continuous daylight followed by six months of darkness each year.

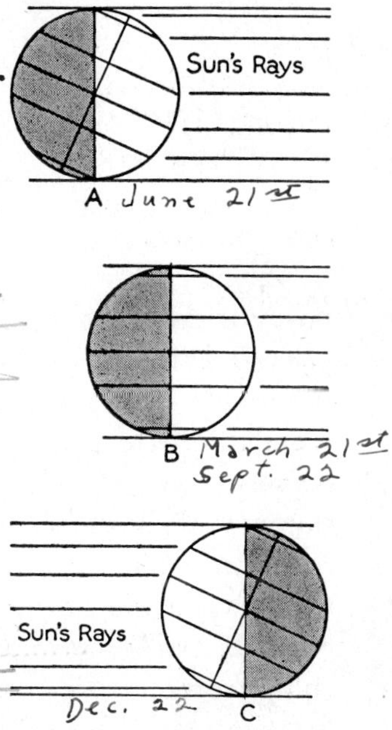

The Seasons. — The four principal mid-latitude seasons and the peculiar conditions at the poles are primarily due to the unequal amounts of heat and light received on the earth at different latitudes during the year. This unequal heating and lighting depends directly on the conditions set forth in the preceding paragraphs, which may be amplified by examining the diagrams in Fig. 19.

In considering the diagrams, we should remember that the heat and light from the sun pass through space in straight lines. The sun is much larger than the earth; therefore, the latter intercepts only the part of the sunlight that falls directly upon it. Disregarding the refraction of light due to the earth's atmosphere, exactly one-half the earth is illuminated at any time.

Fig. 19. — A diagram to illustrate the relations of the earth and the sun's rays at different seasons.

(A) shows the relative positions of earth and sun on June 21st. The north end of the earth's axis is inclined toward the sun. Half the earth is illuminated at one time. The circle of illumination includes all the Arctic circle and excludes everything within the Antarctic circle. More than half of all parallels of latitude are illuminated at one time in the northern hemisphere, less than half in the southern hemisphere.

(B) shows the positions of earth and sun on March 21st and September 22nd. The earth's axis is inclined neither directly toward nor directly away from the sun, but is at right angles to the sun's rays. The length of day and night for all places on the earth are each twelve hours.

(C) On December 22nd the conditions are exactly reversed from those shown in (A). The northern hemisphere is directed away from the sun; its days are, therefore, shorter than in (A). The southern hemisphere now being turned toward the sun has longer days than in (A).

The following table gives the maximum length of daylight for places at different latitudes.

Latitude	Hours	and	Minutes
0	12		0
10	12		35
20	13		13
40	14		51
60	18		30
66½	24		0
80	134		
90	6 months		

It is evident that the conditions are exactly reversed in the two hemispheres. For example, on June 21st, when daylight is 14 hours 51 minutes for all places at 40° North Latitude and 24 hours at 66½° North Latitude, in the southern hemisphere, at corresponding latitudes, daylight is 9 hours, 9 minutes, and 0 hours respectively. On December 22nd, daylight at 40° South Latitude is 14 hours, 51 minutes, but at 40° North Latitude it is 9 hours, 9 minutes.

The Earth's Atmosphere. — *In considering the effects of the relations of the earth and sun, the atmosphere is of primary importance.* It consists of a mechanical mixture of gases which surround and, to some extent, penetrate both the hydrosphere and lithosphere. The observed atmosphere extends above sea level to a height of two hundred miles. Its theoretical height is very much greater. Under normal conditions the air pressure at sea level is 14.9 pounds per square inch. This is equivalent to saying that a complete column of air from top to bottom of one square inch cross-section weighs 14.9 pounds. This weight is sufficient to raise a column of mercury in a barometer to a height of 30 inches. Since the air is a mechanical mixture of gases, it follows that air pressure becomes progressively less with increased altitude above the seas, and heavier gases which exist in greatest amounts at the bottom of the atmosphere give way to lighter gases at higher altitude.

Composition of the Atmosphere. — The important gaseous constituents of the lower air are nitrogen, oxygen, argon, carbon dioxide, hydrogen and water vapor. The latter is very variable, but may displace other gases in amounts up to four per cent by volume. The mobility of the atmosphere is such that at any altitude the composition is remarkably uniform. The following table, adapted from Humphreys,[1] indicates the volume percentages of these gases (except water vapor) at various heights above sea level:

Height, Kilometers	Feet	Nitrogen	Oxygen	Argon	Carbon Dioxide	Hydrogen
0	0	78.04	20.99	0.94	0.03	0.01
5	16,405	77.89	20.95	0.94	0.03	0.01
15	49,215	79.56	19.66	0.74	0.02	0.02
30	98,430	84.48	15.10	0.22	0.00	0.20
100	328,000	1.63	0.07	0.00	0.00	97.84

The table indicates that up to elevations of 16,000 feet, above which very few people live, the percentage of the constituents of the air is quite constant. At elevations of approximately sixty miles, however, very great changes have taken place. In this connection one should remember that the density and quantity of the air decrease rapidly with increasing altitude. The air pressure at an elevation of 19,000 feet is only one-half that at sea level.

Movements of the Atmosphere. — Movements of the air are convection, diffusion, currents and *wind*. The wind, which is of great importance in physiography, may be defined as *air in motion nearly parallel to the earth's surface*. There are many types of

[1] W. J. Humphreys: *Mount Weather Bulletin*, Vol. II, p. 66, 1909.

winds, such as the great planetary winds of the earth, the trades
and westerlies, monsoon winds, winds connected with cyclones and
anti-cyclones, hurricanes, typhoons and tornadoes, local land and
sea breezes, mountain and valley breezes, etc. The air invariably
moves from a region of higher barometric pressure to one of lower
pressure. The chief cause of difference in barometric pressure between two places at the same altitude is the unequal heating of the
air over those regions. Therefore, we may say that *the primary
cause of winds is the unequal heating of the atmosphere directly or
indirectly by the sun*.

This may be illustrated by the very simple land and sea breezes.
In the summer, during the day, the land and, consequently, the air
over the land are more heated than the neighboring sea and the air
over the sea. The air rises over the land, the air pressure becomes
less, and the cooler, heavier air moves in from the sea, creating a
sea breeze. At night the conditions are reversed. The air over
the land becomes colder than the air over the sea, and hence the
wind blows from land to sea, making the *land breeze*.

While the detailed explanation of all winds is not so simple as
in the illustration cited, the principle remains the same; therefore,
the sun is responsible for the chief movements of the atmosphere.

The Atmosphere Tempers the Sun's Heat. — Among its many
physiographic functions, the atmosphere is particularly important in
that it tempers the heat that comes to the earth from the sun. According to Milham,[1] each square yard of the sun's surface constantly emits 14,000 horse power of heat energy. Only a very
small amount of it is received by the earth; yet this heat is of supreme importance in controlling most external geomorphic processes. If it were not for the atmosphere, as the earth rotates, its
sunlit face in the day time would be boiling hot, while the opposite
dark face would be icy cold.

The atmospheric gases absorb a large amount of heat and thus
regulate temperatures. The amount of atmosphere traversed by
the sun's heat at different times of the day and at different seasons
of the year is, therefore, important in determining the amount of
heat received at any locality on the earth. This is illustrated by

W. I. Milham: *Meteorology,* The Macmillan Co., p. 31, 1912.

the fact that if the length of the atmospheric path traversed by the sun's rays be taken as *one* when the rays are *vertical*, it will be *forty-five* when the sun is on the *horizon*.

The Atmosphere also Tempers the Cold. — Much heat is received and absorbed by soil, rocks, buildings, etc., on the earth's surface when the sun is shining. This heat is slowly radiated back into the atmosphere, where much of it is absorbed by carbon dioxide and water vapor. These gases occur chiefly in the lower atmosphere; hence the heat is held near the earth's surface. Because of this condition, the lower atmosphere often is called a thermal blanket for the earth.

The Hydrosphere. — In considering the relations of earth and sun, the hydrosphere is much less important than the atmosphere. However, in the discussions of physiographic processes, it must not be overlooked.

The hydrosphere covers nearly seventy-five per cent of the lithosphere. The accessibility of this moisture is of utmost importance in paving the way for all the dynamic earth forces that have to do with water in any form. In this respect, as in many others already outlined, the earth is unique among all the planets.

The Sun's Dominance in Earth Processes

Accepting the fact that the sun is the source of the heat received by the earth, the following statements will indicate its importance in causing the changes that take place on the surface of the land. Only two of many possible examples will be given.

Cycle of Precipitation. — The sun's influence on the physical activities that modify the surface of the earth is well illustrated by the cycle of precipitation. On the average, about forty inches of water falls on the land each year. The amount varies greatly from place to place, some regions receiving only an inch or two, or less, while other regions may have more than 500 inches a year.

This water, which falls as rain or snow, comes directly from the atmosphere; but it was taken into the atmosphere through evaporation from the surfaces of oceans, lakes, marshes, etc. *The evaporation was caused by the heat from the sun.*

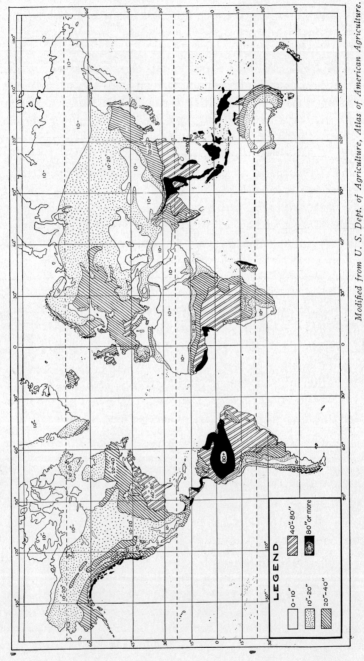

FIG. 20.—Precipitation map of the world.

Modified from U. S. Dept. of Agriculture, Atlas of American Agriculture.

After the water gets into the atmosphere, it is distributed widely by winds. But winds are due largely to the uneven heating of the atmosphere. As the winds carry the moisture-laden air from one place to another, cold air currents may be encountered, or the air may be carried over high mountains. In either case, precipitation in the form of rain or snow may result. The rain water runs off the surface of the land, doing, in total, an incredible amount of work. Snow melts and runs off, or, in favorable places, accumulates to form glaciers, which proceed to do their characteristic erosional and depositional work. Much of the water eventually gets back to the sea from which it came; then the process is repeated, with *the sun's heat being the dominant factor throughout the cycle.*

Wind. — As a second example, let us consider the wind. We have already examined the causes of winds and have noted the importance of wind in the cycle of precipitation. However, the wind is of physiographic importance in many other ways. Wind scoops out great depressions in the surface of the land of arid regions; heaps up dunes, and moves them from one place to another; transports dust; forms waves and shore currents which greatly modify shorelines; etc., etc. Yet, as repeatedly stated, wind is a direct response to the unequal heating of the air by the sun.

Many other illustrations might be given, but these should be sufficient to indicate how important the sun really is in bringing about the great changes that are taking place on land surfaces.

CLIMATE

Climate may be defined as *the sum total of the atmospheric conditions that exist in any region over a long period of time.* The elements that make up climate are *temperature, precipitation, humidity of the air, cloudiness, air pressure and wind.* These elements or conditions of the atmosphere that make up climate vary greatly from place to place and from season to season. The causes of these variations are found in conditions which may be called *climatic controls.* These are (1) position of the particular place on the earth with respect to the sun at different times of the year, (2) latitude, (3) distribution of land and water, (4) position within continents, (5) altitude, (6) position with respect to mountain barriers and other topographic relations, (7) ocean currents, (8) position with respect to prevailing winds, (9) position with respect to great storm paths. All these controls, acting in various combinations on the climatic elements, produce both climate and weather.

Classifications of Climate

As has already been indicated in this chapter, the external geomorphic processes depend largely on climate; therefore, a classification of the climates of the world would help greatly in preparing the way for an understanding of geomorphology. Unfortunately, no adequate simple classification has ever been made. The controls are so varied and their combinations are so involved that any adequate classification becomes a very complex thing.

Older Classifications. — In the past many schemes have been devised to classify climates. One of the oldest, which still is widely used, divides the earth on the basis of latitude into tropical, temperate and frigid zones. Obviously, this simple scheme leaves out precipitation, which is a dominant element of climate, as well as other important elements; and it gives little attention to climatic controls, except latitude and seasons.

Another classification based on the prevailing and secondary winds of the earth has been proposed, but its omissions are quite as great as those of the temperature or latitude scheme. These are but samples of many attempts to invent simple classifications.

Köppen's Classification of Climates. — In this system Köppen recognizes five principal climatic groups which correspond to five principal groups of vegetation. These groups are designated by capital letters A to E. Second, third and fourth letters following the first letter indicate types of climate within the principal group.

A Climates. — A represents tropical rainy climates with temperature of all months above 18° C. (64.4° F.). These conditions are favorable for the growth of sensitive tropical plants (megatherms) which need high temperatures and much precipitation. Af represents a tropical rainy climate with no dry seasons, the rainfall in the driest month being at least 6 cm. (2.4 in.). Am represents a tropical rainy climate with temperatures of all months above

18° C., but with monsoon type of rainfall. In this type there is a short, dry season, but sufficient rainfall to support a rain forest.

B Climates. — These climates are dry with an excess of evaporation over precipitation. The *amount* of precipitation alone does not determine the boundaries of this climatic group, for, obviously, due to evaporation, precipitation in hottest months is less effective in providing water for plant growth than it is when it falls in cooler months; therefore, the *season* in which the moisture falls, as well as annual temperatures and annual precipitation, must be considered. *BW* (W from Wüste meaning desert) represents an arid desert climate; *BS* is a semi-arid grassland, or *steppe* climate. *BWh* (h from heiss meaning hot) is a hot (low latitude) desert climate, while *BWk* (k from the German word kalt meaning cold) is a cold desert climate with average annual temperatures under 18° C.

C Climates. — *C* climates are warm temperate rainy climates with average annual temperature above —3° C. (26.6° F.), but below 18° C. *Cf* represents conditions indicated above with no dry season; *Cw* is a type with a distinct dry winter season; *Cs* represents a Mediterranean type with dry summers.

D Climates. — These are cold, snowy forest climates with the average temperatures of the warmest month below —3° C. and the average temperature of the warmest month above 10° C. (50° F.). This temperature of 10° C. for the warmest month represents the approximate poleward limit of forest growth. As in previous groups *Df* represents a cold, snowy forest with no dry seasons, while *Dw* represents a dry winter season.

E Climates. — *E* climates are polar climates. The average temperature for the warmest month is below 10° C. *ET* is a tundra polar climate with a short growing season, while *EF* is a climate with perpetual frost; the average temperatures for all months are below 0° C. (32° F.). This is the climate of the regions of perpetual snow and ice, such as central Greenland and Antarctica.

Summary. — This classification also uses certain *isothermal* lines connecting places of equal temperature. As is indicated in the brief outline just given, the system is quantitative in that it uses numerical values for temperatures and, to some extent, for precipitation. Because of lack of complete data, many of the boundaries are tenta-

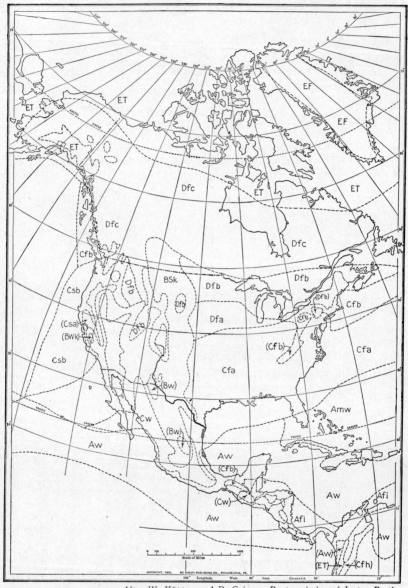

After W. Köppen and R. Geiger.   By permission of Justus Perthes.

FIG. 21.— Climatic zones of North America.

KEY SYMBOLS FOR FIG. 21

A	f	i		: temp. of coldest month above 64.4° F., tropical, wet climates.
				: rainfall of driest month at least 2.4 in.
				: range of monthly temp. less than 9° F.
	m			: dry season exists. Compensated by rains during rest of the year.
			w	: dry season exists. Not compensated by rains during rest of the year.
B				: dry climates.
	S			: semi-arid.
	W			: desert.
			h	: average annual temp. over 64.4° F.
			k	: average annual temp. under 64.4° F.
			s	: at least 70 per cent of rain in winter 6 months.
			w	: at least 70 per cent of rain in summer 6 months.
C	f			: warm temperate rainy, av. temp. above 26.6° F., below 64.4° F.
				: no dry season.
		a		: hot summers, warmest month over 71° F.
		b		: cool summers, warmest month under 71° F.
		c		: cool short summers, one to three months above 50° F
	s			: dry season in summer.
	w			: dry season in winter.
D	f			: temp. of coldest month below 26.6° F., of warmest month above 50° F.
				: no dry season.
		a		: ⎫
		b		: ⎬ as in C above.
		c		: ⎭
E	F			: warmest month below 50° F.
	T			: warmest month below 32° F.
				: warmest month below 50° F. and above 32° F.

tive. The system of letters in series gives an easily understood key to the principal climatic groups and types. The map (Fig. 21) with key shows the classification for North America. Its many advantages over the older classification are obvious. Its most apparent disadvantage is the refinement of details which taxes the memory or makes necessary the use of the key to the symbols.

Modifications of Köppen's System. — Several new classifications of climate have been introduced since Köppen's system was proposed. Thornwaite's and Trewartha's systems are the best examples that are published in the English language. Thornwaite [1] uses essentially Köppen's plan, but makes use of the climatic concepts *precipitation effectiveness* and *temperature efficiency*. He starts with the principle that in the tropical rain forest, where temperatures are always high and rainfall is constantly abundant, the climate must be most favorable for the rapid development of vegetation. These optimum conditions decrease, on the one hand, to the tropical desert, where *rainfall approaches zero*, and, on the other, to regions where the *temperature approaches zero,* that is, a climate of perpetual frost.

Trewartha [2] uses Köppen's system with slight modifications that, in general, simplify the classification.

Conclusions

These suggestions regarding climate are intended to call attention to the importance of the subject in geomorphic studies. The two subjects are closely interrelated, each having an important bearing on the other. In studying physiographic processes, the best results will be obtained through constant use of good climatic maps. Large scale wall maps or those found in any modern physical geography, such as Bartholomew's *The Oxford Advanced Atlas*, are best for this purpose.

[1] C. Warren Thornwaite: *The Climates of the Earth*, Geog. Rev., Vol. XXIII, pp. 433–440, 1933.
[2] Glenn T. Trewartha: *An Introduction to Weather and Climate*. Mc-Graw-Hill Book Co., Inc., pp. 189–354, 1937.

REFERENCES

1. C. G. Abbott: *The Earth and the Stars*. D. Van Nostrand Co., 1926.
2. J. G. Bartholomew: *The Oxford Advanced Atlas*. Oxford Univ. Press, 1936.
3. Thomas A. Blair: *Weather Elements*. Prentice-Hall, Inc., 1937.
4. John C. Duncan: *Astronomy*. Harper and Bros., 1930.
5. W. G. Kendrew: *Climates of the Continents*. Oxford Univ. Press, 1927.
6. ———: *Climate*. Oxford Univ. Press, 1930.
7. W. Köppen: *Grundriss der Klimatologie*. Walter de Gruyter Co. (Berlin), 1931.
8. ——— and R. Geiger: *Handbook der Klimatologie*. Gerbrüder Borntrager (Berlin), 1930.
9. C. Warren Thornwaite: *The Climate of the Earth*. Geog. Rev. Vol. 23, pp. 433–440, 1933.
10. Glenn T. Trewartha: *An Introduction to Weather and Climate*. McGraw-Hill Book Co., Inc., 1937.
11. Chas. A. Young: *General Astronomy*. Ginn and Co., 1916.

CHAPTER IV

MATERIALS OF THE LITHOSPHERE
ELEMENTS AND MINERALS

In order to understand how the relief features of the earth are formed, it is necessary to know something of the composition of the materials of the lithosphere. Having learned the characteristics

Richard Ragle.

FIG. 22. — The effect of tilted rocks of unequal resistance on topography. The ridge is a cuesta.

of the important rocks, we can more easily see how the various external and internal earth forces acting on them have produced our present topography.

We know very little about the materials of the *whole lithosphere* through direct observation. It is true that man has studied very

50

intensively the rocks and minerals which are available to him, but these constitute only a small fraction of all the materials of the earth. Scientists have secured specimens from the slopes of Mount Everest at an elevation of more than 27,000 feet which prove that the mountain was once beneath the sea. One can study the materials on the walls of a great canyon, such as the Grand Canyon of the Colorado River, and learn much about the geologic history of the region. The deepest mines in the world are in South Africa, where a depth of more than 9,500 feet has been attained. Several well borings for oil have reached depths of from 12,000 to more than 15,000 feet, and, through examination of the drill cuttings, one can determine the nature of the rocks at any depth in the holes. However, all rock exposures so far available to man are small compared with the 4,000-mile radius of the earth. It is evident, therefore, that the following discussion must deal only with the materials of the outer part of the lithosphere.

As stated in Chapter I, the word lithosphere really means rock sphere. Rocks, then, constitute most of the solid materials of the earth. Rocks are divided into three great groups, igneous rocks, sedimentary rocks and metamorphic rocks. Nearly all rocks contain two or more minerals. That is to say, *rocks are composed of certain rock-making minerals.* In case of coarse-grained rocks, the minerals are readily identified. If the rocks are very fine-grained, it may be necessary to use a microscope to identify the constituent minerals. Minerals, in turn, are composed of elements, which are very simple units of matter or material into which all substances may be divided.

We shall now study, in order, the elements, rock-forming minerals and rocks that together constitute the solid part of the earth.

Elements

Chemists have recognized some 92 elements in the materials of the earth. Of these, 8 make up about 98 per cent of the atmosphere, hydrosphere and outer part of the lithosphere. Six other less important ones bring the amount up to more than 99 per cent.

THE MOST IMPORTANT ELEMENTS

	Symbol	Per cent in air, water and outer lithosphere
1. Oxygen	O	approximately 50.00
2. Silicon	Si	" 26.00
3. Aluminum	Al	" 7.45
4. Iron	Fe	" 4.20
5. Calcium	Ca	" 3.25
6. Sodium	Na	" 2.40
7. Magnesium	Mg	" 2.35
8. Potassium	K	" 2.35
9. Hydrogen	H	" 0.90
10. Titanium	Ti	" 0.30
11. Carbon	C	" 0.20
12. Phosphorus	P	" 0.08
13. Sulphur	S	" 0.06
14. Chlorine	Cl	" 0.17
		" 99.71

Elements Combine to Form Minerals

Some minerals consist of only one element. Examples are diamond, which is pure carbon, sulphur, native gold, native silver, and native copper. These, however, are not rock-forming minerals in the sense in which the term is usually understood, and they are of relatively rare occurrence.

In general, two or more (in many cases many more) elements combine in definite proportions to make a mineral.

Among the simpler combinations are the following:

(1) Oxides formed by the union of oxygen with other elements, such as quartz, SiO_2, or magnetite, Fe_3O_4.

(2) Sulphides. These do not occur as important rock-making minerals, but they illustrate simple combinations of elements. Examples are pyrite, FeS_2; galena, PbS.

(3) Carbonates. Two carbonates, calcite, $CaCO_3$, and dolomite, $(Ca.Mg) CO_3$, are very common rock-forming minerals. They result from the union of calcium, carbon and oxygen, or, in case of dolomite, of calcium, magnesium, carbon and oxygen.

(4) Chlorides. These are illustrated by rock salt or halite, $NaCl$.

(5) Sulphates. Gypsum, $CaSO_4.2H_2O$, is a good example.

(6) Silicates. The silicates, which consist of silicon and oxygen in union with other elements, are very abundant in all three great groups of rocks. Examples of silicates are the feldspar orthoclase, $K_2O.Al_2O_3.6SiO_2$; muscovite, a white mica, $K_2O.3Al_2O_3.6SiO_2.2H_2O$. In this mineral the silicon and oxygen have combined in definite proportions with three other elements.

MINERALS

A mineral is an inorganic substance having a definite chemical composition and usually a definite molecular arrangement. The chemical composition has been illustrated by the examples just given. It is determined by the chemist, who resolves the mineral into its component elements and determines the amount of each.

Molecular arrangement of a mineral refers to the geometrical pattern in which the molecules (combinations of elements) are grouped. Most minerals occur as crystals; some may be either crystalline or amorphous (without crystal form) while a few occur only in amorphous condition.

It is unusual to find minerals with definite crystal outlines when they are combined to make rocks. This is due to the fact that in igneous and metamorphic rocks, two or more minerals are likely to form at the same time, thus interfering with each other's growth. In sedimentary rocks the component minerals usually have been partly decomposed or disintegrated by erosional processes. Minerals that exhibit their crystalline form are much more likely to occur in cavities in the earth where crystal growth has been unobstructed.

Properties of Minerals

The characteristics of minerals by which they may be identified will be described in the following paragraphs. These, for convenience, may be called chemical and physical properties. Determination of the chemical properties requires tests with the blow pipe or with chemical reagents. While these tests are important and are necessary to the identification of many minerals, they will not be included in this discussion, since it is possible to determine most of the rock-making minerals (those of chief interest to the physiographer) through their physical properties.

Physical Properties of Minerals. — These are the characteristics of minerals which, when known, usually permit easy identification of any particular mineral. The more important properties are *crystal form, color, hardness, cleavage, luster, fracture, specific*

Fig. 23. — Minerals. A — a quartz crystal. B — amorphous quartz. C — mica with one perfect cleavage. D — orthoclase showing two good cleavages. E — calcite with three perfect rhombohedral cleavages. F — labradorite showing multiple twinning. (The lines run diagonally from upper right to lower left.)

gravity, diaphaneity and associations. One physical characteristic only is rarely diagnostic, but when combinations of properties are considered together, they usually serve to distinguish one common mineral from another.

Crystal System. — *All crystals* are included in six crystal systems. Each system includes all crystals whose forms may be described by reference to certain crystal axes. *Crystallography,* the description and classification of crystals, is a science in itself, which is far too complicated to be included in this textbook, even if it were desirable to do so. It has already been shown that minerals rarely exhibit crystal patterns as they occur in the common rocks of the earth; therefore, a knowledge of crystallography is of little help to the physiographer who will study the minerals in order to determine the composition of rocks. For these reasons, crystallization may be omitted from further discussion.

Color. — The color of a mineral is very useful in its identification. A few minerals have more than one color, hence it is not always a distinctive feature. Ordinarily, the color is due to the chemical composition of a mineral, but surface stains or minute traces of impurities or fractures within the mineral may give rise to unusual colors.

Hardness. — This is a very important property, especially valuable in both field and laboratory. The hardness of any mineral may be closely determined by comparison with the following standard mineral scale:

SCALE OF HARDNESS

1. Talc	6. Feldspar
2. Gypsum	7. Quartz
3. Calcite	8. Topaz
4. Fluorite	9. Corundum
5. Apatite	10. Diamond

Very few minerals are as soft as talc, and few are harder than quartz.

With a little experience one may learn to determine the hardness of many rock-making minerals through use of the following common substances: the fingernail will scratch talc and gypsum, but not calcite; a common pin is harder than calcite, but usually will not scratch fluorite; a well-tempered pocket knife blade will barely scratch feldspar; plate glass lies between (6) feldspar and (7) quartz in the scale of hardness.

In determining the relative hardness of two minerals by scratching one with the other, a sharp edge or corner of the scratching mineral should be used on a smooth face of the other. It is important to discriminate between an actual scratch mark and the powdered mineral that will be left if the scratching mineral is softer than the other.

Cleavage. — Many minerals have the property of breaking along one or more *smooth planes*. This is due to the molecular arrangement within the mineral, and is important for identification purposes. Micas, for example, have *one* perfect cleavage; feldspars break with two good cleavages; calcite has three cleavages; quartz has no cleavage. The angles at which cleavage planes meet may be important. For instance, calcite cleavage planes meet in acute and obtuse angles giving a rhombohedral form.

Luster. — The appearance of a mineral due to the way light is reflected from its surfaces is called luster. Common descriptive terms are used as follows: metallic, resembling *polished* silver; adamantine, that of a diamond; pearly, like that of a pearl; resinous, that of resin; oily, like oil; earthy, like that of dull dry earth.

Fracture. — Many minerals which do not break with smooth planes (cleavage) on all sides exhibit certain characteristic qualities of their broken surface. For example, flint breaks with very smooth curved faces which exhibit perfect conchoidal (shell-like) fracture. Some minerals break with splintery fracture; others may have a smooth fracture, etc.

Specific Gravity. — The density of a mineral compared with water is its specific gravity. Quartz, one of the common rock-making minerals, has a specific gravity of 2.6; while magnetite, an iron mineral, specific gravity 5.2, is twice as dense. The specific gravities of most of the rock-forming minerals range from 2.6 to 3.5; therefore, this property is relatively unimportant in differentiating these minerals.

Diaphaneity. — This property has to do with the transmission of light through a *thin piece* of a mineral. If objects can be seen through the mineral, it is said to be *transparent*; if some light passes through, but objects are not distinguishable, the mineral is *translucent*; if no light passes through, the mineral is *opaque*.

Associations. — Certain minerals, such as quartz and orthoclase, or augite and olivine, are very likely to occur together in rocks. The fundamental cause of such associations is usually chemical, but the actual occurrence together is a physical condition that often is helpful to the person who is studying either minerals or rocks. Moreover, the fact that some minerals *seldom if ever* associate with others is of equal importance. Thus, the student who knows that quartz and olivine rarely occur together in rocks will not expect a white mineral, which may *look like* quartz, actually to *be* quartz, if he finds unmistakable green olivine in a rock. Also, it is well to note that certain dark minerals have common associates, while light-colored minerals have others. This principle is of much value in studying many types of rocks of all three great groups. Further details will be found in appropriate places.

Rock-making Minerals

More than 1,500 minerals have been identified and described by mineralogists, who are adding to the number almost daily. Of this vast number, less than 25 make up the great bulk of the known rocks of the earth. The others, although of interest to mineralogists, crystallographers and, in part, to economic geologists, are of no practical importance in an introductory study of rocks.

The purpose of introducing the following short list of the more important rock-making minerals is to enable the student, through their use, to recognize the important varieties of igneous, sedimentary and metamorphic rocks which together make up the lithosphere. Wherever possible, the descriptions should be supplemented by study of actual specimens, both in the field and laboratory.

Additional Descriptions. — Several of the minerals described in the table belong to mineral families or natural groups. Muscovite and biotite are prominent members of the *mica group*. It will be noted that with the exception of color and composition they have essentially the same properties.

The *feldspar group* is represented in the table by orthoclase, microcline, albite, oligoclase and labradorite. The whole feldspar group has been divided into two sub-groups — orthoclase and plagioclase. The basis of the subdivision is the difference in angles at which the cleavage planes meet. In orthoclase the planes meet at 90°. In microcline, which has the same composition as ortho-

ROCK-MAKING

A. Commonly Found in

Name	Composition	Color	Hardness	Cleavage
Albite	$Na_2O . Al_2O_3 . 6SiO_2$	White	6	2 good
Augite	$CaO . MgO . 2SiO_2$ with Fe	Black	5–6	2 good
Biotite	$(H,K)_2O . Al_2O_3 . 2(Mg,Fe)O . 3SiO_2$	Black	2.5	1 perfect
Hornblende	$CaO . 3(Mg. Fe)O . 4SiO_2$ with Na and Al	Black	5–6	2 good
Labradorite	$CaO . Na_2O, Al_2O_3 . 4SiO_2$	Gray-blue	5–6	2 good
Microcline	$K_2O . Al_2O_3 . 6SiO_2$	W—red, green	6	2 good
Muscovite	$K_2O . 3Al_2O_3 . 6SiO_2 . 2H_2O$	Silver—gray	2.5	1 perfect
Oligoclase	$Na_2O . CaO . Al_2O_3 . 6SiO_2$	W—gray	6	2 good
Olivine	$2(Mg,Fe)O . SiO_2$	Green	6.5	None
Pyroxene	$CaO . (Mg,Fe)O . 2SiO_2$	Green	5–6	Poor
Quartz	SiO_2	W—rose, smoky	7	None

B. Commonly Found in

Calcite	$CaCO_3$	W—yellow	3	3 perfect
Chert	SiO_2	W—gray	7	None
Dolomite	$(Ca,Mg)CO_3$	White	3.5–4	3 perfect
Flint	SiO_2	Black—dark gray	7	None
Gypsum	$CaSO_4 . 2H_2O$	W—gray—brown	2	1 perfect
Halite	$NaCl$	W—gray—yellow	2.5	3 perfect
Kaolinite	$Al_2O_3 . 2SiO_2 . 2H_2O$	W—yellow—brown	1–2	1 perfect
Quartz	SiO_2	W—rose, smoky	7	None

C. Commonly Found in

Actinolite	$CaO . 3(Mg,Fe)O . 4SiO_2$	Green	5–6	2 perfect
Chlorite	$5MgO . Al_2O_3 . 3SiO_2 . 4H_2O$	Green	2–2.5	1 perfect
Epidote	$4CaO . 3(Al,Fe)_2O_3 . 6SiO . H_2O$	Green	6–7	1 perfect
Garnet	$3CaO$ or $3MgO$ or $3FeO . Al_2O_3 . 3SiO_2$	Red, brown, black	7	None
Serpentine	$3MgO . 2SiO_2 . 2H_2O$	Green	2.5–5	None
Talc	$3MgO . 4SiO_2 . H_2O$	Green-White	1	1 perfect
Tremolite	$CaO . 3MgO . 4SiO_2$	White, pink, gray	5–6	2 good

MINERALS

Igneous and Metamorphic Rocks

Luster	Fracture	Specific Gravity	Diaphaneity
Vitreous	Uneven	2.6	Translucent
Vitreous	Uneven	3.4	Opaque
Vitreous-pearly	Ragged	3	Transparent
Vitreous-pearly	Uneven	5-6	Opaque
Vitreous-pearly	Uneven	2.7	Translucent
Vitreous	Uneven	2.5	Transparent-translucent
Vitreous-pearly	Ragged	2.7	Transparent
Vitreous	Uneven	2.6	Transparent-translucent
Vitreous	Conchoidal	3.4	Transparent-translucent
Vitreous	Uneven	3.5	Opaque
Vitreous	Subconchoidal	2.6	Transparent

Sedimentary Rocks

Luster	Fracture	Specific Gravity	Diaphaneity
Pearly-vitreous	Uneven (rare)	2.7	Transparent
Waxy-dull	Conchoidal.	2.6	Transparent-opaque
Vitreous-pearly	Smooth	2.8	Transparent-translucent
Vitreous	Conchoidal	2.6	Translucent
Pearly	Conchoidal	2.3	Transparent
Vitreous	Conchoidal	2.1	Transparent
Pearly-earthy	Uneven	2.6	Transparent-translucent
Vitreous	Subconchoidal	2.6	Transparent

Metamorphic Rocks in Addition to A

Luster	Fracture	Specific Gravity	Diaphaneity
Vitreous-pearly	Uneven	3	Transparent-translucent
Pearly	Ragged	2.7	Transparent-translucent
Vitreous	Uneven	3.5	Translucent-opaque
Vitreous-resinous	Uneven-Subconchoidal	3.1-4	Transparent-translucent
Resinous-pearly	Conchoidal	2.5	Translucent-opaque
Pearly	Smooth	2.7	Transparent-translucent
Vitreous-pearly	Uneven	3	Transparent-translucent

clase, the planes meet at almost 90°. In the plagioclase feldspars, represented in the table by albite, oligoclase and labradorite, the cleavage planes meet at slightly less and slightly more than 90°.

The minerals hornblende, actinolite and tremolite belong to the *amphibole group*. Hornblende differs from the others in that it is of common occurrence in the primary (igneous) rocks of the earth, while actinolite and tremolite usually occur as secondary minerals (developed from others) in metamorphic rocks.

Pyroxene and augite also are members of one group, the *pyroxene group*.

Many other rock-making minerals are known, but usually they are of rare occurrence or are not readily recognizable. Therefore, they are omitted from the brief list given above.

Mineral Distinctions. — In spite of the physical properties indicated in the table, some of the minerals are difficult to distinguish even when in good-sized pieces. This difficulty increases when the minerals occur as small grains in rocks. It is here that associations of minerals become very important.

There are, however, some hints that may be helpful. Hornblende and augite look much alike, but hornblende usually occurs in needle-like grains in rocks, while augite is more likely to occur in rectangular blocky grains or masses. Also, the cleavage planes of hornblende meet so as to form diamond-shaped patterns, while those of augite meet practically at right angles.

White orthoclase is easily confused with albite and oligoclase. Close examination, however, frequently shows a single line (edge of *twinning* plane) running lengthwise through the orthoclase, while many fine lines, due to *multiple twinning*, cross the albite and oligoclase grains.

Twinning. — In single twinned (Carlsbad twinned) feldspars, one-half the crystal has grown as if it were rotated 180° with respect to the other half, thus giving the twinning plane referred to above. Most plagioclases are multiple twinned; that is, one thin slice of the crystal grows in normal position, a second slice is rotated 180° on the first, the third slice is parallel to the first, fourth is parallel to the second, and so on. The twin layers may be exceedingly thin, but in some feldspars, such as those mentioned above, *espe-*

cially labradorite, the layers are coarse enough to be easily seen by the unaided eye. Labradorite may exhibit a marked play of colors, green, red, orange, etc., due to the breaking up of light rays by multiple twinning.

REFERENCES

1. J. A. and E. S. Dana: *A System of Mineralogy.* John Wiley and Sons.
2. Edward H. Kraus and Walter F. Hunt: *Mineralogy.* McGraw-Hill Book Co., 1928.
3. L. V. Pirsson and A. Knopf: *Rocks and Rock Minerals.* John Wiley and Sons, 1926.
4. Austin F. Rogers: *Introduction to the Study of Minerals and Rocks.* McGraw-Hill Book Co., 1921.

CHAPTER V

MATERIALS OF THE LITHOSPHERE. ROCKS

The three great groups of rocks, igneous, sedimentary and metamorphic, which together make up the lithosphere, differ greatly in mode of origin, occurrence, and physical properties. All have their own peculiar influences on the rate and nature of erosion and on the resulting topography. It is necessary, then, to be able to distinguish these groups and to recognize their important subdivisions if one is to understand fully the origin and history of land forms.

IGNEOUS ROCKS

Igneous rocks, as the word *igneous* implies, *are rocks formed through the solidification of molten materials.* They are sometimes called *primary* rocks because they represent the rocks from which all others, except certain organically formed sedimentary rocks, have been derived. The term *primary rock* also is related to the theory that the earth was at one time in a completely molten condition. Accordingly, as the earth solidified through cooling, the *first* rocks were, of course, igneous. This theory has been widely, but by no means universally, accepted by geologists.

Igneous rocks are believed to have been formed at all ages in earth history, and they are being formed at the present time. About 500 active or recently active volcanoes are known. In eruption many of these emit streams of hot lava which cool to make igneous rock. The sources of lava are not well understood. Some geologists believe that the lithosphere is molten below a depth of 25 to 30 miles. However, there is considerable theoretical and seismic evidence against such a view. It is quite certain that at such a depth the heat is so great that rocks are *potentially* molten, but probably the pressure of the overlying material is so great that they cannot actually be liquid. When great movements of the earth's

62

crust occur, due to internal stresses, pressure is relieved sufficiently to allow local masses to become liquid, thus furnishing material for the various phenomena of vulcanism.

Classification of Igneous Rocks

The variety of known igneous rocks is very great. They vary in color, in texture, in mode of occurrence on and in the earth, and, most important of all, in mineral composition. Altogether, they constitute the great bulk of the lithosphere. Rocks that were formed ages ago have been subject to earth movements that tend

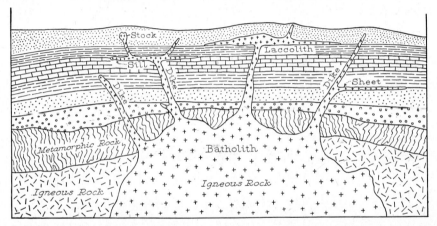

FIG. 24. — A diagram to show the hypothetical relations of intrusive rocks.

to change their characteristics. Many igneous rocks are fine-grained and must be studied by means of a special microscope. Petrologists have developed elaborate classifications, based on chemical and microscopic analyses, which indicate gradations in composition and texture from one rock type to another.

The classifications which follow are simple as compared to those suggested in the last paragraph. However, they are sufficiently detailed to permit the recognition of rock types and occurrences of importance to the physiographer. The bases for the classifications are (1) the types or modes of occurrence, (2) the textures, (3) the mineral composition of the igneous rocks, (4) colors of the fine-textured rocks.

Mode of Occurrence

All igneous rocks are divided into two groups, depending upon the conditions under which they solidified. Those which have been ejected from a volcano or some other vent and have accumulated and solidified on the surface of the earth are *extrusive rocks*. *Intrusive rocks* are those formed through the solidifying of molten material which was forced up *toward but not to* the surface of the earth. The depths below the surface at which such intrusives form vary greatly from place to place.

Extrusive Rocks. — These rocks may be further subdivided through recognition of the ways in which molten material is forced to the surface of the ground. In the *explosive* type of volcanic eruption, accumulations of gases cause the lava to be thrown violently into the air. It is blown into fragments which fall to the earth as solid particles. In the *quiet* type of eruption, lava wells out of volcanic craters or fissures in the earth, and spreads out in relatively thin sheets which soon become solid.

Explosive Types. — The fragmental igneous rocks produced by violent explosions occur in several different forms and in different sizes. Usually large pieces are vesicular due to the accumulation and escape of gases during solidification. Large pieces are called bombs; those about the size of a walnut are lapilli; very fine material is called volcanic ash or, more correctly, volcanic dust. Beds of fine material that have accumulated in water and which present a stratified appearance are tuff. Mixtures of coarse and fine materials composed of angular materials are breccias or agglomerates.

Quiet Types. — Molten rock material (magma) which has flowed out of some opening in the earth and has congealed on the land is called a *lava flow*. It may happen that successive flows give rise to layers of lava being piled one on another. In many parts of the earth, lava flows, doubtless from several vents, now cover areas of hundreds of square miles, and some of the combined flows are thousands of feet thick. The upper and lower surfaces of individual flows exhibit glassy texture, vesicular structure and ropy, stringy appearance, characteristic of lava flows, that can be seen forming from present-day volcanoes.

FIG. 25. — Agglomerate made up of extrusive, fragmental igneous rocks, Specimen Mountain, Colorado.

Junius Henderson.

FIG. 26. — A recently solidified lava flow from Kilauea, Hawaii. The lava is of the "pahoehoe" type.

Intrusive Rocks. — The principal types of occurrence of these rocks are batholiths, laccoliths, stocks, sheets or sills, dikes and necks.   Intrusions that solidified at *great* depth are called *plutonic* rocks.

Batholiths. — These are very large, irregular but elongated masses of igneous rock.   They are invariably associated with mountain ranges.   At the time of their formation they were deeply buried by overlying rocks.   Subsequent erosion may have exposed

FIG. 27. — A laccolith stripped of its sedimentary rock cover, Bearpaw Mountains, Montana.

their upper portions, but no one has ever seen the bottom of a batholith.   The surfaces of batholiths are very irregular.   In many cases, if the overlying rocks could be stripped off, exposing the whole upper surface of a batholith, relief of thousands of feet would be disclosed.

Laccoliths. — Laccoliths are huge, somewhat lenticular masses of igneous rock that have been forced between layers of stratified rock. Due to the rapidity of the movement of liquid material, the beds overlying the central part of the intrusion have been arched up hundreds or even thousands of feet.   Eventually, erosion may remove the sediments from the top of the intrusion, leaving highly inclined strata on the sides (Fig. 27).   Many groups of mountains and small ranges in western North America have been formed by such intrusions. Unlike batholiths, which may be forced into any kind of rock, laccoliths are found only in stratified rocks. The bottoms of laccoliths are relatively flat, while the tops are of an irregular, domed shape.

Stocks.—Stocks are relatively small, somewhat rounded, igneous intrusions. Like batholiths they may occur in any kind of rock.

Courtesy New Mexico State Tourist Bureau.

FIG. 28. — Shiprock, a much-eroded stock. The sedimentary rocks into which it was intruded have been removed by erosion, leaving the more resistant igneous rock standing high above the wind-swept plain, New Mexico.

Sills or Sheets.—These are layer-like masses of igneous rock that have been forced between beds of sedimentary or metamorphic rocks. Their upper and lower surfaces conform closely to the position of the overlying and underlying strata. Thick intrusions of this type are commonly called sills. Thin ones are sheets. Some sills are several hundred feet thick and have a lateral spread of many miles. Sills and sheets may be intruded into either flat-lying or tilted beds, or movements of the earth may deform the whole series of beds including the intrusives. The igneous rocks of the sills commonly are more resistant to erosion than are the surround-

FIG. 29. — Two sills of basic rock intruded into sedimentary rocks, Yellowstone National Park. Note the fine columnar jointing.

U. S. Geol. Survey.

FIG. 30. — One of the great Spanish Peaks dikes, Colorado. The sedimentary rocks into which the dike was intruded have been eroded away. The horizontal lines on the face of the dike indicate their former position.

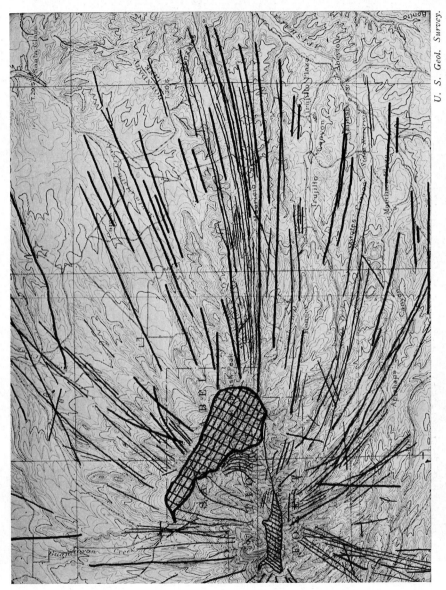

FIG. 31. — The dike system of the Spanish Peaks, Colorado. Some dikes can be traced for 20 miles. Many make the cores of pronounced ridges. The area shown in this figure is 285 square miles. *U. S. Geol. Survey.*

ing rocks. Therefore, sills may be exceedingly important in the development of topographic forms.

Dikes.—Dikes are somewhat like sills and sheets in that they are relatively long and thin. But *unlike* them, dikes cut any kind

FIG. 32. — A volcanic plug about 100 feet in diameter, northwestern Colorado.

of rocks and usually occur in a position highly inclined to a horizontal plane. Where they occur in sedimentary rocks they cut across the bedding planes at an angle in contrast with sills that are parallel to the stratification planes. Dikes vary in thickness from a few inches to hundreds of feet and in length from a few feet to many miles. Most dike rocks are much more resistant to erosive agents than are the rocks into which they were intruded, although some are not. After the older rocks have been worn away, dikes usually make great walls of rock, as in Fig. 30, or form the cores of long ridges.

Necks.—In an active volcano there is a vent or opening which connects the heated, deep-seated material within the earth with the surface. In the dying stages of the volcano, lava may rise and solidify in this conduit well below the surface of the earth. After extensive erosion, these masses of igneous rocks, which are roughly circular in outline, are disclosed. Such intrusions are called volcanic necks or plugs.

Summary.—After reading these brief descriptions of intrusions, it is well to remember that all types are formed at varying depths below the earth's surface. If they are exposed now on land surfaces, it is because the rocks which once covered them have been removed by erosion. Many intrusions which do *not* appear on the surface of the land have been encountered in mines. Intrusions are most numerous in mountain regions where earth forces have been intense. They occur also in many volcanic regions. The influence of these various types of intrusions on present topography will be indicated in more detail in later chapters.

Igneous Rock Textures

Igneous rocks solidify under a great variety of physical conditions, as indicated in the preceding paragraphs. If the molten material cooled slowly at great depth, the minerals that make up the resulting rocks may be very large. On the contrary, if the rock formed on or near the surface of the earth, the rate of cooling may have been so rapid that there was no time for individual mineral growth, and a natural rock glass without mineral grains results. Intermediate conditions give intermediate results in the size of grains. *Texture* refers to the size and arrangement of the grains or other physical conditions of the materials that make up the rocks.

Classification by Textures. — Regardless of mineral composition, all igneous rocks can be classified on a basis of texture.

Granitoid, Phaneritic or Holocrystalline.—Any igneous rock whose grains are recognizable with the unaided eye belongs in this group. The grains may be from the size of fine shot to more than an inch in length. Typical examples are granites and diorites. Nearly all plutonic rocks are holocrystalline.

FIG. 33. — Textures of igneous rocks. A — an even-grained granite showing phaneritic texture. B — a porphyry. C — a felsite. D — a vesicular basalt. E — obsidian showing glassy texture.

Dense or Aphanitic.—Rocks of this texture are distinctly granular, but most of the grains are too small to be identified without the aid of a microscope. Basalts, felsites and other dense varieties found chiefly in dikes, stocks, sills and non-glassy lava flows are representative of this group.

Glassy.—The rock is composed chiefly or entirely of natural glass. Some grains may be present. Many extrusive rocks and

CLASSIFICATION OF IGNEOUS ROCKS

Family	Average Chemical Composition	Chief Mineral Composition	Holocrystalline Texture	Dense Texture	Glassy
Granite Chiefly light-colored	SiO$_2$ 70.0% Al$_2$O$_3$ 15.0 Fe (oxides) 2.6 Others 12.4	*Quartz* *Orthoclase* ± Albite Biotite Muscovite Hornblende	Granite Biotite granite Hornblende granite Pegmatite Binary Granite	Rhyolite Quartz Porphyry (Field classification felsites)	Obsidian Pitchstone Perlite Pumice
Syenite Chiefly light-colored	SiO$_2$ 60.8 Al$_2$O$_3$ 17.2 Fe (oxides) 5.0 Others 17.0	*Orthoclase* ± Acid plagioclase Hornblende Biotite Augite (rare) Nephelite	Hornblende syenite Biotite syenite Augite syenite Nephelite syenite	Trachyte Phonolite (Field classification felsites)	Obsidian (rare)
Grano-diorite Light to intermediate in color	SiO$_2$ 64.3 Al$_2$O$_3$ 16.5 Fe (oxides) 4.7 Others 14.5	*Orthoclase* *Acid plagioclase* *Quartz* (small amount) ± Hornblende Biotite	Grano-diorite Quartz diorite Monzonite	Dacite Quartz andesite (Field classification felsites)	Obsidian (rare)
Diorite Intermediate to dark in color	SiO$_2$ 59.0 Al$_2$O$_3$ 17.0 Fe (oxides) 6.7 Others 17.3	*Plagioclase* *Hornblende* ± Biotite Augite	Diorite Biotite diorite Augite diorite	Andesite (Field classification: if light-colored —felsite; if dark-colored—basalt)	Obsidian (rare)
Gabbro Chiefly dark-colored	SiO$_2$ 49.1 Al$_2$O$_3$ 16.6 Fe (oxides) 10.8 Others 23.5	*Basic Plagioclase* (labradorite chiefly) *Augite* ± Olivine (very common) Hornblende	Gabbro Olivine gabbro Hornblende gabbro	Basalt Olivine basalt (Field classification basalt)	Obsidian (rare)
Basic rocks Chiefly composed of *one mineral* Dark colors predominate	SiO$_2$ 38–50 Al$_2$O$_3$ 4–8 Fe (oxides) 10–13 Others 29–48	*Pyroxene* *Olivine* *Hornblende*	Pyroxenite Olivinite, dunite Hornblendite	Limburgite	

others that occur in thin sheets or dikes and have cooled very quickly belong to this group. Obsidian, pitchstone, pumice and perlite are common varieties.

Porphyritic.—Any rock in which large and small grains or large grains and glassy matrix occur are called porphyries. Great variations in the size of grains may occur. It is believed that many porphyries have resulted from two periods of cooling.

Fragmental.—While not strictly a textural term, fragmental suggests the condition in which many extrusive volcanic rocks occur. Volcanic breccias, dust and tuff belong in this category.

Classification Based on Mineral Composition

We come now to the determination of igneous rocks based on their component minerals. This classification is based on the fact that starting with molten rock material of certain general chemical composition, rock-making minerals form and associate themselves in rather definite groups. Each assemblage of minerals, therefore, results in a rock which can be assigned to a certain family. Only the very simple families with their most common constituents will be described.

Granite Family. — This family *always* contains quartz and orthoclase which are called *essential minerals*. Usually one or more of the *accessory minerals,* albite, biotite, hornblende and muscovite are present. The word granite has two meanings: first, it designates the name of the family which is made up of the minerals just named; second, it designates the coarse-grained members as distinguished from the dense, glassy or fragmental forms of this family. The family names as they appear in the table have similar significance.

Varieties.—There are many varieties of the granite family whose distinctions are based chiefly on composition and texture. For example, granites that contain considerable of the accessory mineral hornblende are called *hornblende granite*. Certain granites occur with the quartz and orthoclase arranged in large irregular masses and usually with large segregated masses of biotite or muscovite. Such granites are *pegmatites.*

Rhyolite is a dense rock with the mineral composition of a granite.

Granite porphyry is an entirely holocrystalline rock, but there is a marked contrast in the size of the grains.

Pumice, obsidian and *pitchstone* are glassy members of the granite family. They have few or no mineral grains, but their chemical composition agrees with that of an average granite.

Color.—The colors of granites depend upon the amounts of the various minerals present and upon the size of the grains. Most granites are light-colored. If there is an abundance of orthoclase present, they may appear reddish or pink; or if the black minerals hornblende or biotite are very abundant, the rock may be dark gray.

Syenite Family. — Rocks of this family consist largely of orthoclase feldspar with subordinate amounts of one or more of the accessory minerals, albite, hornblende, biotite (rare), augite (rare), nephelite and leucite.

Varieties.—Like granites the individual holocrystalline syenites are usually named for some accessory mineral; thus, there are *hornblende syenites, nephelite syenites, etc. Syenite porphyry* refers to a syenite with contrasting grains. *Trachyte* is the common dense member of the syenite family. Glassy members are *pumice, obsidian,* etc.

Color.—Syenites usually are light-colored.

Diorite Family. — Diorites are composed of hornblende and various feldspars. The hornblende equals or exceeds the amount of feldspar present. Other minerals may occur in very subordinate amounts.

Varieties.—Andesite is the fine-grained form of diorite. Frequently it is porphyritic. Glassy forms, when they occur, are obsidian, pitchstone, etc.

Color.—The colors are black, dark gray, dark brown and green.

Gabbro Family. — The members of this family contain pyroxene and one of the calcium plagioclase feldspars, usually labradorite. Olivine may occur in considerable amounts. Biotite and hornblende are rarely present.

Varieties.—If much olivine is present, the holocrystalline rock is called *olivine gabbro*. The dense form is *basalt*. If discernible olivine grains are present, it is *olivine basalt*. Glassy forms are rare, but obsidian and pitchstone may occur.

Color.—The coarse-grained varieties are dark gray, green or black. Basalt is black or dark gray.

Intermediate Families. — These are intermediate gradations from one family to another. A good example is the sub-family of *grano-diorite*. As the name implies, the members of this group have some of the characteristics of both granite and diorite. The component minerals are orthoclase and soda-plagioclase in about equal amounts, a subordinate amount of quartz, and usually a small amount of either biotite or hornblende.

Varieties.—*Monzonites and quartz diorites.* These are coarse-grained varieties, while the dense varieties include *dacites* and *quartz andesites*. Porphyritic textures are very common in this group, thus giving monozonite porphyry and dacite porphyry. Glasses are not determinable except through chemical analyses, but the usual terms, obsidian and pitchstone, apply.

Color.—The colors are intermediate. Grays, light greens and light browns predominate.

Rare Basic Rocks. — Certain rocks not representative of a whole family and composed largely of one mineral are rather common in the earth. Thus we have *hornblendite,* a coarse-grained rock made up chiefly of hornblende; *pyroxenite,* one composed largely of pyroxene; *olivinite* or *dunite,* a rock containing mostly olivine. The dense forms cannot easily be distinguished from basalts. Colors are usually black or green.

Field Classification of Dense Rocks. — It has been noted in preceding paragraphs that the mineral composition of the dense rocks can be determined only through the expert use of a petrographic microscope. This being the case, it is necessary to use a simple classification of dense rocks based on color.

Felsites.—Any dense, light-colored, igneous rock is called a felsite. The colors may be pink, white, light gray, light green or light brown. If such a rock is porphyritic, it may be called a *felsite porphyry*. Most dense rocks and associated porphyries of the granite, syenite, and grano-diorite families will be included in these terms.

Basalt.—*Any* dense, dark-colored, igneous rock is a *basalt* or, if porphyritic, a *basalt porphyry*. These terms include most of the dense rocks and related porphyries of the diorite and gabbro families and of the basic rocks named above.

Chemical Compositions of Igneous Rocks. — There is a rather close agreement between colors and mineral and chemical compositions. For example, the percentages of silica, SiO_2, in rocks

Colo. Geol. Survey.

Fig. 34. — Sedimentary rocks, alternating beds of shale and limestone, near Pueblo, Colorado.

of the granite family range from 65 to 80; while the iron oxides average about 2.6 per cent. The minerals and rocks are largely light-colored. In the gabbro family silica averages about 50 per cent, while the iron oxides amount to 19.0 per cent. Dark colors of both minerals and rocks, especially basalts, prevail in this family.

SEDIMENTARY ROCKS

Sedimentary rocks, as the word sediment implies, are composed largely of fragments of older rocks and minerals that have been more or less thoroughly consolidated and arranged in layers or strata. Some sedimentary rocks, however, are formed through organic agencies, and some are the result of direct precipitation of minerals from salt waters.

The modes of occurrence of sedimentary rocks are very different from those of igneous rocks. The former never occur in massive forms, such as sills, batholiths, laccoliths, etc., but always are stratified.

Most sediments are deposited in seas, lakes or streams, hence, they are water deposits, although in some places vast quan-

Fig. 35. — Typical sedimentary rocks. A — conglomerate. B — thin-bedded sandstone. C — massive sandstone. D — shell limestone. E — shale. F — flint.

tities are laid down directly on the land surface and are called continental deposits. All sedimentary rocks are likely to contain fossils (remains of ancient life). Also, they may exhibit ripple marks, raindrop prints, and mud cracks, if they were deposited in shallow water or on beaches or tidal flats. Usually the fragments of rocks and minerals that make up the *clastic* (composed of fragments) sedimentary rocks are well rounded, due to wear by streams or waves.

The grains of many clastic rocks are cemented together by silica, SiO_2, calcite, $CaCO_3$, or iron compounds. Some are consolidated simply through the pressure of overlying rocks.

Classification of Sedimentary Rocks

While many varieties of sedimentary rocks are known, they are much easier to distinguish than are the varieties of igneous rocks. The following table includes the more important varieties, and indicates in part the composition and mode of origin of the different rocks.

CLASSIFICATION OF SEDIMENTARY ROCKS

Clastics, mechanically formed	Non-clastic, organically formed	Non-clastic, formed by chemical precipitation
1. *Sand rocks*—deposited in water Sandstone Arkose Conglomerate	1. *Calcareous rocks*—shell fragments of marine or fresh water animals Limestone Chalk	1. *Calcareous rocks* Some limestones Dolomites Travertine
2. *Clay rocks*—deposited in water Clays Shale	2. *Carbonaceous rocks*—compressed and altered vegetable material Peat Lignite Coal	2. *Siliceous rocks* Novaculite Flint
3. *Dust and sand* Loess—wind-blown dust deposited on land Tuff — wind-blown volcanic dust deposited in water or on the land Sand—Wind-blown sand deposited on the land	3. *Siliceous rocks*—made up of tiny particles of silica secreted by organisms Diatomaceous earth Infusorial earth Geyserite (this also may be a chemical precipitate)	3. *Salts* Halite, NaCl Gypsum, $CaSO_4 . 2H_2O$ Anhydrite, $CaSO_4$ Potash Borax and many others
4. *Glacial deposits* Tillite (Drift) deposited on land or in water		

Due to methods of accumulation of the materials, the typical rocks indicated by the table may be very pure; or, in many cases they may be quite impure. Thus one may find beds of pure limestones in one place which laterally grade into shales; or pure quartz sandstones may occur which laterally or vertically grade into shales. Many other similar variations are known.

Clastic Rocks. — The rocks of the lithosphere are decomposed and broken up by agencies which will be discussed in Chapter VII. As a result, fragments of many different kinds of rocks and minerals accumulate on the land surface in the form of soil, dust and coarser fragments with variable size and shape.

Wind, streams, glaciers, and, in case of fragments that are formed on shorelines, waves and currents move these materials from one place to another. If the transporting agents deposit the material on land, the resulting rocks, after some consolidation, are called continental deposits; if they are deposited in seas, they become marine deposits; if laid down on lake bottoms, they are lacustrine deposits; while if they are deposited on the floors of streams, they are alluvial or flood-plain deposits.

As a rule, the continental deposits are poorly assorted, and only roughly, if at all, stratified; while the materials deposited in seas are well assorted and well stratified.

Sand Rocks.—Sandstones are composed chiefly of quartz grains, although many other mineral grains may be found. Usually the grains are rather small and are well rounded. When cemented by silica or iron oxide (hematite), the rock is very resistant to erosion and may be very important in the production of typical topographic forms. The colors vary greatly in these as in all other clastic rocks.

Arkose is a coarse sand rock composed largely of angular orthoclase feldspar and quartz grains in roughly equal amounts. Silvery mica may occur in these rocks.

Conglomerates are still coarser sand rocks. They are made up of sand grains with pebbles and boulders of varying sizes. The boulders may be several feet in diameter. Many conglomerates are continental in origin. If laid down in seas, they represent near shore deposits. Firmly cemented sand rocks resist erosion well, and are of great importance in local topographic development. They cap mesas, stand as great cliffs (Fig. 48), and, in many other ways, affect the development of land surfaces.

Clay Rocks.—These are chiefly lacustrine or marine deposits, but flood-plain deposits are common. The materials are primarily the mineral kaolinite with any other finely divided mineral matter. *Clays* are rocks composed almost entirely of kaolin. They are soft, break down easily by mechanical agents, and are easily eroded by wind, waves, streams and glaciers. They are, however, very insoluble, and resist chemical weathering to a marked degree. Pure clays are white, but in nature clay rocks of almost every color imaginable are found, due to small amounts of various coloring materials that may be present. *Shales* are impure clays which contain considerable proportions of minerals other than kaolinite. Their occurrence and behavior under erosional agents is essentially like that of clays.

Dust. — For our purposes dust may be thought of as any solid material small enough to be held in the air and to be carried long distances by the wind. Its chief sources are dry lands, cultivated fields and volcanoes. Dust may be carried for thousands of miles by the wind. It has been stated, probably correctly, that every square mile of the land surface contains dust from every other square mile of dry land of the earth. Where it has accumulated in large amounts, it forms the following sedimentary rocks.

Loess is very fine-grained material deposited by wind on the land. Unlike most sedimentary rocks, it is poorly, if at all, stratified. It is usually light brown or dull yellow in color. A peculiar property of loess is its ability to stand in vertical cliffs. It is poorly consolidated and is easily eroded. Due to its finely divided condition and to the remarkable wealth of soluble mineral plant foods which it contains, loessial soils are very fertile.

Tuff is pulverized igneous rock or volcanic dust which has been blown with explosive violence from a volcano. It may or may not be carried long distances by winds. It may accumulate on the land or in water. In the latter case it usually is well stratified, and it may contain well-preserved plant, insect and animal fossils. Tuff is composed largely of grains of glass. It is, therefore, very insoluble, makes a poor soil, and decomposes very little under the influence of chemicals in the air or ground. It is easily eroded by mechanical agents.

Non-clastic Rocks Organically Formed. — As is indicated in the table, these rocks are formed by both animals and plants.

Calcareous Rocks. — Limestones are the most important members of this group. While freshwater limestones are known, they are believed to be far less important than are marine limestones. These have a somewhat complicated history. The carbon dioxide of the air, in the presence of moisture, attacks rocks and minerals containing calcium. The result is calcium bicarbonate, which is carried in solution by streams and underground waters to the oceans. Average ocean water contains about 1.17 parts of $CaCO_3$ for every 1,000 parts of sea water. This is used by corals, oysters and many other marine organisms to build their shells or skeletons. Some plants (algae) also secrete $CaCO_3$. After the organisms die, their shells and skeletons may be ground to pieces by waves and ocean currents. These fragments, both coarse and fine, are accumulated in layers, and, when cemented together, form limestones.

Limestones occur in both thick and thin layers and in a great variety of colors. Due to their solubility, limestones tend to erode readily through chemical agents both on the surface and below the surface of the earth. Underground they are sites of caves and sinks; above ground they may be of much importance in controlling local topography, especially where they are thick-bedded.

Chalk is a soft friable rock made up of calcium carbonate in amorphous form secreted by tiny organisms called foraminifera. Small fragments of other shells, some composed of lime and others of silica, usually occur sparingly in chalk. It is of little physiographic importance, although chalky soils may be very fertile.

Carbonaceous Rocks. — These, unlike all others so far described, are of direct vegetable origin. In marshes, peat bogs and swamps situated at sea level, vegetable material may accumulate to great thickness. If such thick masses of partially decomposed vegetation become covered by sediments washed in by streams, coal of various grades finally results. *Peat is* the poorest and first grade of coal formed. It is brown in color and shows, under a microscope, its vegetable parentage. *Lignite* represents a more advanced stage in the coal-making process. The original vegetation has been considerably changed; volatile gases are less and the percentage of carbon is greater. The colors are brown or black. *Coal* occurs in many varieties, of which the most common are *bituminous, semi-anthracite and anthracite.* All are black. All occur interstratified with sandstones and shales. Although of little physiographic importance, coal is, of course, of great economic value.

Siliceous Rocks. — Diatomaceous, or infusorial earth, is a *loose*, white, gray or brown rock made up in large part of tiny siliceous shells formed by microscopic, single-celled plants. The earth looks and feels much like chalk, but is more gritty, and, unlike chalk, it does not effervesce in acids. Although it is in considerable demand for economic purposes, it is of little importance physiographically.

Geyserite is silica deposited from the hot water of geysers. It is white, gray or yellowish brown in color, depending on impurities. Algae aid in the deposition of this material; although it may be deposited directly by chemical precipitation. Locally, where geysers occur, minor but interesting topographic forms result from the deposition of this material.

Non-clastics Formed by Chemical Precipitation.— Oceans, salt lakes and underground waters contain many different salts in solution. Under favorable conditions these salts may be precipitated through evaporation of the water. Some, but not all, such precipitates are arranged in layers, and may be covered by stratified shales or sandstones, thus forming a series of sedimentary rocks.

Calcareous Rocks. — Some *limestones,* which are composed of $CaCO_3$, and *dolomites,* which are magnesium limestones, $Ca,Mg(CO_3)_2$, are formed by direct chemical precipitation. Usually these rocks are more dense and compact than are limestones that are formed through organic agencies. Colors and physiographic significance are the same as for other limestones.

Travertine is found both beneath and on the surface of the ground. In caves it occurs as stalactites and stalagmites and in

many other irregular forms. On the surface it is chiefly associated
with hot springs. The beautiful terraces of the hot springs of
Yellowstone Park are composed of this material; algae aid in its
deposition. The color of travertine, when pure, is white; but many
other colors are known.

Siliceous Rocks. — Novaculite and flint are good representatives of this group. Both are very fine-grained, white, gray or
black rocks which break with distinct conchoidal fracture. Novaculite is believed to have been deposited from spring water; while
flint is deposited from sea water in irregular, rounded masses in
limestones and chalk. Both have some economic but little physiographic importance.

Other Salts. — Many other salts, including nitrates, borates,
sulphates and chlorides occur as sedimentary rocks. Since they are
of little interest to the physiographer, only a few examples will be
given.

Halite, NaCl, a rock salt, is found in layers between other stratified rocks in many parts of the world. Through the solvent action
of ground water, caves may be formed in salt. If the roofs of the
caves fall in, salt sinks and depressions similar to those made in
limestone may be formed.

Gypsum, $CaSO_4.2H_2O$, is of widespread occurrence and great
economic importance. It is particularly likely to occur interstratified with red sandstones and shales. Massive gypsum, or alabaster,
is largely used for statuary and other decorative purposes.

Potash salts, consisting of nitrates, and others occur in Germany
in layers with a total thickness of several thousand feet. In New
Mexico there are somewhat similar beds. They are of great economic value in that they furnish materials for fertilizers and also
for explosives.

METAMORPHIC ROCKS

The word *metamorphose* really means change of form, but, as
used in geology in a more restricted sense, *metamorphic rocks include those rocks that have been changed either in form or composition without disintegration.* Based on the original types before
metamorphism, all metamorphic rocks may be classified as meta-

igneous or meta-sedimentary. The changes that take place may be physical or chemical or both. One mineral may be changed to another; the arrangement of mineral grains may be changed; individual grains may be fused due to extreme heat; new materials may be added from other sources.

Agents of Metamorphism. — The agents that produce the changes are chiefly heat, compression and solutions, acting singly

Fig. 36. — Metamorphic rocks. A — gneissoid granite. B — quartz-mica schist. C — mica schist. D — slate. E — quartzite. F — marble.

or together. In *contact metamorphism* molten rock comes in contact with other solid rocks. The heat and, in many cases, solutions derived from the liquid material change the surrounding rocks. An example is a dike intruded into limestone. Near the borders of the dike the limestone may be entirely changed to marble, which is, of course, a metamorphic rock.

However, metamorphic processes may operate on a much grander scale. For example, in New England and Pennsylvania, heat through friction and compression produced by great mountain-making forces have changed limestones to marbles, shales to slates, and bituminous coal to anthracite. Also, in those regions igneous rocks have become laminated, due to movements which rearranged the minerals within the rock. Great forces acting over large areas give rise to *regional metamorphism* of the rocks.

As a result of metamorphism, some rocks are made more resistant to erosion; while others become less resistant than they were before. Naturally, the topographic forms produced by different forces acting on such rocks will be very different in different cases. For these reasons, a knowledge of the important types of metamorphic rocks is of value to the physiographer.

Classification of Metamorphic Rocks

As has already been indicated, these rocks may be classified according to original materials as meta-igneous and meta-sedimentary rocks; or, on the basis of metamorphic processes, they may be classified as contact and regional metamorphic rocks. The first classification assumes that the original rock is determinable, and the second assumes that the immediate cause of the metamorphism is determinable. It frequently happens that neither is possible; therefore, the following classification, based largely on structure but with some regard for original composition, is used. Only the more common varieties are included.

Distinguishing Features. — While type specimens of the metamorphic rocks usually are easily recognizable, it should be understood that there are gradations from one type to another. Thus, a sandy shale after metamorphism may be a quartz-mica schist; but with an increased amount of sand and less shale in the original, it may become an impure quartzite. Some gneissoid rocks are difficult to distinguish from schists. Many other gradations are known, but usually are of little importance in physiography.

Physiographic Importance. — Quartzites, quartz schists, slates and phyllites are harder and more resistant to erosion than are their

CLASSIFICATION OF METAMORPHIC ROCKS

Division	Chief varieties of original rocks	Descriptions
Foliated 1. Gneisses	Conglomerates or any granitoid igneous rock	Gneisses are granular rocks in which the original grains have been rearranged into more or less perfect bands or layers.
2. Gneissoid granites, syenites, etc.	Granitoid igneous rocks. The name of the rock family indicates the composition	Same as above. Gneissoid granite indicates a coarse-grained rock of the granite family whose minerals are arranged so as to give a banded structure.
3. Slates and phyllites	Shales and other finely divided argillaceous materials	They may have almost any color. A definite cleavage or fissile structure is always present due to compression and recrystallization of minerals with parallel arrangement.
4. Schists	Either fine-grained igneous or clastic sedimentary rocks. The latter are more common.	Well foliated granular rocks. Usually named for the dominant mineral. Ex.: mica schist, talc schist, hornblende schist, etc. Almost any color.
Non-foliated 1. Quartzite	Sandstone	Spaces between grains of the original rock have been completely filled through (a) intense heat and compression or (b) silica brought in by and deposited from solution. As a result the quartzite is harder than the original sandstone and tends to break through rather than around the grains.
2. Marble	Limestone or dolomite	In marble the original materials have been recrystallized. As a result, the rock takes a high polish. Usually impurities which give red, green, black or gray colors are introduced during the process of metamorphism.
3. Serpentine	Basic igneous rocks such as gabbro or pyroxenite	Greenish to black color, massive or platy. Composed chiefly of serpentine with silica, iron, olivine, etc. Used extensively for decorative purposes.

unmetamorphosed equivalents. On the other hand, most gneissoid rocks, serpentine, soapstone and some schists, erode more easily than do the rocks from which they were derived. Metamorphic rocks occur especially in mountain regions where structural conditions incident to mountain growth are in evidence. Due to the combined influence of composition and structure, these rocks may have much to do with the details of the topography of such regions.

REFERENCES

1. R. A. Daly: *Igneous Rocks and the Depths of the Earth.* McGraw-Hill Book Co., 1933.
2. Alfred Harker: *Petrology for Students.* Cambridge Univ. Press, 1902.
3. L. V. Pirsson and A. Knopf: *Rocks and Rock Minerals.* John Wiley and Sons, 1926.

CHAPTER VI

EARTH MOVEMENTS AND STRUCTURES

Geomorphology often is called "the last or present chapter in earth history." This designation is quite appropriate, for the subject is primarily concerned with the *present* surface of the land. But even a cursory examination of land forms reveals the fact that many of them are largely dependent upon the structure of the underlying rocks for their shape or position. In other cases the general results of *gradational* processes are clearly modified by earth movements. Final analysis of land forms indicates plainly that crustal movements resulting in the deformation of both small and large regional areas have combined with the external physiographic processes in a multitude of ways to bring about our present landscapes. One frequently hears such phrases as "solid as a rock" or "stable as the earth," the ideas conveyed being those of great solidity or stability. Contrary to such notions, it is evident that the earth is, and probably always has been, a very unstable body. The evidence for this statement is all around us, and we may now proceed to examine it.

As a first example, let us try to see what the physiography of North America was like some 75 or 100 million years ago, and then trace it through, in broad stages, to the present time. During the middle of the Upper Cretaceous period, a great epicontinental sea covered some 4,000,000 square miles of central western North America. It extended from the Gulf of Mexico to the Arctic Ocean (Fig. 337). The Appalachian Mountains were much lower than they are now, but the Basin Ranges and probably the Sierra Nevadas were higher. The Rocky Mountains were not in existence.

Confining our attention now to the Rocky Mountain region, we find that the seas have drained back to the ocean basins, and a great mountain system, thousands of miles long and many miles wide, has been elevated by earth movements. In addition, the plains east of the mountains have been raised in some places to a

Don Kemp.

FIG. 37. — Vertical sedimentary formations showing varying resistance to erosion, Mexico.

height of more than 6,000 feet above sea level, while some of the plateau lands west of the mountains have been elevated to even greater heights.

The denudation of the mountains, plateaus and plains by glaciers, wind and streams to produce the present landscape was made possible by earth movements. It might be interesting to ask what the physiography of North America would be now, if there had been no earth movements of any sort, anywhere, since Upper Cretaceous times. The question can be answered better after reading the succeeding chapters, but it may be stated categorically here that there would be very little physiography; for part of the continent would be covered by shallow seas, and the rest would be a monotonous plain only slightly above sea level. Other more local examples of the results of earth movements are sedimentary rocks containing marine fossils, now found thousands of feet above the sea in the Rockies and Alps; warped shorelines of seas and lakes; long fractures, *faults*, in rocks; submerged wharves and piers; and earthquakes. Countless other examples might be given.

Types of Earth Movements

The term *diastrophism* includes all crustal movements of the earth. These may be divided into (1) sudden and relatively slight movements, such as (a) those that produce earthquakes, and (b) earthquakes themselves; (2) slow but relatively large movements, (a) *orogenic* (mountain-forming), and (b) *epeirogenic* (continental). Faults which cause earthquakes and the resulting earth tremors occur quite as commonly beneath the oceans as beneath land surfaces. Earthquakes are important from a human point of view because of the devastating results, but are of relatively little importance in physiography. The continental and mountain-making movements, on the contrary, are of utmost interest and importance in all studies of land forms.

Earthquakes

"An earthquake is a vibration or oscillation of the surface of the earth caused by a transient disturbance of the elastic or gravitational equilibrium of the rocks at or beneath the surface."[1] Earth-

[1] J. B. Macelwane: *Seismology, Physics of the Earth* VI, p. 1, National Research Council, 1933.

quakes may be natural or artificial, depending upon whether they are due to natural causes or are caused by man. Great explosions, railway trains, heavy trucks, the razing of the walls of large buildings illustrate causes of minor, man-made earthquakes. Natural earthquakes are *volcanic, tectonic* and *plutonic*, depending upon the cause and position of the stresses. *Volcanic earthquakes* precede, accompany and frequently follow volcanic eruptions. Usually they are not particularly severe, although they are very numerous in volcanic regions. Apparently, they are caused by sudden violent displacements of lava in or beneath the conduits of volcanoes. *Tectonic earthquakes* are caused by sudden movements of the earth's crust, usually at depths of from 3 to 15 miles below the surface of the ground. These movements which break the rocks apart and displace them along definite planes are *faults*. Tectonic earthquakes vary greatly in intensity, but some are very severe. *Plutonic earthquakes* are less well understood than are the other types. They occur less frequently and originate at depths of from 150 to 420 miles. Due to the great pressures that exist at such depths, it is not generally believed by geologists that sudden breaks can occur in the rocks. Therefore, highly theoretical causes, such as chemical explosions, recrystallization of minerals, molecular changes in minerals attained in "unsymmetrical manner," and others, have been offered to explain this type of earthquake. Gutenberg[1] and Richter, however, in a critical analysis of deep focus earthquakes, conclude that "the mechanism of origin of shocks seems to be the same at all depths." They classify earthquakes as *normal* when the shock occurs at depths of 50 kilometers (about 30 miles) or less, *intermediate* when the shock originates at depths between 70 and 250 kilometers, and *deep-focus* when the depth of the disturbance is between 250 and 700 kilometers (about 420 miles).

Frequency. — Many earthquakes occur every day. Based on the number of recorded shocks during a year, the earth is quaking at one place or another on the average of at least once in every two and one-half hours. Regions particularly susceptible to earthquakes

[1] B. Gutenberg and C. F. Richter: *Depth and Geographical Distribution of Deep-Focus Earthquakes.* Bulletin, Geol. Soc. America, Vol. 49, pp. 249–298, 1938.

may have several shocks in one day. The shocks are perceptible if people recognize them, or they may be so light as to be imperceptible, yet are recorded by delicate instruments called seismographs.

Earthquake Zones. — Due to peculiar geologic conditions, certain regions of the earth are recognized as earthquake zones (Fig. 38). Typical of these are volcanic areas, steep continental slopes, youthful or growing mountains, and the regions, such as both the East and West Indies, where two continents and two ocean basins meet. More than 50 per cent of all earthquakes occur in youthful mountains, of which the Andes, Himalayas and Coast Ranges of the United States are good examples. About 40 per cent occur on or near the borders of the continents where the slopes are relatively steep from the highlands of the continents to the floors of the ocean basins. The other 10 per cent are widely scattered over the earth.

Although most shocks occur where they are expected, some come in quite unexpected places. For example, in 1929 there were strong earthquakes in Cabot Strait between Nova Scotia and Newfoundland, while in 1935 severe shocks occurred near Helena, Montana. No place on earth can be regarded as entirely secure from earthquakes.

Duration and Repetition of Shocks. — An earthquake can do an incredible amount of damage in a surprisingly short time. The great San Francisco earthquake of April 18th, 1906, was all over in less than one minute. The Italian earthquake of 1908, which caused the loss of 150,000 lives, lasted only 23 seconds. The Japanese earthquake of 1923, in a few seconds, killed about 140,000 people, and directly, or indirectly through the fire which followed the shock, caused a property loss of more than two and one-half billion dollars.

Usually the first heavy shocks are followed by numerous lighter ones. Nine hundred and thirty-six after-shocks were recorded in four days following the Japanese quake of 1923. During the first year following the major shock at Helena, Montana, in 1935, there were more than 2,100 minor shocks.

Apparent Intensity of the Shocks. — Students of earthquakes have repeatedly pointed out that it is difficult to determine the

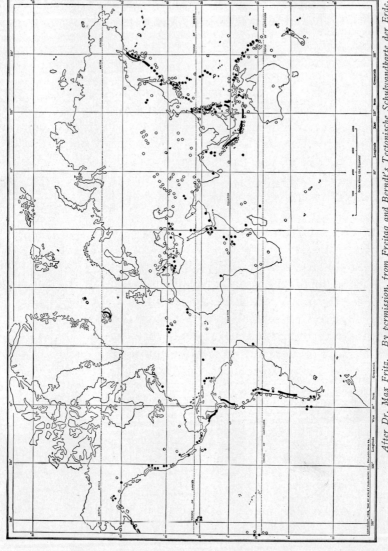

After Dr. Max Fritz. By permission, from Freitag and Berndt's Tectonische Schulwandkarte der Erde.

FIG. 38.—Earthquake and volcanic regions of the earth. The open circles show earthquake centers. The black circles and solid black lines denote regions of present or recent volcanism.

actual intensity of an earthquake which depends upon the amplitude of the waves, acceleration, frequency and other mathematical factors. The *apparent intensity* is indicated by the damage to buildings and other engineering structures and to the disturbance of soil and rocks. In general, earthquakes are more destructive to structures built on loose rocks or filled ground than to those built on firm, solid rocks. Also, greater damage occurs near the *epicenter* than far from it. The epicenter is the point or line on the earth's surface directly above the place of the origin of the shock. In all cases the degree of intensity depends upon the violence of the original disturbance that caused the shock, the angle at which the waves reach the surface of the ground and upon the distance from the focus of the shock to any place on the earth's surface. Very deep-seated shocks, therefore, are usually less destructive than are shallower ones.

The Focus of the Shock. — The term *focus* means the point or localized zone where earth vibrations originate and from which they radiate. In cases where the place of origin is small, the focus may be thought of as a point within the earth. However, many earthquakes occur as a result of movement on fault planes of great length. In the California earthquakes of 1906, there was movement along the old San Andreas fault for a distance certainly of 190 miles, and probably of more than 350 miles. In this case the focus was not a single point, but, rather, a plane at least 190 miles long and 3 miles deep. Where a sudden slip on a long fault occurs, some observers regard the place where the *first* violent activity occurred as the focus for the whole shock; actually, the focus changes from one place to another as the rocks break apart.

Earthquake Waves. — When rocks suddenly break within the earth, vibrations are set up which are called earthquake or seismic waves. Due to reflection, refraction and interference, simple waves become complicated, but for our purpose we may consider only three types. These are (1) Preliminary or P waves, also called longitudinal waves or waves of condensation. These waves travel outward in straight lines in all directions from the focus of the shock. They are the fastest of all earthquake waves, having an average velocity of 3.3 miles a second and a maximum of nearly double that rate. (2) Secondary S or shear waves, also called transverse waves because they vibrate at right angles to the direction of the propagation, closely follow the P waves. The velocity of the S wave is about one-half that of the P wave, but the S wave is more destructive. (3) After the P or S waves reach the surface of the earth, a surface wave L may be set up which travels with a lower velocity than the other two around the surface of the earth. It is also very destructive.

Nature of Earth Movements. — It is necessary to distinguish clearly between cause and effect when considering these movements. The disturbances which *cause* earthquakes may involve movements of from a few inches to many feet. In the California earthquake of 1916 the maximum displacement along the San Andreas fault was 20 feet. Soundings made in Sagami Bay before and after the Japanese earthquake of 1923 indicate a total movement on the two sides of the fault of more than 1,800 feet. These, however, represent movements which *caused* the earthquakes.

The movements resulting from the passage of earthquake waves through the earth are very much less. A *rapid* horizontal or vertical movement of one inch constitutes a very disastrous shock. In exceptional cases the ground may roll into swells and troughs like ocean waves, but the total height of such swells probably is not more than two or three feet. Apparently the movement in loose soil or remade ground is much greater than in solid rock.

The Effects of Earthquakes on Topography. — Here again one must be careful to distinguish between cause and effect. The actual effects of earthquakes on topography are comparatively small, although many *minor* effects may be found. Landslides occur; loose mantle rock is cracked open or caused to slump; small circular openings like miniature volcanic craters are formed in soil and unconsolidated rock; irregular cracks may occur parallel with or transverse to the faults that caused the earthquake. All these may be important in aiding subsequent erosion, but in themselves they are of little topographic importance.

Sea Waves. — Submarine earthquakes may cause sea waves of great size and velocity. Where such waves dash on a low, thickly inhabited coast, they may do tremendous damage. Also, they are important agents of erosion if they break on unconsolidated rocks, such as those of deltas and beaches. These waves are frequently (incorrectly) called tidal waves.

Destructiveness of Earthquakes. — The literature on earthquakes is full of descriptions of the damage to life and property, and the horrors attending great earthquakes. Naturally, the greatest disasters are in thickly populated regions. In a violent earthquake trees are snapped off; buildings are shaken down; bridges collapse; roads are cracked open or are blocked by landslides; railroads are put out of commission; telegraph wires are torn down. On coasts, wharves and breakwaters are destroyed, ships are grounded, and sea waves rush in over the land, leaving ruin and desolation in their wake. In large cities, fires almost inevitably follow earthquakes. In the 1923 Tokio earthquake, far more damage was done by fire than directly by the quake. The same is true of the San Francisco earthquake of 1906 and of many others.

Man-made Structures in Earthquake Zones. — Through past experience in earthquake regions, engineers and architects have learned much about building large structures, so that they will withstand the shocks. Flimsy bamboo houses commonly used in many Oriental countries are doomed to destruction, if a severe earthquake occurs. A poor grade of brick structure with cheap mortar and careless construction is likely to collapse. Well-built wooden structures stand up well under the shocks. Steel-framed and reinforced concrete buildings usually withstand even violent shocks. If possible, large structures should stand on solid rock; if it is necessary to build them on sand or remade ground, they should stand on piles or foundations set deeply into the loose ground, so that they will sway with the ground. Elasticity, the ability to yield to the earthquake stresses, or to move with them, is an important factor in earthquake-proof construction. Not only buildings, but dams, bridges, water pipes, sewers and all other structures demand the attention of skilled engineers in earthquake zones.

Continental (Epeirogenic) Movements

Every continent, including Antarctica, offers unmistakable evidence of both downward and upward movements since Pre-Cambrian times. The proof of such movements is found in marine sedimentary rocks of Paleozoic, Mesozoic or Cenozoic age, which lie within the continents upon well-eroded older rocks. The occurrence of such sediments in the positions indicated is definite proof of downwarping of broad areas of the continents which allowed the sea water to cover gradually these depressed regions. Sediments carried by streams from neighboring land areas were deposited in these epicontinental seas. Proof of the subsequent upwarping of the continents is evident in the fact that these marine sedimentary rocks are now found high above sea level, well within the borders of the present continents.

The question naturally arises, when considering the statements in the preceding paragraph, "Is it the land or sea which changes level?" If sea level rises or falls due to upward or downward movements of the ocean floor, obviously such rise or fall should be recorded on *all the continents* at the same time. However, when all the records are examined, no such evidence is found, except during the Pleistocene Ice Age, when the sea level fell, due to locking up of the ocean water on the land in the form of glacial ice; and then rose again when the ice melted. During many geologic periods some continents apparently have remained above sea level at the time that other continents were partly covered by marine waters. Therefore, we may conclude that the continents, individually, have been subjected to great earth movements. This statement is further verified by studying in detail local areas on the individual continents. This examination shows plainly that both the downward and upward movements have varied greatly in nearby regions. For example, in east central Colorado the total thickness of Cretaceous sediments is only 6,500 feet, while in northwestern Colorado, only 150 miles away, beds of the same age are more than twice as thick, thus indicating that the downwarped basin was much deeper in the latter region. Also, on the plains of southeastern Colorado, due to uplift, certain Cretaceous sediments (the Dakota beds) are now 6,000 feet *above* sea level, while in northeastern Colorado the same beds have been reached by drills at a depth of 2,000 feet *below* sea level.

To understand this situation, it should be noted that the Dakota formation, which was widely deposited over west central North America at the beginning of the Upper Cretaceous epoch, was depressed by continental movements and covered by more than 6,000 feet of sedimentary rocks all during Upper Cretaceous times. At the close of this period, the Dakota was approximately 6,000 feet below sea level over all of eastern Colorado. Subsequent movements raised southeastern Colorado some 12,000 feet, but northeastern Colorado only 4,000 feet. Such differential uplift within a small region in the heart of a great continent furnishes the best possible evidence of great epeirogenic movements.

Recent Movements. — Seashores and lake shorelines of the various continents afford abundant evidence of recent movements. The following examples are indicative of conditions that are found on many continental borders.

Downward Movements. — At the east end of the Island of Crete, ancient buildings are now submerged. Immediately off the coasts of Maine, British Columbia and southern Alaska are numerous islands which clearly were once part of the mainland. The seaways between the islands are former lowlands now submerged. Much of the north coast of the Gulf of Mexico appears to be slowly subsiding. Chesapeake Bay and the lower part of the St. Lawrence River valley are "drowned valleys" (*estuaries*) due to subsidence of the land which has let the sea water advance far up the valleys.

Upward Movements. — The Atlantic coastal plain of southeastern United States is underlain by marine sedimentary rocks that not long ago, geologically speaking, were beneath the sea. Their present position above water indicates a broad regional uplift of the land. Where coast lines have been relatively stable for some time, the sea develops wave-cut plains, sea caves and other characteristic forms (see Chap. XII). The present occurrence of such forms well above the sea level also indicates recent uplift. On the shores of ancient Lake Bonneville, in Utah, wave-cut terraces were made as the water level became progressively lower. The terraces still remain, forming gigantic stairs. However, they have been warped and tilted by diastrophism since they were formed by the waves. Raised beaches of northern England and Scotland, raised coral reefs of Peru and Cuba, salt water barnacles still attached to cliffs in Alaska, 1,000 feet above the sea — all tell the same story of recent differential uplift.

Conclusions. — The data just presented can be augmented by other evidence from each of the continents. It is impossible to escape the conclusion that all the continents are relatively unstable and that movements of great variety and extent have occurred throughout earth history. These great diastrophic changes have

D. F. Higgins.

FIG. 39. — The partially dissected terrace above the beach is a recently uplifted wave-cut plain, northern Africa.

revived and rejuvenated the continents and have allowed new relief features to be developed. It may be prophesied with confidence that similar movements will continue during the coming ages.

Mountain-making (Orogenic) Movements

These movements are closely associated with continental movements, both in time and in their nature. However, orogenic movements are due to the concentration of great forces within the earth which, through folding or faulting, usually both, raise more local land masses than continents high above their original positions. The rate of movement is so slow that little or no evidence of it could be determined during the average life of any person. Yet through many hundreds of centuries of growth, the mountains have finally attained their present heights.

Periods of Mountain Growth. — Every geologic era and probably every period from far back in the Archeozoic era has been a time when mountains were growing somewhere on the earth. The oldest mountains long ago were removed by erosion, but their roots may be yet found in the distorted metamorphic rocks of Archeozoic and Proterozoic ages. The Appalachians, which were greatly uplifted in the Pennsylvanian and Permian periods, have endured to the present time. It is doubtful, however, if they would have done so had it not been for repeated uplifts since their first period of growth. The Himalayas, Andes and Coast Ranges of western United States have been growing in comparatively recent times. The Rockies are intermediate in age, having attained their maximum growth probably by the end of the Pliocene epoch. A more detailed discussion of the history and development of different types of mountains is given in Chapter XVI.

The Causes of Diastrophism

The causes of earthquakes already have been discussed in this chapter. Fundamentally, however, they are definitely related to the more basic causes of continental and mountain-making movements. A full discussion of the hypotheses that have been advanced to explain these movements involves problems of theoretical geology that are out of place in an introductory textbook. The many theories are definitely related to different conceptions of the physical condition of the interior of the earth.

The Earth Is a Contracting Body. — The internal temperatures and pressure of the earth are very high. Earthquake waves that pass through deep portions of the earth indicate a marked difference between the materials at depth and those that make up the outer crust. The "crust" may be thought of as a shell some 36 miles thick. Regardless of one's theory of the interior of the earth, the principle is generally accepted by geologists that the earth is gradually contracting to a smaller and smaller volume. This shrinkage may be due in part to loss of heat, but probably chiefly to physical and chemical changes that are taking place in rocks well within the earth. As contraction goes on, stresses are set up between the outer crust and shrinking interior. The crust finally yields, sinking in some places and rising in others. This unequal yielding seems to explain the great continental movements. Mountain-making movements occur on the sites of former geosynclines where the stresses are concentrated. Folded and faulted mountain structures indicate that *lateral compression* is the chief factor in the *original* mountain growth. After the mountains have been raised and greatly eroded, *vertical* adjustments may take place, causing renewed uplift.

Structures Due to Diastrophism

All varieties of rocks are deformed by earth movements, but massive homogeneous igneous rocks do not show the results of such movements as clearly as do stratified sedimentary or metamorphic rocks. With few exceptions, sedimentary rocks are deposited in a horizontal or near horizontal position. Therefore, if they are found departing much from that position, deformation is indicated. The chief types of rock structures due to diastrophism are broad warps and folds, faults, and joints.

Dip and Strike. — In order to interpret correctly folded and faulted structures, the terms dip and strike should be clearly understood. *Dip.* — Sedimentary or stratified metamorphic rocks that are now in a horizontal position have no dip. If the beds are not in horizontal position, they must slope in some direction. Dip denotes two things: (1) it represents the *angle* that the beds slope measured from a horizontal plane (Fig. 40); (2) it denotes the *direction* of the *downward* slope of the beds. Thus the dip of the beds which have been tilted to an angle of 45° and which now slope due south is recorded as follows: Dip 45° S.

Strike is the *direction* in which uptilted beds intersect a horizontal plane. The direction of strike is at right angles to the direction of dip. On geologic maps it is customary to indicate the dip by an arrow which points with the direction of slope. The strike is indicated by a bar at right angles to the arrow. Of course, both the dip and strike directions on a map are plotted accurately to conform to the geographic positions previously determined on the ground.

Broad Warps. — Continental movements usually result in broad upwarped or downwarped areas of the earth's surface. These may extend from a few miles to hundreds of miles in length and width. The upwarped regions are *geanticlines*, while the downwarped areas are *geosynclines*. The great plains of western North America have been upwarped, so that from their highest elevation in central Colorado they slope gradually toward the Arctic Ocean, the Mississippi basin and the Gulf of Mexico, thus representing a great *geanti-*

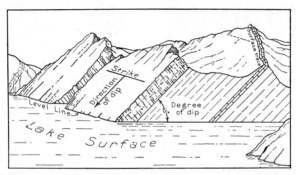

FIG. 40. — Dip and strike. The reference plane for measuring the angle of dip is any horizontal plane. Here it is represented by the lake surface. Note that outcrops do not necessarily follow the strike of the beds.

cline. Hudson Bay and the Baltic Sea illustrate geosynclines now covered by sea water. Many small folds or faults may occur within either geanticlinal or geosynclinal areas.

Folds. — Actually the broad warps just described are folds, but they are so large that they can be understood only through wide regional studies. The term "fold" usually is applied to smaller structures which result from the bending of layers of rocks. They may be simple or very complex in form, due to the varying nature and intensity of the earth forces that produced them. The length and width of folds may be from less than an inch to scores of miles.

Monocline. — The simplest type of fold is the monocline which involves only *one* inclination of the rocks. The terrace-like structure of the rocks may give rise to surface topography of similar form.

Anticline. — In a normal anticline the layers dip in opposite directions away from the crest or axial plane of the fold. In many cases the ends of anticlines dip downward making *closed folds* which are favorable structures for the accumulation of oil and natural gas. Anticlines are symmetrical if the dips of the sides are approximately equal; unsymmetrical if the dip on one side is much steeper than on the other. Gentle anticlinal folds may have dips as low as one or two degrees. Steep anticlines have dips of from 45° to nearly 90°. Anticlines are particularly common in and on the borders of folded mountains, but are by no means confined to such localities. They occur widely throughout the central and western

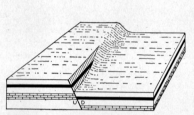

FIG. 41. — A monoclinal fold playing out into a fault.

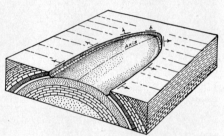

FIG. 42. — An eroded anticline.

plains of North America, and similarly in many other plains and plateau areas.

Due to the tension developed during their formation, the tops of anticlines are likely to be cracked and broken, thus making them very susceptible to erosion. It frequently happens that streams have carved deep valleys in the tops of anticlines. If resistant rocks are exposed by erosion, ridges may eventually be developed that clearly outline the anticlinal structure (Fig. 43). After long erosion the flanks of folded mountains are carved into long parallel ridges and valleys. The valleys are cut in soft layers of sedimentary rock, while the ridges are composed of more resistant layers.

Syncline. — A syncline is a downwarped fold — just the reverse of an anticline. The sides of a syncline dip *toward* each other, meeting at the bottom of the fold. If synclines are closed due to the downward plunge on all sides of the rocks that make up the structure, the resulting form is basin or canoe-shaped. The sizes vary as greatly as in case of anticlines. Synclines occur very com-

Richard Ragle.

FIG. 43. — An eroded anticline, northern Colorado.

W. O. Thompson.

FIG. 44. — A syncline and an anticline, both tightly compressed, Alberta.

monly beside anticlines. Great intermontane basins with synclinal structure often are found between two anticlinal mountain ranges. After long erosion and uplift, synclinal structures often underlie hills and ridges. In such cases it is evident that the synclines, being

R. D. Crawford.

FIG. 45. — A hill with underlying synclinal structure, Sawatch Range, Colorado.

compressed, are more resistant to erosion than are the adjacent anticlines.

Anticlinorium. — As the word suggests, anticlinoria are structures found in folded mountains. The form of an anticlinorium is

FIG. 46. — Cross-section through an anticlinorium and a synclinorium.

that of a large anticline with minor synclinal and anticlinal structures incorporated in it. In such structures it is evident that the forces were applied unevenly and that the rocks yielded unequally.

Topographic Results of Folding. — Folds lay the groundwork for a great variety of topographic forms. Minor terraces due to recent monoclinal folding, or mountain ranges due to the upheaval of enormous anticlines are but suggestions of the influence of this type of deformation on topography. Far more important even than these direct relationships are the indirect ways in which folds help to determine the land forms that are later produced by agents of erosion.   Thus we find long parallel ridges and valleys carved out of uptilted sedimentary rocks of varying composition, or straight regular shorelines developed by waves on rocks of uniform composition that dip toward the sea.   These relationships between structures of rocks and topography form much of the subject matter for the chapters that follow, and need not be considered further here, except to reemphasize the fact that deformations of the earth, whether great or slight, are of fundamental importance in determining the subsequent topography of any region.

Don Kemp.

FIG. 47. — Horizontal beds of similar resistance to erosion as those shown in Fig. 37. Here the massive sandstone capping the mesa protects the underlying shale from erosion.

Faults. — A fault is a fracture or fissure in the earth along which one side has moved with reference to the other side.   The surface, usually called the fault plane, on which the movement took place may be smooth or curved; it may be vertical or inclined at any angle to a horizontal plane, which is the plane of reference.   The fissure may be tight or there may be a zone of fractured rock many feet wide within which the faulting took place.   The movement may occur vertically, horizontally, or in any other direction.   Even pivotal faults with a rotary movement are not uncommon.

Faults are closely related to folds. Any type of fold may pass into a fault (Fig. 41). Where anticlines have become unsymmetrical and finally recumbent, due, apparently, to forces acting chiefly

James Johnson.

FIG. 48. — The "Third Flatiron" near Boulder, Colorado. The steeply dipping beds of massive conglomerate are more resistant to erosion than is the granite behind them.

in one direction, the under limb of the anticline may become stretched until the rocks finally give way and a thrust fault results.

In highly compressed mountain regions, such as the southern

Appalachians, faults are likely to occur parallel to the general strike of the folds. In other cases faults may occur at angles of about 45° to the strike of the folds. Such definite relationships of faults and folds indicate that their fundamental cause is the same. Whether rocks subjected to deformation will fold or fault apparently depends upon the strength of the rocks and the rapidity of the applied forces.

Faults represent zones of weakness within the earth in which movements are likely to occur repeatedly through long periods of time. Where this happens, the faults are known as *active* faults. They are illustrated by the renewed movement along the San Andreas fault in 1906 which caused the

FIG. 49.—A fault in metamorphic rocks, near Central City, Colorado.

California earthquake, or the movement in 1935 along an old fault which caused the Helena, Montana, quakes. Wide fault zones permit rapid weathering and erosion. Therefore, the trace of great faults on the earth's surface usually is easily followed (Fig. 51).

FIG. 50.—A thrust fault developed by lateral compression.

Blocks of the earth may be either elevated or depressed due to faulting. The Basin Ranges of Nevada and of the plateau of Mexico are bounded by great faults. An interesting example of a relatively depressed block is the region of the Dead Sea in Palestine, where a long strip of land was left down, while the surrounding land was faulted up around it. Many minor topographic forms, such as benches or terraces, small valleys and cliffs are direct results of faulting.

Royal Canadian Air Force Photo.

FIG. 51. — A view near the mouth of French River, Ontario, north of Lake Heron. The long narrow water courses probably coincide with minor faults.

Descriptive Terms Applied to Faults. — Many types of faults, such as dip faults, strike faults, branching faults, etc., are known.

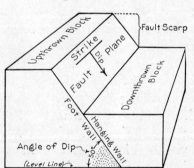

The technical terms applied to different parts of faults are numerous, but most of them are of little importance to the physiographer and will be omitted from this discussion.

Parts of a Fault. — Figure 52 illustrates a typical fault with the names of the important parts. The *fault plane* is the surface along which movement takes place. The *dip* of the fault plane is the angle between

FIG. 52. — The parts of a simple fault.

the fault and a horizontal plane. It is measured and recorded as

FIG. 53.—A slickensided surface. The small grooves and polished face indicate the relative directions of movement; in this case from left to right or right to left.

indicated above. The strike of the fault is the direction of its intersection with a horizontal plane. The *trace is* the outcrop of the fault plane on the land surface. It is the same as the strike, if the land is flat. The *downthrow* side is the side that has been moved down relative to the other side, which is called the *upthrow* side. It usually is impossible to determine which side actually moved.

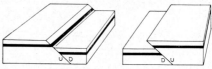

FIG. 54.—The block on the left represents a normal fault, the one on the right is a reverse fault.

The *hanging wall* is the upper wall of the fault, and the *foot wall* is the lower wall, when the fault plane is not vertical. In case of a vertical fault, there is neither hanging nor foot wall. The _scarp_ is the cliff or steep slope made on the land surface due to faulting. Many well-preserved fault scarps have very highly polished rock surfaces, _slickensides_. Shallow grooves on these surfaces indicate the relative directions of movement of the rocks along the fault plane.

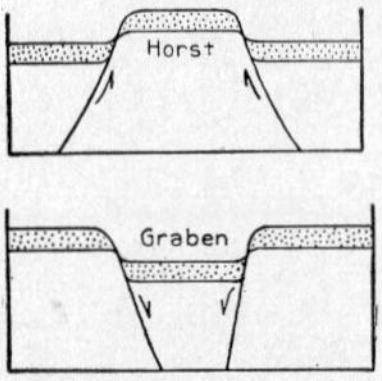

Types of Fault Structures. — By definition a _normal fault_ is one in which the hanging wall is on the downthrow side (Fig. 54). A _reverse fault_ is one in which the hanging wall is on the upthrow side. This also is called a _thrust fault_. If the dip of the thrust fault plane is low, it is called a _low angle thrust_. Faults of this type with displacement of many miles are common to the Rocky Mountains of Montana, Alberta, and many other mountainous regions. A _horst_ is an upthrow block which stands above blocks of the earth that have stood stationary

FIG. 55. — Diagrams of a horst, an upraised block between two faults, and a graben, a strip of land depressed between two normal faults.

or that have been depressed. It is bounded on at least two sides by fault planes. A _graben_ is a trough or depression of land between two normal faults. A _ramp valley_ is a depression left down where masses of land have been upthrust, one on either side of the intervening strip. A _branching fault_ is a fault which is distributed among two or more branches. Under such conditions large zones of weakness may be created which allow rapid erosion. _Strike and dip faults_ are parallel to the strike or dip, respectively, of tilted beds. Parallel ridges, composed of the same resistant layer of rock, often are the joint results of strike faulting and erosion. _Step faults_: not infrequently several parallel faults dipping in

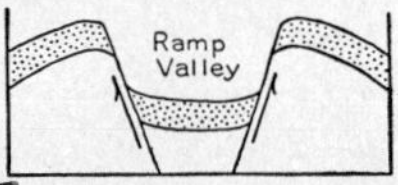

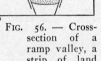

FIG. 56. — Cross-section of a ramp valley, a strip of land left down between two upthrust blocks.

the same direction are found in a single region; these are step faults. If the fault scarps have not been removed by erosion, the whole structure is like a gigantic stairway, the scarps being the risers between the steps.

The Topographic Expression of Faults. — Immediately after a fault has occurred, it is evident that a fault scarp marks its course.

Many recently made fault scarps are still available for study in such regions as western United States, Mexico, Chile, the Dead Sea depression and central Africa. The faults may be single or multiple, and they exert a strong influence on the present topography. In older geologic regions, such as eastern North America and much of western Europe, actual scarps are rare, for erosion has reduced the land surface hundreds or thousands of feet below the surface on which the original fault scarp was formed. In such cases all effects of the original fault may have been removed; but if rocks of very different composition were brought together by the faulting, usually a trace of the ancient fault is indicated in the present topography. Figure 58A illustrates the history of a faulted region where the original scarp was entirely removed by erosion; but because of more rapid erosion of the weaker beds (a) and (b) than of the resistant rock (c), the fault plane below the original fault scarp has been exhumed, giving rise to a _fault-line_ scarp. Many

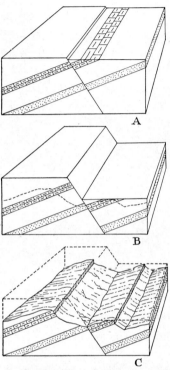

FIG. 57. — The development of parallel ridges through strike faulting and erosion.

such scarps are not so clear cut as the one represented in the diagram. They exist under all sorts of conditions. The fault surface may be buried by alluvium or greatly dissected by streams or other agents of erosion. Due to weakening of the rocks by faulting and to the difference in resistance, valleys are likely to form on the fault

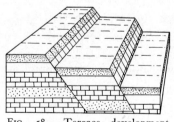

FIG. 58. — Terrace development through step-faulting.

lines. In any geomorphic studies of faulted regions, it is important (although often difficult) to distinguish between original scarps in a first cycle of erosion and fault-line scarps that may be products of a second or even later cycle.

Joints. — Regardless of their composition, all consolidated rocks on and even far below the earth's surface are intersected by cracks or fractures. Where there has been no displacement of the walls, such fractures are known as *joints*. Joints may stand in a vertical position, or they may be inclined at any angle. Often fractures run

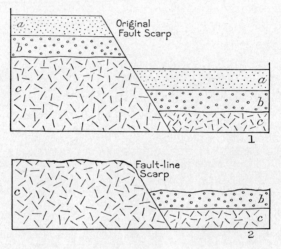

FIG. 58A. — A diagram to show the development of a fault-line scarp.

through the rocks in several directions, giving rise to *joint systems* or *patterns*. Where the rocks are uniformly divided by joint systems, cubical or rectangular blocks result. The faces of joints usually are remarkably smooth planes, but in some cases they are rough or curved. Joints are formed in several different ways. The largest and strongest joint systems are clearly the results of earth movements, which result in *tension, compression* or *shear joints*. Other joints are due to the release of pressure on rocks as a result of erosion; still others are due to the cooling and consequent shrinkage of lava, to the drying of unconsolidated sediments, particularly mud and silt; and one peculiar variety is the result of the saturation by heavy rains, followed by quick drying out of consolidated but poorly cemented sandstones. Near the surface of the earth, joints are likely to be open because of rock-weathering, but, as disclosed in mines and tunnels, at a comparatively shallow depth below the land surface, most joints are tight fractures in the rocks. It often happens that blocks of freshly quarried granite fail to show any joints; yet, after exposure to the air for a few days or weeks, cracks appear.

Jointing Due to Earth Movements. — These structures are well illustrated wherever great highlands have been upheaved. Joint patterns at right angles and others meeting at 45° angles predominate; although irregular patterns are not uncommon. It is an inter-

S. P. Turner.

Fig. 59. — The flat slabs of granite are the result of sheet-jointing which is believed to be caused by release of pressure through unloading by erosion, Pine Mountain, Georgia.

esting fact that in Colorado, where hundreds of square miles of granite rocks are exposed, the jointing is so great that there are few places where large-dimension blocks suitable for buildings or monuments can be quarried.

Jointing Due to Release of Pressure. — The weight of average solid rock in the outer part of the lithosphere is about 165 pounds per cubic foot. At a depth of a mile below the land surface in *granite* rocks, the pressure on each square foot of rock surface, due to the weight of the overlying material, is about 875,000 pounds. Where thick layers of rock have been removed from land surfaces by erosion and where deep canyons have been cut into the earth, obviously there is a tendency for the underlying rocks to expand, due to release of pressure. Great joints that appear parallel to highly eroded rock surfaces or parallel to canyon walls are believed to be formed in this way.

Jointing Due to Cooling Lava. — Most molten materials *contract upon cooling.* Lavas are no exception. Both lava flows on the surface of the land and intrusions, such as sheets and dikes, are

Junius Henderson.

Fig. 60. — Columnar jointing in basalt, Eugene, Oregon.

likely to develop very regular joint systems (Fig. 29). The joints start at right angles to the planes of cooling, and grow into the cooling mass of rock. Columns with four, five or six faces, all concave outward, are of frequent occurrence. These columns vary greatly in size, but thicknesses of several feet and length of scores of feet are not uncommon.

Joints Due to the Drying Out of Rocks. — These joints are of two distinct though related types. Mud cracks may be seen in such places as in ditches and on flood-plains and tidal flats after the water has been removed and the silt has dried out. In semi-arid and desert regions, where evaporation is very rapid, joints making hexagonal patterns are abundant in well-stratified but poorly cemented sandstones (Fig. 74). It is evident that the porous sandstone becomes saturated with water during a heavy rain; then dries out quickly after the rain is over, resulting in a very slight contraction in the surface of the sandstone.

Influences of Joints on Topography. — The direct influences of joints on topography are probably not very great, but indirectly they aid and, to a considerable extent, direct all agents of erosion.

As will be described in the next chapter, they are of tremendous importance in the weathering of rocks. The courses of small

D. F. Higgins.

FIG. 61. — Vertical joints in sedimentary rocks, Egypt. Note the complete control of erosion by the joints.

E. G. Fine.

FIG. 62. — Colorado National Monument, Colorado. Erosion along vertical joints has left great monoliths of massive sandstone.

streams often follow joint systems, while stream erosion, particularly on the outer bends of meandering rivers, is made more rapid and effective by joints. Glaciers and waves would be much less effective erosive agents, if they were working on perfectly solid, rather than on jointed, rocks.

REFERENCES

1. W. M. Davis: *Nomenclature of Surface Forms on Faulted Structures.* Bull. Geol. Soc. Am., Vol. 24, pp. 187–216, 1913.
2. Charles Davison: *Great Earthquakes.* Thomas Murby and Co., London, 1936.
3. J. S. Geikie: *Structural and Field Geology.* Gurney and Jackson, London, 1905.
4. B. Gutenberg and C. F. Richter: *Depth and Geographical Distribution of Deep-Focus Earthquakes.* Bull. Geol. Soc. Am., Vol. 49, pp. 249–298, 1938.
5. W. H. Hobbs: *Earthquakes.* D. Appleton and Co., 1907.
6. C. K. Leith: *Structural Geology.* Henry Holt and Co., 1928.
7. J. B. Macelwane and F. W. Sohn: *Geodynamics*, Theoretical Seismology, Pt. 1. John Wiley and Sons, 1936.
8. National Research Council, Committee of: *Seismology*, Physics of the Earth VI, 1933.
9. C. M. Nevin: *Principles of Structural Geology.* John Wiley and Sons, 1931.
10. J. A. Steers: *The Unstable Earth.* E. P. Dutton and Co., 1907.
11. Bailey Willis and Robin Willis: *Geologic Structures.* McGraw-Hill Book Co., 1929.

CHAPTER VII

PREPARING THE LAND FOR EROSION — ROCK WEATHERING

In this chapter we shall discuss the different ways in which the solid rocks of the earth are broken up and decayed. The term *weathering* usually is applied to these processes, although there are

O. L. Quale.

FIG. 63. — Stone Mountain, Georgia. The smooth outlines of this great granite dome are due to sheet-jointing, exfoliation and chemical weathering on rocks of very uniform composition.

objections to this usage, for *some* of the forces involved have little to do with either the weather or the atmosphere. Others, however, are direct results of atmospheric conditions, therefore, *weathering* is retained with reservations.

R. D. Salisbury, a great teacher of physiography, used to say to his classes that "one of the chief functions of streams is to carry the land to the sea." One might add with equal emphasis that important functions of wind, glaciers, waves and shore currents are to

move materials of the land from one place to another, and in so doing to develop a remarkable variety of topographic forms. Before any considerable amount of the lithosphere can be moved by surface agencies, the rocks must be broken or even thoroughly decomposed. The importance of these processes easily m a y be underestimated. Most of them are carried on slowly and in an inconspicuous fashion; but their results are fundamental to an understanding of the manifold phases of erosion. *Weathering, then, is the first step and a most important step in erosion of the land.* The agencies of weathering

FIG. 64. — A granite cliff. The layers are a result of chemical exfoliation, aided by frost action, Colorado.

are chemical, mechanical and organic. It will be found that both the processes and their results overlap to a considerable degree.

CHEMICAL WEATHERING

Oxygen, carbon dioxide and water vapor are important constituents of the lower atmosphere. When *dry* both oxygen and carbon dioxide are very inert, but *in the presence of moisture* they are very active chemical agents. Through their attack, rocks are decomposed, new secondary minerals are formed, and the original hard firm rocks of the land surface are altered to easily eroded materials. Similar results occur underground. It is a well-known fact that much water which falls as rain or snow sinks into the ground to become ground-water. Pure water is a very poor solvent, although some materials, such as rock salt (sodium chloride), are easily dissolved; but underground water charged with oxygen or carbon dioxide from the air may cause much decomposition of sub-surface rocks.

Carbonation. — Carbon dioxide and water form a chemical reagent capable of attacking any mineral which contains one or more of the elements iron, calcium, magnesium, sodium or potas-

H. E. Gregory, U. S. Geol. Survey.

FIG. 65. — The arch is being formed by percolating waters which dissolve out the cementing material of the massive, porous sandstone allowing blocks to drop.

sium. The elements are taken into solution, causing the minerals and, of course, the rocks which contain them, to crumble and decay. Referring to the composition of the various rock-making minerals in Chapter IV and to the composition of the various rocks described in Chapter V, it is evident that many rocks of all three great groups may be decomposed through this process.

Decomposition of Granite. — To illustrate the decay of rocks through carbonation, we may use granite, which is one of the most common igneous rocks. An average granite contains chiefly ortho-clase, with smaller amounts of quartz, biotite and albite. Carbon dioxide plus water equals H_2CO_3, which is carbonic acid. This acid, with excess water, attacks orthoclase with the following results: orthoclase $(K_2O.Al_2O_3.6SiO_2) + H_2CO_3 + 2H_2O =$

J. G. Lester.

FIG. 66. — Solution basins in granite, Georgia.

K_2CO_3 (in solution) $+$ kaolinite $(Al_2O_3.2SiO_2.2H_2O) + 4SiO_2$. Thus, through the decomposition of the orthoclase, we have potassium carbonate going off in solution with two solids, a new soft, solid secondary mineral, kaolinite, and solid free silica left.

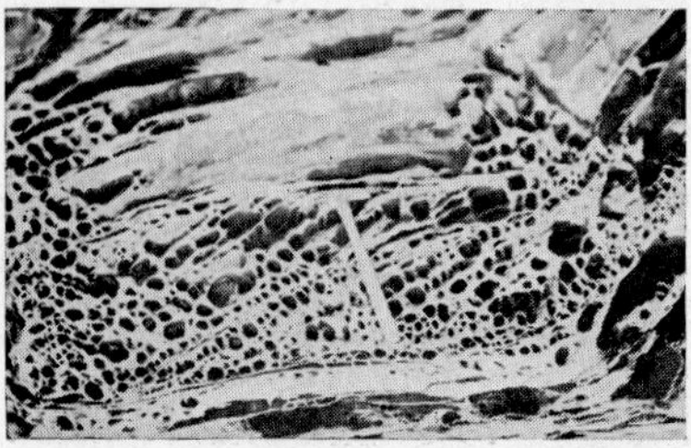

The quartz grains of the original granite are not attacked by carbonic acid, but are loosened as the feldspar is decomposed. Albite, $Na_2O.Al_2O_3.6SiO_2$, is changed in a manner exactly similar to that in which orthoclase is decomposed. Sodium carbonate goes off in solution; kaolinite and free silica are left.   Biotite, $(H,K)_2O.Al_2O_3$.

R. C. Moore, U. S. Geol. Survey.

FIG. 67. — Weathering of sandstone. The sand grains were loosened by chemical action, then blown away by the wind.

$2(Mg,Fe)O.3SiO_2$, contains three elements, potassium, magnesium and iron, which may be taken into solution as carbonates, leaving secondary minerals of varying composition, depending on the completeness of the process.

Decomposition of Gabbro.— Starting with a gabbro, which consists chiefly of labradorite, $CaO.Na_2O.Al_2O_3.4SiO_2$, and augite, which is a complex silicate of calcium, magnesium, iron and aluminum, we find in the two minerals four elements, Ca, Na, Mg and Fe, that are susceptible to the attack by carbonic acid. The result yields soluble carbonates of calcium, sodium magnesium and iron, solid free silica, clays, and other secondary minerals.

Decomposition of Limestone. — Pure limestone is composed of calcium carbonate which, dissolved by carbonic acid, yields calcium

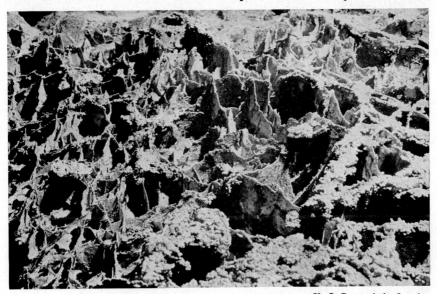

U. S. Dept. of the Interior.

FIG. 68.— Solution cavities in and deposition of calcium carbonate on limestone, Wind Cave National Park, South Dakota.

bicarbonate, $Ca,H_2(CO_3)_2$. Many limestones contain shale, sand or chert, but these do not seriously interfere with the carbonation process. On the surface of the land carbonic acid from the air and beneath the surface the same acid in ground water take limestone into solution. The great limestone caverns of the world are formed through the solvent action of ground water charged with carbonic acid.

Oxidation.— Oxygen and water do not react on as many elements as does carbonic acid. However, iron yields readily to oxidation.   As a result, minerals containing iron are decomposed and rocks decay.   The familiar examples of rusting iron and steel illustrate this process.   The surface of bright hard steel, upon exposure to moist air, soon becomes rusty due to the formation of the soft yellow or brown mineral limonite, $Fe_2O_3.2H_2O$.

Hydration. — Hydration is the process by which water is included in the composition of new minerals that are derived from old ones.   In the last example, under oxidation, the original form

S. P. Turner.

FIG. 69. — The widening of joints in granite by solution, Pine Mountain, Georgia.

of the iron was changed through the addition of both oxygen and water.   In the decomposition of feldspars we have already noted that the composition of the secondary mineral kaolinite includes two molecules of water.   Many other secondary minerals have water in their make-up.   Usually this results in an increase of volume of the new mineral.

Soils. — Although soils will be discussed in more detail later, it should be noted here that the chemical decay of rocks is of utmost importance in the formation of soils.   Soil may be defined as *finely* *divided rock material which contains mineral matter in soluble form that will support the growth of plants.* Residual soils, that is, those soils which lie directly on the rocks from which they were derived, are composed of secondary minerals, soluble salts, humus and fragments of the undecomposed original minerals. In favorable situations, residual soils scores or even hundreds of feet thick indicate the depth to which these chemical processes may operate.

MECHANICAL AGENCIES

The rocks of the land are disintegrated by many different mechanical agents. Wind carrying sand, streams carrying sediment,

Roy Coffin.

FIG. 70. — A talus, just back of the trees, and loose rock fragments in wrinkles on the slope that will add to the talus when they are brought down by gravity, Colorado.

glaciers and waves — all wear down the rocks through mechanical abrasion. These processes will be described in detail in later chapters. Here we shall consider (1) freezing water, (2) expansion due to chemical changes, and (3) exfoliation due to sudden changes of temperature.

Freezing Water. — When water freezes it expands by about one-tenth its volume. The expansive force is about 2,000 pounds per square inch. Water which gets into cracks in rocks and freezes tends to wedge the rocks apart. It forms the great blocks seen on the tops of high mountains and on the walls of canyons. In middle and high latitudes and at high altitudes, it is the most important single agency in disintegrating rocks. Where temperature conditions permit repeated freezing and thawing, small cracks soon be-

R. D. Crawford.

FIG. 71. — A talus, Chaffee County, Colorado.

come larger until blocks of rock are well separated or even dislodged from their original positions.

Talus. — Talus is a heap or sheet of coarse rock waste that has accumulated at the foot of a cliff or on a steep slope. The rocks are usually angular and vary in size from huge boulders to fragments of comparatively small dimensions. The talus is largely the result of frost action and gravity. If the course of the falling blocks has been directed by channels in the canyon walls, the resulting deposits at the foot of steep slopes frequently take the shape of *talus cones* (Fig. 72).

Expansion Due to Chemical Changes. — During carbonation, oxidation and hydration processes, particularly the latter, the new

R. D. Crawford.

FIG. 72. — Talus cones on the left. On the right, rock fragments slide for more than a mile down the mountain and out into the valley through the white-appearing rock channel. The light color is due to powdered rock made by the slides.

secondary minerals formed may have a volume much greater than that of the original minerals.[1] In the *concentric or spheroidal* weathering of granites, gabbros and other feldspathic rocks, the loose curved layers or scales (Fig. 73) clearly are due to expansion caused by the growth of secondary minerals.

Chemical Exfoliation. — This term, relatively new in geologic literature, indicates an important result of chemical expansion. It has long been an observed fact that curved scales

W. A. Waldschmidt.

FIG. 73. — Spheroidal weathering in basalt. The boulder in the center is about 4 feet in diameter, Golden, Colorado.

[1] C. K. Leith and W. J. Mead: *Metamorphic Geology,* Henry Holt and Co., p. 92, 1915.

up to many feet in length and from a fraction of an inch to a hundred or more feet in thickness form on the surface of massive rocks in many different parts of the earth. Various writers have concluded that these scales were the result of extreme and sudden temperature changes. Blackwelder [1] has analyzed the whole question of *exfoliation*, and concludes that it may be brought about by (a) *fire*, which would occur rarely except in forested regions; (b) by *frost action*; (c) *the wedgework of salts*, and (d) *possibly by roots*. He doubts

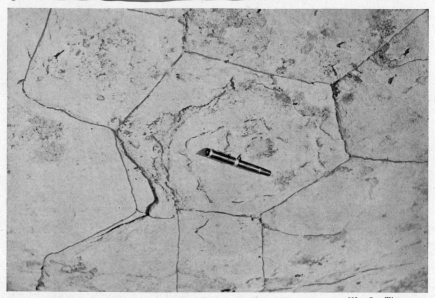

W. O. Thompson.

FIG. 74. — The thin scales on the surface of the sandstone were wedged off by growing salt crystals. The hexagonal jointing is the result of quick drying out of the porous sandstone after heavy rains.

the ability of solar heat to cause exfoliation, and notes that exfoliation is more pronounced in humid than in arid regions. In conclusion he states: "*In chemical exfoliation the sheets are notably decayed and discolored. The work is performed by solutions which penetrate slowly along the cleavage cracks of crystals and between the grains and there induce the formation of new minerals of larger volume.*" This conclusion that expansion is due to the growth of

[1] Eliot Blackwelder: *Exfoliation as a Phase of Rock Weathering.* Jour. Geol., Vol. 33, pp. 793–806, 1925.

new minerals of larger volume is generally accepted to explain the *thick* curved scales so often found in humid regions.

Wedging of Salt Crystals. — Another type of chemical expansion on a small scale is clearly due to the wedging of salt crystals. In many arid and semi-arid regions thin scales form on the surface of poorly cemented sandstones. These are formed as follows: rain falls on and sinks into porous sandstones, dissolving soluble salts that are in the rocks. Later the rocks are heated by the sun; the water rises by capillary action and is evaporated a short distance below the surface. As the water evaporates, salt crystals form and, due to the expansion incident to their growth, scales of sandstone are loosened and slightly raised. These aid erosion in two ways: they loosen the grains, thus permitting more rapid removal by wind and water; and they furnish sand grains which act as cutting tools for the wind.

Exfoliation Due to Sudden Temperature Changes. — It seems evident that extreme changes in temperature are less important in disintegrating rocks than was once supposed. Yet *exfoliation* or *spalling does* occur under some conditions due to extreme heating by the sun, followed by sudden cooling of the rocks. On many bare slopes in the mountains of Colorado and Wyoming, Latitude 38° to 45° N., one may observe curved scales on the rocks. These scales seldom are as

FIG. 75. — Exfoliation of granite due to temperature changes, Colorado.

much as 2 inches thick in the center and are usually only a fraction of an inch thick at the edges. The surface area of the scales may be from a few inches to 3 or 4 square feet. They are much more numerous on south slopes than on north slopes. The scales and the underlying rocks show little or no evidence of decay. Similar spalling has been described on Stone Mountain in Georgia, where the climate is much more humid. There, according to reliable witnesses, spalls have broken off the granite with noise like the report of a rifle. Many authorities regard temperature changes as the largest single factor in breaking up the rocks of the earth ; but certainly frost action is much more important in all humid regions

J. G. Lester.

FIG. 76. — Exfoliation in granite, Arabia Mountain, Georgia.

where much freezing of water in rocks occurs; and the question is debatable in arid regions.

ORGANIC AGENCIES

Both plants and animals aid in preparing the land for erosion. However, not all their activities are destructive. Vegetation is of utmost importance in many places in holding soil, dust and sand in place, while at present a modern animal, man, is interesting himself as probably he has never done before in *preventing erosion.*

Destructive Work of Plants. — The roots and even the trunks of trees and large shrubs wedge rocks apart, thus aiding erosion. The roots of many different plants, both large and small, gradually work their way into tiny crevices in the rocks. As they grow, the enlarged cracks become channels for the movement of mineralized water, which carry on their characteristic work of decomposing the rocks. Also, humus acids incident to plant growth aid the other chemicals in causing rocks to decay.

Destructive Work of Animals. — Burrowing animals, such as gophers and prairie dogs and even the lowly earthworm, add their bit to the destructive agents that are preparing the land for erosion. Anyone who has ever examined the mounds of prairie dog colonies must be impressed by, first, the large amount of soil and dirt that is excavated, and, second, by the rapidity with which wind may remove this material. The chemical and mechanical results of the work of earthworms, although less obvious, are, nevertheless, very great.

Man's Destructive Work. — Ever since man reached approximately his present industrial attainments, he has been a serious offender in aiding erosion. For centuries the Chinese denuded their land of trees. In more recent times, for example, in New England and in the Appalachian Mountains, lumbermen have slashed all the trees in the forests. They have permitted forest fires which not only burned the tops, but destroyed all underbrush and humus in the soil. As a result of such deforestation, all the soil may have been washed away clear down to the solid rocks. In many parts of the semi-arid western United States, men broke up the sod, cultivated the land for a few years; then left it to grow up to tumbleweeds and sunflowers, or to blow away. Through unwise methods of tilling the land on steep and even gentle slopes in humid regions, man has permitted countless tons of soil to be removed by running water. Bennett states that of 9,250,000 acres of agricultural land examined in the Brazos River Watershed, Texas, 66 per cent is suffering seriously from sheet washing. Although it is not an offense against nature, in mining districts man has brought millions of tons of rock from the depths to the surface of the earth. In these and in scores of other ways he has helped to prepare the land for erosion.

RESULTS OF WEATHERING

Mantle rock, or regolith, is the loose debris consisting of rocks and minerals in various stages of decay which overlies solid or *bed rock*. It is formed through one or more of the processes that already have been described. *Transported mantle rock* which has been carried from one place to another and deposited by streams, glaciers or wind is usually given some name which indicates the agent of transport and deposition. Thus, we have *alluvial or fluvial* deposits made by streams, *glacial drift* deposited by glaciers, and *loess* and *dunes* which are wind deposits.

Movements of Mantle Rock. — On very flat plains, on the tops of broad plateaus, in heavily forested regions, and in regions where the ground is permanently frozen, mantle rock may remain in its original position indefinitely. In general, however, it is soon moved from its place of origin. *Minor movements*, induced by gravity and ground water, include such important processes as *earth creep*, *solifluction*, *slumps*, *landslides* and related phenomena. These are fully described in Chapter XIII on the work of ground-water. All

E. G. Fine.

Fig. 77. — Chemical weathering and wind erosion on sandstone, Red Canyon, Utah.

these are of tremendous aid in preparing the material for more distant removal by the *major processes*, which are *slope wash, mud-flows, streams, glaciers, wind, waves* and *currents*. The work of these major agents is discussed in detail in the appropriate places in the following chapters, and need not be considered here.

Effects of Climate on Weathering

It is evident from the preceding discussion that the weathering processes will function very differently under varying climatic conditions. *In cold climates* mechanical weathering is of primary im-

Don Kemp.

FIG. 78. — Mountains southwest of Monterey, Mexico. Note the difference in the erosion of the steeply tilted sedimentary rocks on the side of the mountains and the horizontally bedded sediments on top.

W. O. Thompson.

FIG. 79. — Chemical and wind erosion on calcareous sandstones and shales, southern Wyoming.

portance. Some chemical and organic weathering go on, but they are quite subordinate to the mechanical processes. *In frozen ground* all chemical and organic processes of weathering are at once stopped, and can be continued only after the ground thaws out. *In temperate humid climates all* the weathering processes are exceedingly active. *In dry temperate climates* the mechanical weathering probably overshadows chemical work, although there is considerable difference of opinion on this point. *In temperate climates at high altitudes* there is no doubt about the greater effectiveness of mechanical weathering. *In warm and hot humid climates* chemical weathering is at a maximum, for moisture and heat accelerate leaching and solvent action of all salts, making chemical work far more important than mechanical weathering. *In dry, hot climates* the conditions probably are reversed, and mechanical weathering predominates.

Local climatic effects are definitely related to geographic position. For example, assume a high, east-west trending mountain range at about 45° N. L. Also assume equal snowfall on both sides of the range, with the precipitation coming intermittently all months from August to June. On the *north* slope much of the early snow may lie on the ground all winter; while on the *south* side of the range there will be much more melting with consequently more water getting into the cracks of rocks where it freezes. Repeated freezing and thawing will take place during the fall and spring months, thus causing much greater breaking up of the rocks on the *south* than on the *north* slope. Other *local* influences of position or topography can be found almost everywhere that detailed investigations are made.

SOILS

No discussion of weathering is complete that omits consideration of soils. Indeed, of all geologic processes none are so important to man as are those which help to form soil. Although some plants are now being grown on a small scale in laboratories without any soil, it is generally true that all vegetation, all land animals, birds and insects depend directly or indirectly on soils for their very lives.

The general relationship between weathering and soil formation to physiographic processes has
already been indicated or will be
shown in succeeding chapters; it
follows that the study of soils is
often of great help in determining
the complete physiographic history
of any region. It is a well-known
fact that geologists and physiographers alike make large use of
vegetation, which varies greatly
with different types of soil, to determine the nature of concealed
outcrops. Even old river meanders,
sand bars, faults and other structures may be indicated by different
types of vegetation. Through the
use of aerial surveys and photographs, supplemented by ground
work, much valuable information is

FIG. 80. — Weathering of granite —
the material near the pick is thoroughly decomposed. Fresh rock
appears at the bottom and at the
upper right side of the picture.

easily obtained that otherwise
would be almost unavail-
able. Furthermore, t h e
geographer is much con-
cerned with soils when considering the environmental
factors of plants and animals. For these reasons a
brief statement of the very
complex subject of soils is
desirable at this point.

Pedology

*Pedology is the science
of soils.* It represents an
attempt to recognize the
soil as an independent unit

Richard Ragle.

FIG. 81. — The strips of vegetation parallel to
the ridges indicate different types of underlying sedimentary rock, foothills of central
Colorado.

or natural body with definite morphologic and physiologic features, and with specific physical properties, chemical composition and biologic make-up. *This is the extremist's point of view.*

A more moderate attitude toward pedology is held by Robinson,[1] who defines pedology as *the study of the soil from the standpoint and by the methods of pure science.* He considers pedology to be a closely interdependent group of studies which include (1) geology, in that it has to do with weathering processes and the formation of the regolith; (2) chemistry and physics, as related to the complicated colloidal system and chemical compositions of soils; (3) biology, the part that deals with a complex flora and fauna in relationship to soil environment.

History. — The development of pedology has had an interesting history. Originally it was largely geologic, biologic and agromic in nature. Later the physical and chemical studies of soils were emphasized. During the last twenty years the relations of soils to climate have been the chief subject of studies by many Russian and some German and American pedologists. These studies have led to classifications of soils based largely on the climatic conditions under which they were developed. The emphasis in this direction has been so great that soil groupings, with their accompanying natural vegetation, are primarily classifications of climate.

The Classification of Soils

The Bureau of Soils of the United States Department of Agriculture recognizes more than 1500 soil types. This classification is based on origin, accumulation, size of grains, composition, constituent plant foods, development after deposition, and many other factors. Obviously, any simple statement which covers all these factors is impossible.

Only two classifications will be given here. The first may be regarded as a geologic classification. It is based on the origin and methods of accumulation of soils. *In general this grouping is most valuable to the geomorphologist.* The second classification follows, with slight modifications, that used by the Bureau of Soils to

[1] C. W. Robinson: *Soils, Their Origin, Constitution and Classification.* 2nd Ed. Thomas Murby and Co. (London), 1936.

indicate the major soil groups of the United States. Its basis is essentially climatic; although, to a certain extent, it indicates physiographic conditions. This grouping, although much more complete and satisfactory from the standpoint of pedology, is seldom of particular value to the physiographer except in one very important phase. It does help him, through the extent of leaching and chemical changes that have occurred since the soil was deposited, to determine climatic changes and age relationships.

Geologic Classification

In this simplest of all classifications of soils, they may be divided into two groups, _residual soils_ and _transported soils._

Residual Soils. — Where residual soils lie in place on the parent rocks, the underlying rocks show the composition of the materials from which the soils were derived. Deep residual soils indicate that weathering and soil formation have been going on very rapidly or for a very long time without much erosion. The recognition of the latter condition often is very important to the physiographer. These soils are unstratified, but where fairly deep show gradual transitions from the surface layers down to the parent rocks. In humid regions deep residual soils have almost invariably been much leached; the soluble plant foods may have been largely removed, leaving relatively insoluble compounds of silica, alumina and iron. The amount of humus (organic material) usually is large. Iron tends to become oxidized to the ferric form, giving a red color to the soil, although this color may be masked by black humus. Unleached residual soils derived from granites, impure limestones, gabbros and basalts contain potash, calcium and other salts that were not washed away during the original rock decay. Usually the residual soils of arid regions are very fertile, because they are less leached than are those of humid regions. Residual soils formed from quartz sandstones, quartzites and rather pure argillaceous shales usually are deficient in soluble plant foods. In old residual soils the materials subject to chemical decay finally are so changed that it is difficult to recognize the original nature of the parent rock. Such soils are said to be mature.

Transported Soils. — These include all soils that have been removed from the rocks on which they were formed. During transportation, soils from one locality are mixed with those from many other places; therefore, soil types, based on the parent rocks, cannot be recognized. These soils may have been moved only a short distance by gravity, creep or slopewash, or they may have been carried any distance up to hundreds of miles by streams, wind or glaciers. Both the transporting agents and the present situations of these soils have important bearings on their classification.

Colluvial Soils. — All soils which have been moved largely by gravity only short distances from the place of their origin fall into this class. Avalanches, landslides, mudflows, slump, creep or gravity alone are the chief causes of movement. Usually much coarse material, including talus, is mixed with the soil. Due to the nature of the movement these soils usually are found on or near the foot of relatively steep slopes. They never are well stratified.

Alluvial Soils. — These include all soils which have been carried by streams and deposited by them *on the land*. They may occur in roughly or even very perfectly stratified form. The materials at the time of deposition consist of any rock or mineral fragments that the stream was able to carry. (See Chapter VIII.) Youthful, swift streams may carry pebbles, gravel, sand and silt, while old, slow, sluggish streams transport chiefly finely divided rock materials.

Alluvial soils are found chiefly on the flood plains of rivers, which from time to time overflow their banks, on deltas and, less abundantly, in lagoons, swamps, and in abandoned channels of former streams. The flood-plains of the Missouri and Mississippi in the United States exhibit typical examples of alluvial soils. The classic example of the River Nile in Egypt, which annually brings a new supply of fertile soil to the lands near its mouth, well illustrates the formation of both alluvial and deltaic soils.

Usually organic material is washed in as the soils are deposited. Where climatic conditions are favorable, humus accumulates rapidly. Due to these conditions and to the periodic deposition of new soil, many alluvial soils are thick and are very fertile.

Glacial Soils. — During the Pleistocene epoch of the Quaternary period, which ended only a short time ago (geologically speaking), great glaciers, moving from high latitude centers, advanced over about half of North America and over large areas of Europe (Chapter X). When the ice melted, all the material carried by the glacier was deposited in irregular unstratified form. At the same time thousands of alpine glaciers formed in the mountains. Many were large enough to move far down their valleys. Some reached the adjacent plains. When they melted, the debris that they had carried was deposited as moraines of one type or another. All unstratified debris deposited by glaciers may be called *glacial drift, or till.*

The material of drift or moraines includes all varieties of rocks and minerals passed over by the glaciers from their source to the place of deposition. Some drift is composed chiefly of finely divided materials, such as clays and rock flour. In other places rocks of varying size predominate. Many moraines or drift sheets are hundreds of feet thick. The constituents are wholly *unstratified.* Coarse and fine materials may occur in every possible proportion. Rock fragments are *angular,* as opposed to the rounded ones of alluvial deposits. In many regions the original drift has been changed through the decay of boulders and soluble minerals. The great corn belt of Ohio, Illinois, Iowa and adjacent regions is underlain by soils largely of glacial origin.

In any glaciated region the relative ages of different moraines may be indicated by the amount of decay of the constituent boulders. The very old moraines often exhibit quite thick soils, while the young moraines consist largely of only slightly weathered materials. From the ends and margins of glaciers, meltwater washes out much debris that is deposited beyond the glacial drift in the form of *valley trains or outwash plains.* This shares some of the characteristics of both stream and glacial deposits. The material is stratified as in other alluvial deposits, but if it was not carried far by streams, it is angular or sub-angular in form. Usually large boulders, so conspicuous in moraines, are absent.

Lacustrine Soils.—As we shall see in detail in Chapter XI, many of our present lakes will soon be destroyed. Some basins will be drained; others will be filled with sediment brought in by streams;

still others will be filled by vegetable material. The fate of lakes can be predicted with confidence because of our knowledge of the history of lakes that have been destroyed in the past, and because of our observations of changes taking place in present-day lakes.

Peat bogs and muskeg swamps of northern latitudes in the northern hemisphere represent glacial lakes that have been filled with vegetable material or with a mixture of vegetation and sediment. Some have very fertile soils; others support only a limited plant growth, apparently due to the presence of bacteria which destroy the humus.

The floors of many drained lake basins are covered with well stratified soil. It varies greatly in size of grains and in fertility. The great wheat belt of western Minnesota, North Dakota, southern Saskatchewan and Manitoba is situated on the site of a former lake which was drained by the Red River and its tributaries. This region is now a very flat plain. The underlying soil is fine-grained and very fertile.

Eolian Soils.—Strong winds may carry sand grains for short distances, but they carry fine dust for hundreds or thousands of miles. If the dust is moved into the upper atmosphere by ascending currents, it may remain in the air for years, and be carried completely around the earth. A deposit of wind-blown *dust* is known as *loess*. It may be thick or thin, large or small.

Volcanoes, deserts, dry flood-plains and cultivated fields in semi-arid and even humid regions, in times of drouth, furnish dust to be transported by wind. If the dust is coarse, or if the winds are not strong, the eolian soils may be deposited near the places of their origin. The great mounds of wind-deposited *loess* at Council Bluffs, Iowa, are believed to have been derived locally from the neighboring flood-plains of the Missouri River. However, the tremendous loess deposits of China, which cover a total area of more than 300,000 square miles, were carried across the mountains from the deserts of Central Asia.

Because most loess deposits are derived from deserts or semi-arid regions where the leaching is at a minimum, and also because such soils are composed of finely divided rock materials, they are very fertile. Frequently they may easily be distinguished from associated glacial or alluvial soils by the more luxuriant, natural vegetation which they support.

Dune Soils. — Many dunes are composed almost entirely of pure quartz sand, which is very insoluble and supports almost no vegetation. Other dunes contain much soluble mineral matter, which makes a fertile soil after the dune has become stabilized. Dunes, then, may have no vegetation on them, either because they contain no plant foods, or because they have formed so rapidly that there has not been time for the vegetation to become fixed. Wind-blown sand, when mixed with heavy alluvial clay, tends to lighten the soil and make it more suitable for crop growth.

Major Soil Groups of the United States [1]

General Principles — This grouping of soils is the Russian classification modified by detailed studies of United States Soils by the Bureau of Chemistry and Soils. According to the principles laid down by Russian pedologists, *soil types are definitely related to natural conditions which are primarily climatic and secondarily biologic.* They adopt the view that in all parts of the earth where climates are similar soils are alike. Thus, soils of humid Georgia will differ from those of drier California even when they are formed from similar granites. The soil is a natural body that must be considered as such. It must be studied as a unit apart from its parent rocks. It continues to develop through organic, physical and chemical changes long after its separation from the parent rock. Soils which do not now agree with their climatic environment are explained by assuming that the climate changed after the soils acquired their present characteristics.

Biologic activities are second only to climate in their role as soil-forming processes. *Organic life with other natural forces creates the soil and, conversely, the soil and the same natural forces create organic life.*

Summarizing [2] the factors called by Dokuchaev "soil formers"

[1] The following discussion is based largely on *The Atlas of American Agriculture*, Pt. 3. U. S. Dept. of Agr., 1936, and *Miscellaneous Publication No. 229.* U. S. Dept. of Agr., 1936.

[2] As outlined by Jacob S. Joffe, *Pedology,* Chap. V. Rutgers University Press, 1936.

that contribute to the formation of soils, two groups are recognized: (1) passive soil formers, the minor ones, and (2) active soil formers, the major ones. *Passive soil formers are the parent rocks, topography and geologic age. Active soil formers are (1) climate (including water, temperature, humidity, evaporation and wind), the most active one; (2) the biosphere (plant and animal kingdoms).*

Soil Profile. — Another principle developed by both Russian and American investigators is the recognition of definite soil pro-

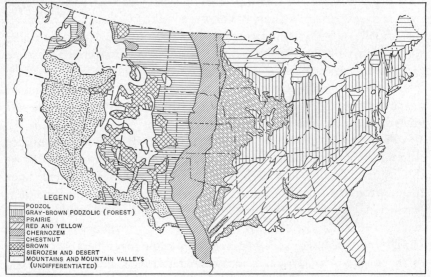

LEGEND
PODZOL
GRAY-BROWN PODZOLIC (FOREST)
PRAIRIE
RED AND YELLOW
CHERNOZEM
CHESTNUT
BROWN
SIEROZEM AND DESERT
MOUNTAINS AND MOUNTAIN VALLEYS
(UNDIFFERENTIATED)

U. S. Dept. of Agriculture.

FIG. 82. — The major soil groups of the United States.

files. Where vertical sections are made through soils, it is found that the soil is made up of layers which, although they may differ greatly in physical condition and chemical composition, yet show a definite genetic relationship. These layers constitute the soil profile. The principal layers or horizons from the top down are designated A, B and C. A and B represent the true soil produced by the soil formers. C is the weathered regolith not yet developed into soil. Rarely, when rock-weathering and the soil-forming processes progress at the same rate, C may not be present. Each horizon in any particular group of soils has its distinctive color, texture and structure.

Definitions. — In order to understand the soil map of the United States (Fig. 82), the following definitions are necessary. Some terms are borrowed directly from Russian classifications, while others are independent of the Russian types and are designed to meet conditions not covered by the Russian classification.

Podzol. — Soils of the northern humid regions under coniferous or mixed coniferous and hardwood forests. The profile shows a thin organic layer at the top, then a gray leached soil which is over a dark-brown horizon. Moisture in the ground has removed the soluble salts, including calcium and magnesium, leaving an acid soil in the A horizon and usually in the B layers; although in some places calcium carbonate is concentrated in the lower part of B. The Podzol is not considered fertile, inasmuch as it does not support a great variety of plants; although it is fertile in so far as forest growth is concerned.

Gray-Brown Podzolic (Forest). — Soils of a moist, temperate climate under deciduous forests. The profile is similar to that of the Podzol and the soil has developed in a similar manner, but there are more soluble salts in this group. The soil is of medium fertility, supports a wide variety of crops, and is amenable to artificial fertilization.

Prairie. — These soils occur in temperate, moist climates, chiefly in the United States. The native vegetation is tall prairie grass. In the profile there is a very dark brown soil grading down through a lighter brown to still lighter colored parent material at a depth of from 3 to 5 feet. The grass vegetation has been able to return sufficient calcium to the surface soil to prevent dispersion of the colloids. The fertility is high.

Red and Yellow. — These soils are found in warm-temperate, moist climates with deciduous forests (largely) over the red soils and coniferous forests (largely) over the yellow soils. In the red soil profile the surface horizon is a thin organic layer. Then comes a grayish-yellow leached soil which lies on a deep-red layer. The yellow soil has the same profile, except that the lower horizon is yellow. Both soils have formed under the influence of podzolization (*leaching of soluble salts*) and *laterization* (*solution and removal of silica, especially from alumina-silica compounds, leaving a soil rich in iron and alumina*). The red soils are of medium fertility, but the yellow soils are low.

Chernozem. — The soils of a temperate to cool sub-humid climate under a natural vegetation of tall prairie grass. In profile the soil is black at the top grading downward into a whitish, calcareous horizon at a depth of from 2 to 4 feet. These soils best illustrate the soil-forming process known as *calcification* (*accumulation of calcium and magnesium in the lower part of the soil, B horizon, with the plants bringing bases and phosphorus from the lower to the surface horizons. Colloids remain saturated largely with calcium and are relatively immobile. Decomposed organic matter remains in the upper part of the soil*). The fertility of these soils is very high.

Chestnut. — Soils of a temperate to cool arid climate under mixed tall and short prairie grass. The profile shows a dark-brown top layer grading at depths of 1½ to 3 feet into a whitish calcareous horizon. Calcification is the dominant soil-development process. The fertility is high.

Brown. — This soil group is typical of a temperate to cool arid climate under short prairie grass. The brown A soil grades into a whitish calcareous horizon at depths of from 1 to 2 feet. Calcification is the dominant soil-developing process. Fertility is high.

Sierozem and Desert Soils. — Grayish soils of temperate to cool arid climates under short prairie grass and desert plants. The grayish surface soils grade down into calcareous, light-colored material at depths of 1 foot or less. The fertility (under irrigation) is high.

Mountain and Mountain Valley Soils. — This broad zonal group of soils, unclassified on the soil map of the United States, includes many different soil units. Thin, rocky soils without a well-developed profile are found on mountain slopes. *Tundra soils* occur in swamps and bogs near the mountain tops. In the mountain valleys alluvial soils of great variety and usually with immature profiles abound.

Tundra. — Although found only in high mountain regions of

the United States in regions too small to be shown on a general map, tundra soils are extensively developed in the northern parts of North America and Eurasia. They are found in cold, humid climates under a natural vegetation cover of mosses, lichens and shrubs. The profile shows dark-brown, peaty layers over grayish horizons over a substratum of frozen ground. *Gleization* is the dominant soil-development process. (Gleization *includes processes found in swamps and waterlogged regions. Anaerobic conditions favor reducing reactions and minimize leaching.*) The fertility is medium.

Laterite. — These soils occur in hot, moist climates under tropical forests. They are extensively distributed in tropical regions, *but do not occur except in small detached areas in the United States.* In the profile a thin organic layer lies over reddish, leached soil which, in turn, is over deep-red lateritic material. *Laterization and podzolization* are the chief soil-forming processes. Fertility is medium.

Summary. — The broad zonal groups of soils just described grade into one another. Many only slightly less important groups are omitted, but the examples indicate the basis for the classification. From the brief descriptions given above, it is evident that the various soils can be thrown into two major groups. These are (1) Pedocals (soils with an accumulated layer of calcium carbonate) which include chernozem, chestnut soil, brown soil, sierozem and desert soils; (2) Pedalfers (soils in which iron or alumina or both accumulate) which embrace tundra, podzol, gray-brown podzolic soil, red and yellow soils and laterite.

REFERENCES

1. E. W. Hillgard: *Soils: Their Formation, Properties, Composition and Relations to Climate and Plant Growth.* Macmillan and Co., 1907.
2. Jacob S. Joffe: *Pedology.* Rutgers University Press, 1936.
3. Charles E. Kellogg: *Development and Significance of the Great Soil Groups of the United States.* U. S. Dept. of Agr., Misc. Pub. No. 229, 1936.
4. C. F. Marbut: *The Soils of the United States.* Atlas of American Agriculture, Pt. 3. U. S. Dept. of Agr., 1936.

5. Geo. P. Marsh: *The Earth as Modified by Human Action*.   Chas. Scribner's Sons, 1898.

6. Geo. P. Merrill: *A Treatise on Rocks: Rock Weathering and Soils*. Macmillan and Co., 1897.

7. E. Ramann: (Translation by Whittles) *The Evolution and Classification of Soils*.   W. Heffer and Sons, England, 1928.

8. G. W. Robinson: *Soils: Their Origin, Constitution and Classification*. Thomas Murby and Co., England, 1936.

CHAPTER VIII

TOPOGRAPHY PRODUCED BY STREAMS OF HUMID REGIONS

In the preceding chapters the composition and structure of earth materials have been discussed, and a background has been prepared

George Grant, U. S. Dept. of the Interior.

FIG. 83. — The Grand Canyon of the Colorado River. The inner gorge is being cut in Pre-Cambrian metamorphic rocks. From the lowest terrace to the flat rim of the plateau the rocks are all sedimentary.

for the study of active erosional forces. This chapter and those that follow will consider in detail the external earth processes and the various relief features that they produce.

Streams are the most widespread and, in many respects, the most important of all erosive agents. Regardless of size, all streams, whether tiny brooks or mighty rivers, are slowly but constantly changing the surface of the land.   If one stands on the rim of a great canyon, such as the Grand Canyon of the Colorado River, it may seem impossible that one stream could cut that great gorge, which is in places more than a mile deep and fifteen miles wide.   Yet that is exactly what has happened.   When we recall the principles of *weathering* (Chap. VII), and combine them with the erosive work of streams discussed in this chapter, it becomes

Photograph by Air Map Corporation of America, Courtesy U. S. War Department.
FIG. 84. — Part of the Mississippi River Delta.

evident that *given sufficient time* there is practically no limit to the work that streams can do.

However, not all the work of streams is destructive.   Streams build great deltas far out into lakes and oceans.   They deposit quantities of debris on their flood-plains, or build up alluvial fans. In other words, they are constructive as well as destructive agents. On this account streams are called agents of *gradation*.   They *degrade* (tear down) the land in some places and *aggrade* (build it up) in other places.   Waves, glaciers and wind are also agents of gradation, but considering the whole earth, streams probably are the most important of all.

Sources of Stream Water

The direct sources of stream water are rain and melting snow which fall on the land. Indirectly much rain or snow water may sink into the ground, move varying distances underground, and emerge in the form of springs or seepages to feed streams. Also many streams rise in lakes which are fed by melting snow banks, glaciers, springs, or seepage waters from the surrounding land.

Precipitation

Since rain and snow are responsible for streams, it is worth while at this point to examine briefly the amount and distribution of precipitation of the earth.

On the average, about 40 inches of water in the form of rain or snow falls on the *land* each year. In high latitudes or high altitudes, it is mostly snow. In intermediate latitudes, both rain and snow may occur; while in low latitudes, snow, except at high altitudes, is unknown. The moisture content of snow varies greatly, but averages about 1 inch of water for 10 inches of snow. A total precipitation of 40 inches on the 56,000,000 square miles of land surface is equivalent to about 36,000 cubic miles of water, enough to cover the state of Indiana to a depth of about a mile.

Distribution of Precipitation. — It is a well known fact that the distribution of rain and snow varies greatly, both in time and in amount, over different parts of the earth. This, naturally, influences the size and number of streams and the nature and amount of work that they can do. In the Atacama desert of northern Chile, the average annual rainfall is less than three inches a year. Some years not a drop of rain falls. In contrast, large areas of the Amazon basin have more than 80 inches of rainfall every year. On the windward side of the higher islands of the Hawaiian group, the annual rainfall is more than 400 inches. The precipitation map of the world (Fig. 20) shows clearly that more than half of all the land of the earth is arid or semi-arid, that is, it receives less than twenty inches of water a year. While streams are of importance in developing topography even in semi-arid and arid regions, it is evident that their greatest activity is in the humid regions of the earth.

In considering the work of streams, the distribution of precipitation at any locality during a year also is important. For example, over an eighty-four-year period,[1] Albany, New York, had an average monthly precipitation of 3.4 inches. During all this time the lowest normal month was February, with 2.47 inches, and the highest was July, with 4.12. These figures indicate a rather uniform precipitation, hence uniform stream flow, throughout the year. In contrast, a 61-year record for San Francisco, California, shows an average monthly rainfall of 1.91 inches. But June, July and August each have a normal monthly rainfall of only 0.02 inch, while the amount for January is 4.82 inches, thus indicating a very irregular annual stream flow in that region.

Runoff

Although nearly 36,000 cubic miles of water falls on the land every year, the annual return flow to the oceans by all the rivers of the earth is only about 6,520 cubic miles. To explain this discrepancy, it is necessary to trace the history of water which falls on the land. Some of this water may be evaporated almost immediately from the ground or from trees and buildings on which it falls. Some runs down slopes, gathering in rivulets to become a stream. Some sinks into the ground. This water soon may be evaporated; it may enter into the growth of vegetation; or it may penetrate deeply into the ground to become permanent ground-water. Water which falls in the form of snow may be soon melted or evaporated, or it may accumulate in snow fields or glaciers where it slowly wastes away. Also some water is caught in depressions of the land and forms lakes and ponds.

Factors Controlling Runoff. — In general, the following conditions *aid* rapid runoff: (1) uniform, heavy rainfall, (2) lack of vegetation, (3) steep slopes, (4) bare impervious rocks, (5) frozen ground-or ground already filled with water, (6) humid regions

[1] Figures from Milham's *Meteorology*, p. 248.

which do not permit rapid evaporation. All these factors favor the direct formation of streams from runoff following precipitation. Opposite conditions reduce or prevent the possibility of streams being formed. Thus if rainfall is of rare occurrence in an arid region, the parched ground may soak up all the water, entirely preventing runoff. Or, in a heavily forested region, the mulch of soil, decayed leaves, broken twigs, etc., may absorb all the water from a light rain. The thoughtful reader will easily reconstruct other conditions that reduce or prevent runoff.

W. O. Thompson.

FIG. 85. — The formation of gullies, the beginning of stream erosion.

CHARACTERISTICS OF STREAMS

Every one knows that streams differ one from another in many respects. Some are large, others are small. Some are thousands of miles long, others are short. In some regions, streams are closely spaced; in other regions they are far apart. One stream may carry a tremendous load of silt, while another may be clear most of the time. Other differences quite as marked and even more important are discovered when studies are made of the complete history of streams.

Location and Distribution. — The location of streams depends upon many factors; the fundamental ones are enough precipitation to support a stream and a downward slope to direct its course. But often these do not satisfy the student of land forms. Why do two streams, for example, the Hudson and Connecticut rivers, flow due south in straight courses only a few miles apart, each with comparatively few tributaries; while the Missouri-Mississippi river system includes streams which flow in every direction, the whole system draining nearly half the United States? Or, why do streams flow directly through great mountain ranges: For example, the Colorado River which flows through the Park Range in Colorado? Obviously, these and similar questions are easier to ask than to answer.

In general, streams are numerous where precipitation is heavy and few where it is light. The location of streams depends not only on the amount of rainfall, but upon earth movements and other factors that will be discussed later in this chapter. Great faults, sharp folds, and particularly broad upwarps or downwarps of the land control the positions of many streams. For example,

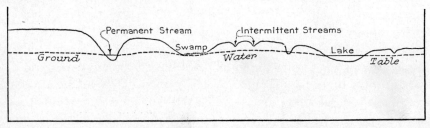

Fig. 86. — The diagram shows permanent streams in valleys that have been cut below the ground-water table and intermittent streams in valleys not cut so deeply.

the Mississippi River system is where it is largely because of the uplift of the Rocky Mountains and High Plains, which directs the streams toward the east, and to the uplift of the Appalachians and Allegheny Plateau, which directs the streams on the west side of the mountains to the west. Downwarping of the Gulf of Mexico region permitted the streams to flow south. However, a slight *upwarping* of this region, coupled with downwarping of northern United States, might quite as easily have directed practically all the interior drainage of North America to the north or northeast.

Permanent Streams. — These are streams which flow throughout the year. Many of them rise in lakes or at the foot of melting snow banks or glaciers which furnish a constant supply of water. Some are supplied with water through direct precipitation which is sufficient to maintain a regular flow. Others, and this includes a very large number, remain permanent *only* because they have cut their valleys deeply into the earth below the ground-water table (Chap. XIII) and receive a constant supply of water through seepage from this underground source.

Intermittent Streams. — These are streams whose sources of water periodically fail. They occur chiefly in regions of seasonal rain or snowfall, and are particularly common to semi-arid regions. Intermittent streams may be divided into (1) spring-fed and (2) surface-fed intermittent streams. *A spring-fed intermittent stream* is subject to fluctuations of the ground-water table. When the table is low, the stream channel is above it and does not get water. When the table is high, the stream flows. *A surface-fed intermittent stream* receives its water from protracted rains or melting snow banks. When the surface supply is gone, the stream disappears. Storms in these regions often are violent; therefore, the streams may grow rapidly for a few hours or days, then decline as quickly as they were formed. On steep slopes such streams may do incredible amounts of work during the brief periods of their existence.

In times of great drought, such as the one that occurred over much of the United States between 1930–1935, many streams that have been regarded as permanent become intermittent. This is due partly to lack of immediate runoff, but chiefly to the lowering of the ground-water table below the beds of the streams.

Ephemeral Streams. — These streams flow only in response to precipitation. They are not fed by springs or by slowly melting snows. According to Meinzer's definition, an ephemeral stream is one that does not flow continuously for as much as one month. Such streams are characteristic of semi-arid and desert regions.

Consequent Streams. — Streams that follow certain courses as a result of (1) initial depressions in land surfaces or (2) slopes that antedated the stream are *consequent streams*. Most of the streams of the earth are of this type, and often their courses are due to crustal deformations of one kind or another. However, simple things, such as buffalo paths, old logging roads, or other man-made depressions may determine the sites of modern consequent streams. Consequent streams are usually definitely in harmony with the slopes of the surrounding land.

Subsequent Streams. — In normal valley development in regions of folded rocks, the main streams (usually consequent) cut their valleys across the uptilted beds. As these valleys are deepened, headward-growing tributaries are started in easily eroded sediments at right angles to the main stream. These tributaries may continue to grow headward until long valleys develop parallel to the strike of the folded beds. Streams in such situations are *subsequent*, and their positions are in direct response to rock structures. The ridges composed of resistant rocks that occur between two parallel strike valleys are called *hogbacks* or *cuestas* (Fig. 87).

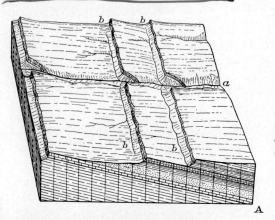

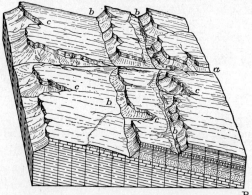

Obsequent Streams. — These also are streams which have developed in certain positions by adjustment to rock structures. After the valley development of consequent and subsequent streams, obsequent streams may form at right angles to the subsequent streams and flow opposite to the direction of flow of the original consequent stream. The drainage

FIG. 87. — The development of subsequent and obsequent streams. (A) represents a region with a consequent stream (a) flowing to the right — subsequent streams (b) are cutting headward at right angles to (a). In diagram (B) obsequent streams (c) flow down the back sides of the ridges at right angles to (b) and in a direction opposite to (a).

patter (Fig. 87) developed by a group of consequent, subsequent and obsequent streams is rectilinear in form and known as *trellis drainage*.

Insequent Streams. — Streams that develop their valleys on flat-lying sediments or on massive rocks, such as granites, without strong structural control are called *insequent streams.* Their drainage pattern being tree-like in form is called *dendritic drainage*. This is the most common of all drainage patterns.

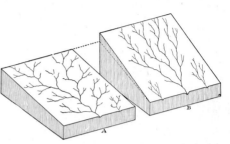

Antecedent Streams. — It may happen that after a stream's course has become well established, movements of the earth, intrusions or extrusions of lava occur which tend to deflect the stream. If it is strong enough to persist

Fig. 88. — Insequent (dendritic) drainage development on homogeneous rocks (A) of gentle slope, (B) of steeper slope.

in its course in spite of the deflecting forces, it is called an *antecedent stream*. Such streams and their courses are out of harmony with the surrounding slopes. An interesting example of this type of stream occurs in southwestern Colorado (Fig. 89). The Dolores River established its course in a northwestward direction from the San Juan mountains to eastern Utah, where it joins the Colorado River. Later, the Paradox Valley anticline began to grow diagonally across the course of the Dolores. However, the river cut its valley downward as rapidly as the anticline was formed, and threw out tributaries which cut headward to the east and west along the crest of the anticline. The present course of the river is entirely out of harmony with its surroundings.

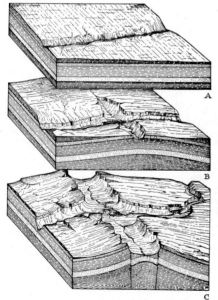

Fig. 89. — The history of the Dolores River, an antecedent stream, as described in the text, Colorado.

Superimposed Streams. — It frequently happens that streams start cutting their valleys in rocks of certain composition and structure, and later, as erosion goes on, the streams reach and are obliged to cut into originally buried underlying rocks of very different composition and structure. Eventually, after the overlying rocks are worn away, the streams are found in most unusual places, such as on the crests or sides of sharp anticlines or crossing resistant rocks which in normal drainage development they would have avoided. Such streams whose courses have been predetermined by the rocks in which they first started to cut their valleys are *superimposed* (Fig. 90). Most superimposed streams are quite out of harmony with their structural surroundings. They are easily confused with antecedent streams, but a thorough examination of the region usually determines their origin.

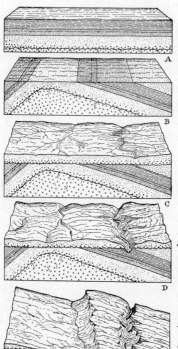

FIG. 90. — The development of superimposed streams. (A) represents a series of undeformed sedimentary rocks. (B) shows the same region folded and eroded. In (C) a new series of beds has been deposited on the older folded beds, and a new erosion cycle has started. (D) is a continuation of (C). By the time stage (E) is reached, the beds deposited in (C) have been removed and the streams are cutting valleys deeply into the old folded beds as a result of their superposition.

Accidents to and Adjustments of Streams

After streams have formed and have started to cut their valleys, many things can happen to them. They may be captured by other streams; they may be drowned; glaciers may change their courses; lava flows or landslides may dam their valleys and pond or divert the streams; the source water may be cut off by diastrophism, draining of lakes, or climatic changes. Floods also change the courses of streams, obstruct their valley, and in other ways prevent their normal development.

Stream Capture. — In regions of folded rocks, stream capture of youthful and mature streams is of very common occurrence. Also when streams meander widely over floodplains, stream capture is common, due to lateral cutting and intersection of meanders.

A simple example of stream capture is shown in Figure 91. Three consequent streams are flowing across a series of tilted rocks. Stream B has much more water than streams A and C, therefore, it cuts its valley deeper. It is able to develop headward tributaries along the easily eroded bed S. These tributaries eventually cut clear through to streams A and C, and since the bottoms of the valleys of the tributaries are *lower* than the valleys of streams A and C, those streams are diverted to B and are said to be captured. The valleys of A and C below the point of capture, now having no water, are called *wind gaps.*

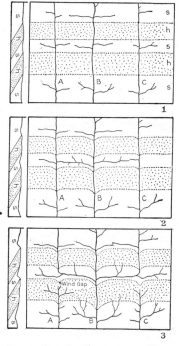

FIG. 91. — A diagram to illustrate stream capture as described in the text.

Drowned Streams and Valleys. — Many examples of drowned streams are known. They can be found on practically all submerged coasts. As the coasts sink or as sea level rises, the streams become drowned and sea water backs up into the main valley and its tributaries (Fig. 92). The Hudson River Valley is drowned as far north as Troy, 150 miles above its mouth. Also its submerged channel can be traced by soundings out over the continental shelf for a distance of about 150 miles from its present mouth. Chesapeake Bay and the lower St. Lawrence Valley are drowned river valleys (estuaries), as is Puget Sound. The coasts of southern Greenland and Norway afford excellent illustrations of drowned valleys, fiords, which differ from estuaries in that they were shaped by glaciers before they were submerged.

Ponded Streams. — Many mountain streams are ponded by landslides which make temporary or permanent dams (Fig. 237). As a result, the sediment carried by the stream above the lake or pond is deposited in the still water, and clear water flows from the pond, tending to reduce the erosive power of the stream.

Streams are sometimes ponded by great quantities of vegetation and silt torn out of their banks which lodge on sandbars and make temporary dams. *Alluvial fans, lava flows, uplifts of the stream floors by earth movements,* and *glaciers* also may pond streams and may even divert them to new courses.

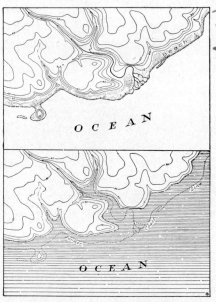

Man-made dams are of great importance in not only ponding streams but in changing their whole behavior. The great Fort Peck dam in Montana will not only create a lake in the Missouri River valley 181 miles long, but it will regulate the flow of the river all the way from the dam to the Mississippi River.

Due to the Boulder Dam, the load that the Colorado River acquires above Lake Mead will now be deposited in the lake.

FIG. 92. — The upper diagram illustrates a coast and valleys before submergence. The lower view shows the same region after submergence.

This load of silt, sand and boulders amounts to 137,000 acre feet annually. Formerly most of this annual load reached the Colorado River delta; therefore, it is evident that the delta-building activities of the river from now on will be greatly reduced. Erosion below the dam also will be reduced, for the stream will have to acquire a new supply of cutting tools to replace those deposited in Lake Mead.

Adjustments Due To Glaciers. — These adjustments are of unusual interest to the physiographer. Many streams were formed long before the Pleistocene epoch, when both continental and valley glaciers were widespread over northern Europe and North America. As the continental glaciers advanced far into the United States from Canada, they changed the courses of hundreds of streams. Good illustrations of these changes occur in Ohio, Illinois, Iowa, North and South Dakota, and in many other states. To give only one example, Calhoun [1] and Alden [2] have shown important changes in the courses of the Missouri and its tributaries. Before the Pleistocene glaciation the Missouri apparently flowed into Hudson Bay. Due to the advance of the successive ice sheets, it was finally diverted to the Mississippi and the Gulf of Mexico. Its pre-glacial course was far to the north of the present one in central Montana.

Valley glaciers also have changed the courses of many streams. Camp-bell gives a striking illustration of such a change in case of the Eagle River in west central Colorado (Fig. 94). Homestake Valley was filled by a glacier which ponded Eagle River and forced it to cut a new outlet. In the com-

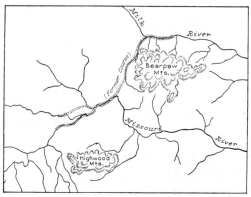

After W. C. Alden, U. S. Geol. Survey.

FIG. 93. — Change in the course of the Missouri River in Montana, due to glaciation.

paratively short time that has elapsed since the river was diverted, it has cut a canyon more than 500 feet deep through solid granite.

These examples show that many things may happen to streams, and that *present* valleys may not indicate the complete physiographic history of the streams that now are in them.

[1] F. H. H. Calhoun: *The Montana Lobe of the Keewatin Ice Sheet.* U. S. G. S. Prof. Paper 50, 1906.

[2] W. C. Alden: *Physiography and Glacial Geology of Northeastern Montana and Adjacent Areas.* U. S. G. S. Prof. Paper 174, 1932.

Floods. — Nearly all streams experience floods at some time in their history. Some streams flood every year. If the floods are not great and the streams remain within their banks, little damage is done; but if the streams overflow their banks, t h e damage may be very great. Floods, in some respects, are much like earthquakes in that there are well defined flood zones in which floods periodically occur. The analogy may be carried further by noting that m a n y streams rarely flood, yet occasionally a disastrous flood occurs without warning.

Causes of Floods. — There are many causes of floods: a dam may fail, as in the case of the St. Francis dam, California, in 1928; ice jams may cause the river water to back up and flood the surrounding low lands. This frequently

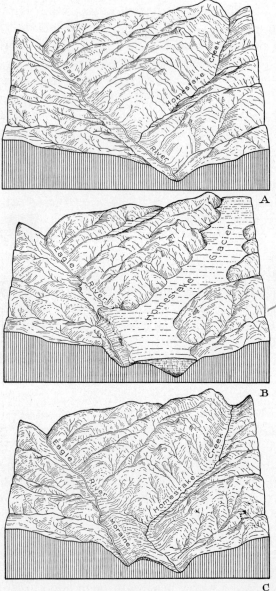

After M. R. Campbell, U. S. Geol. Survey.

FIG. 94. — Change in the course of Eagle River, Colorado, by the Homestake glacier.

happens to the Connecticut River of New England. Rapidly melting snows, particularly if accompanied by heavy rains, cause many streams to flood. Abnormally heavy rainfall may cause floods. If the ground is frozen or already saturated with water from previous rains, the runoff may be practically 100 per cent. Many of the rivers on the west side of the Appalachians flood in the winter and early spring due to protracted storms. Occasionally one comes from the Gulf of Mexico only to be immediately followed by one from the west. In the Rocky Mountains and adjacent plateau regions, unusually heavy rains called *cloudbursts* often cause small streams to rise several feet in a few minutes.

Flood Damage. — The wide plains (flood-plains) adjacent to old or mature streams usually are covered with very fertile soil. On this account large numbers of people inhabit these plains. When, due to floods, great rivers overflow their banks, the damage may be stupendous. Nearly every year newspapers record such floods in some part of the United States. In 1921 the Arkansas River flood between Canon City and the Kansas state line caused damage to property of more than $100,000,000. One of the most destructive floods on record occurred in China in 1887, when the Hoang-Ho swept over its flood-plain causing a loss of more than 1,000,000 human lives. In mountain streams the loss of life usually is much less, but roads, railroads, bridges and houses may be swept away and telephone and telegraph lines torn down. These manifestations of flood damage are relatively easy to evaluate. Often, however, intangible damage is very great. Fertile soil may be washed away; cultivated fields may be strewn with boulders, sand, and all sorts of debris. Soil losses in China and in many parts of the United States are terrific. When we realize that it takes several thousand years to produce a foot of good soil, the loss due to floods becomes more apparent.

Flood Prevention. — This is a matter of immediate national importance in the United States. The Chinese people centuries ago cut the forests from mountains, hills and other water sheds. Succeeding generations have paid a heavy penalty through flood losses, involving loss of property, life and famine. In many parts of the United States there has been similar deforestation. *Forests tend to reduce the rate of runoff and to prevent floods;* therefore, reforestation of all denuded water sheds will do much to control floods. Storage reservoirs for flood waters, straightening of river channels, man-made levees, higher bridges and fewer obstructions to the free flow of water—all help. The forecasting of floods, which is now being done on a large scale, will allow people to move out of regions likely to be flooded, but, of course, will not prevent the floods. Devastating floods will occur in the future just as they have in the past, but the damage can be greatly reduced in civilized countries when people decide to institute proper methods of flood control.

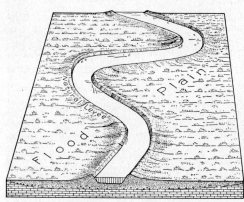

FIG. 95. — A diagram to illustrate the development of natural levees on a flood-plain.

Topography due to Floods. — The cutting and transporting power of streams increase rapidly with increase in volume and velocity of the water. It follows then that streams in flood do more work than under normal conditions. Erosion on land slopes is increased; streams widen and deepen their channels; cut new channels; deposit debris irregularly on flood-plains, thus creating depressions which fill with water making ponds and lakes. In the flood of 1892 the Hoang-Ho cut a new channel and reached the ocean 300 miles north of its old mouth.

Natural levees are made by many rivers. They are long embankments formed by the alluvium deposited by rivers where they overflow their banks. The slopes from the levees to the adjacent flood-plains are anomalous in that they are *away* from the streams rather than toward them as in normal conditions. The principle of formation of levees is easily understood. As long as streams are confined within their banks, the water is concentrated and definite currents are established. Where they overflow their banks, the current is partially dissipated, the carrying power is decreased, and deposition begins.

THE WORK OF STREAMS — EROSION

It has already been stated that one of the chief functions of streams is to carry the land to the sea. While doing it, a great variety of topographic forms are produced. If we follow a typical stream from its source to its mouth, examining its processes and testing its waters, we find that its work naturally falls into the following divisions. These are (1) getting a load, (2) transportation

FIG. 96. — Part of the bed load of a stream, that cannot be moved in times of low water.

of the load, (3) wearing away the rocks both loose and solid against which the water flows (corrasion), (4) taking materials from the rocks into *solution*. These, together with *weathering*, which prepares the rocks of the earth for removal, are all involved in the process of *stream erosion*.

The Load. — The sediment carried in suspension, together with the bed load, that is, gravel, pebbles and boulders rolled along the bottom of the channel, and the material carried in solution, constitute the stream's load. This material gets into the water in various ways. Some fine material is washed in by rain or melting snow. Some creeps down the sides of the valley, much slides or tumbles down due to gravity. The streams cut out soft materials from the bottom and sides of their valleys, undermine their banks, and abrade the hard rocks in their channels, wearing off pieces of rocks that are small enough to be carried away. Larger boulders are undercut and allowed to turn over. Weathering of the sides of the valleys and the banks of streams is probably the most important single factor in making rock material available for removal by streams.

Transportation. — The amount of material carried to the sea each year by all the rivers of the world is stupendous. It has been estimated that the rivers of the United States alone transport annually at least 800,000,000 tons; actually the amount is probably much more. Approximately two-thirds of this is in suspension and bed load (the material rolled along the bed of the stream); the rest is in solution. It would take 160,000 freight trains of 100 cars each, every car carrying a normal load of 50 tons, working all the time to carry as much material to the sea as is carried by the rivers of the United States.

The Transporting Power of Streams. — Many factors are involved in determining the transporting power of streams. Two of fundamental importance are (1) the size of the debris and (2) the velocity of the stream. Fine material is readily carried in suspension, but with increasing coarseness a size is finally reached which cannot be so carried. The coarse material that is swept along the bottom as bed load rolls, jumps or skips along through the process known as *saltation*. The velocity of a stream depends largely upon the slope, size and shape of the channel and upon the volume of water. With a constant slope and shape, increased volume means increased velocity. If the shape of the channel and volume are constant but the slope is greater, velocity is increased. Where the volume and slope are constant, the velocity is greater in straight smooth channels than in winding irregular ones.

Many experiments have been made to determine the capacity of streams to move their bed load. None have been entirely satisfactory, and different figures have been used to express the relationship between velocity and the transporting power of streams. According to Gilbert, the capacity of a stream to move its bed load

varies with the 3.2 power to the 4.0 power of the velocity. Using
the latter figure, it is equivalent to saying that *if the velocity is
doubled, the stream's power to move objects on the bottom is increased 16 times*. This principle applies primarily to the size of
the particles moved and explains the tremendous carrying power of
streams in times of flood. When the St. Francis dam in California
failed in 1928, blocks of concrete weighing more than 10,000 tons
were carried more than half a mile down the valley.

Courtesy U. S. War Department.

FIG. 97. — The original jetties constructed by Captain Eads. Most of the old east
jetty is submerged but is shown in the view to the right of the present one, south
of Port Eads.

Many years ago Captain J. B. Eads made use of the principle
that with a constant slope streams can do more work in straight than
in crooked channels. In spite of much adverse criticism, he constructed jetties on South Pass, one of the distributaries of the Mississippi River on its delta. He believed that by confining the water,
the river would keep its channel free of sediment and would permit
ocean-going boats to ascend the river to New Orleans. The first
jetties were placed at the full width of South Pass, but were found
to be too far apart, and a second one was constructed on one side,

thus *narrowing* the channel (Fig. 97). Since the completion of the latter, the river has kept its channel open just as it was supposed to do.

In the normal history of a river, most of the coarse material which it carries is dropped and picked up many times. This is well illustrated by the shifting of sand bars in the Platte, Missouri, and Mississippi rivers. Shifting of bars is well known to every trout fisherman who has waded out to fish the riffles of a moderately swift stream and has felt the rounded gravel and cobblestones roll beneath his feet!

W. O. Thompson.

FIG. 98. — A gravel and cobblestone bar being cut to pieces by the stream that made it, Red Deer River, Alberta.

Corrasion. — Corrasion is the mechanical abrasion by streams caused by one particle of rock striking another. Clear water has little abrading power. But streams that carry grains of sand and gravel or that roll one pebble or boulder against another cut, polish, and finally wear away the rocks with which they come in contact. The well-rounded and often highly polished boulders that are strewn along streams both large and small attest the remarkable amount of corrasion that goes on.

Corrasion is largely responsible for the ability of streams to deepen their valleys. The best cutting tools are quartz sand grains, which are harder than most rocks with which they come in contact.

An important reason for the present great depth of the Grand Canyon of the Colorado River is the easily available large quantity of quartz sand which the river can use.

Solution. — The amount of rock material carried in solution to the sea by the rivers of the world is surprisingly large. This is ac-

FIG. 99. — Pot holes and corrasion of granite boulders in a mountain stream, Colorado.

quired in several ways. Through the process of carbonation described in Chapter VII, vast quantities of soluble salts drain into streams; underground waters also dissolve many rocks and minerals and bring this material to the streams through springs and seepages; solution processes, however, also are active in the running water. Soluble minerals are removed both from the materials that are being carried and from the rocks of the bed and banks of the stream. Murray estimated that on the average there are 762,587 tons of mineral matter, about half being calcium carbonate, in each cubic mile of river water. We have already learned that more than 6,500 cubic miles of water is carried to the sea annually by the rivers of the world; therefore, if this estimate is correct, it is evident that *nearly 5 billion tons of mineral matter is taken into solution from the land and carried to the seas each year.*

Summary. — We are now prepared to understand the close relationship that exists between weathering and the work of streams. When both mechanical and chemical weathering are rapid (especially on bare slopes), the erosive work of running water will be great. If the rocks are of such a nature that weathering is slow, the results will be reflected in the valley development of the streams. Where the land is heavily forested, stream erosion will be slow, for the forest cover tends to regulate and reduce runoff, and also the roots of trees help to hold the soil in place.

Rate of Erosion. — There is no entirely satisfactory answer to questions regarding the rate of stream erosion. The factors that govern the process are complex and too variable to allow sweeping statements. In one region actual measurements may show that soft shale hills are eroded as rapidly as one foot in one year. In another place the erosion of a massive quartzite is so slow that it cannot be measured.

Perhaps the best way to get at the problem is to take average conditions over large areas. According to the United States Geological Survey, the area of the drainage basin of the Mississippi River is 1,265,000 square miles. Basing the rate of erosion on the amount [1] of material that is transported to the Gulf of Mexico each year, it apparently takes between 5,000 and 6,000 years to lower the whole drainage basin one foot. This rate is too high for erosion by *streams* over the whole United States, for in the Appalachian and New England states, forests and lakes retard stream erosion; while in the Columbia and Colorado plateau provinces and in the

---

[1] Estimates of this amount vary greatly and cannot be determined accurately on account of the unknown amount of bed load. The figure most generally accepted has been 550,000,000 tons, but Richard J. Russell's detailed studies of the Mississippi delta lead him to believe that the average annual discharge by the river is not less than 730,000,000 tons.

Great Basin it also is less than in the Mississippi basin. The estimated rate of stream erosion over the whole United States is one foot in 8,000 to 9,000 years.

THE WORK OF STREAMS — DEPOSITION

It is obvious that deposition is a complementary process of erosion. The conditions that cause a stream to deposit its load are

Whitman Cross, U. S. Geol. Survey.

FIG. 100. — Alluvial fans, San Juan Mountains. After the first (upper) fan was formed it was partly cut away and the valley floor was lowered. Then the small fan was deposited.

exactly opposite to those that permit it to carry a load. Therefore, a reduction in either gradient, volume or velocity will cause deposition.

Deposits on the Land. — Most streams deposit and pick up part of their load many times. The material may be picked up almost immediately or, in certain situations, it may remain on the land for hundreds or even thousands of years. The velocity of streams is checked when they flow from steep to gentle slopes causing the deposition of *alluvial* fans and plains. Such deposits are wide-spread along the flanks of high mountains in western North America. Small, swift tributary streams may deposit small alluvial fans and cones in the valleys of larger but more sluggish streams which the main streams cannot carry away. Also swift tributaries to streams in plateaus and mountains bring in alluvium which is not left in the form of fans or cones, but rather is strewn along the floor of the main valleys, causing the overloading of the streams. Old and mature rivers overflow their banks, building up natural levees and flood-plain deposits. These may attain great thickness. In the irrigated districts of western North America many large canals are built to carry water from the streams to the farm land. It is a very noticeable fact that immediately below the intakes of such canals, the streams deposit much of their load due to the reduction in the volume of water.

Deposits in Water. — Where rivers empty into lakes, seas or even, in exceptional cases, other rivers, the velocity is reduced and deposition may occur. If the waves and currents of the body of water into which the river empties are not strong enough to carry away the sediment brought in by the stream, a *delta* is formed at the mouth of the river. Deltas grow seaward by continued deposition. The deposits block the stream channels, causing distributary streams. Each distributary stream has less volume than the original river, hence there tends to be further deposition.

Streams in many cases become very sluggish, due to the low gradient of their valleys and to the large loads that they carry. As a result, they tend to deposit sand bars here and there along their courses. Bars are particularly likely to form on the *inside* of broad bends due to eddies that bring in material that the stream is removing from the outside of the bend. In many places the valleys become so clogged with debris that the flow of the stream is divided among many channels, thus creating an *anastomosing* or *braided* stream (Fig. 102).

Overloaded Streams. — Many streams acquire more load than they can carry, and thus become overloaded. This condition is found in all types of topographic regions. Thousands of mountain streams are so loaded by debris brought in by steep-gradient tributaries

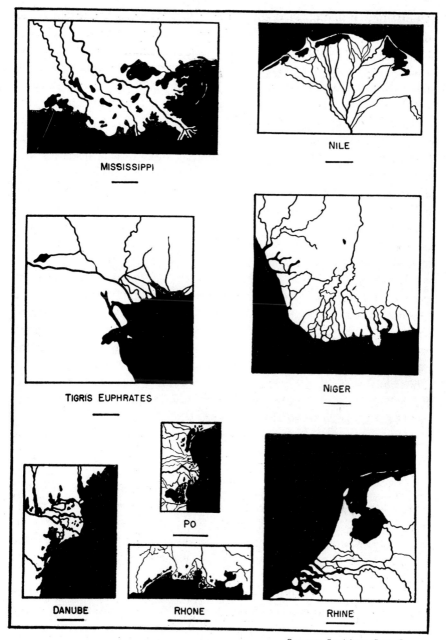

MISSISSIPPI

NILE

TIGRIS EUPHRATES

NIGER

PO

DANUBE

RHONE

RHINE

Courtesy Louisiana Geol. Survey.

FIG. 101. — Some great deltas of the world. The horizontal bar below the name of each delta represents a distance of approximately 31 miles.

that their valley floors are actually being *raised* instead of *deepened* as one might expect in regions of high relief. Such valleys may finally be filled to depths of many feet by alluvium and consequently greatly widened. The streams may be braided and may appear to be old when actually they are only well started in their work of wearing away the land. In regions of lower relief, overloading is even more common. Under all conditions of overloading the streams tend to become selective, transporting more of the finer or lighter

FIG. 102. — The Arkansas River near LaJunta, Colorado. An old, braided stream.

material and depositing more of the larger or heavier parts of their load.

Graded Streams. — In the early stages of a stream's history, under normal conditions, more material is being transported than is deposited along the stream course. The natural result is to *degrade* the valley by both deepening and widening it. As time goes on, the gradient of the valley floor is reduced, and the stream's carrying power is diminished until finally a condition is reached in which the stream's load and transporting power are approximately balanced. The stream, then, is said to be *graded* or *at grade.* Because of differences in the original (usually very irregular) gradient and in the resistance of rocks that are being eroded, not all of the stream reaches this condition at the same time.

When a stream is at grade it must drop some of its old load, if it is to transport new material received from any source. If its load decreases (unless the stream is at baselevel), it begins to deepen its valley. If the load increases, part of it is deposited, and the

W. O. Thompson.

FIG. 103. — The Red Deer River, Alberta. An overloaded stream in mature surroundings.

stream tends to split up into channels, thus becoming braided, or to swing in broad curves, meanders, over its valley floor.

TOPOGRAPHY RESULTING FROM STREAM EROSION

Having examined the ways in which streams do their work, we now are ready to discuss the topography produced by stream erosion. In considering this subject, it will be helpful to attempt to visualize the great variety of conditions under which streams exist and carry on their activities.

First, let us examine some swift mountain stream, for example, the Animas River in Colorado. This stream just south of Silverton is flowing in a deep narrow canyon. From the top of the high mountains, less than three miles away, to the bottom of the canyon there is a drop of more than 5,000 feet. Evidently the amount of work already done is very great, but the floor of the canyon is still 8,000 feet above sea level, and the river can continue to cut much deeper into the land; therefore, the amount of work yet to be done in wearing away the land is even greater than that already accomplished. In contrast with the Animas River, let us examine the St. Johns River near Palatka, Florida. This, like the Animas, is a young river, but it never will do much work. Its surface is only ten feet above the Atlantic Ocean. The highest ground anywhere near the river is only 95 feet above sea level. The gradient of the St. Johns is less than 6 inches to the mile, while that of the Animas is 100 feet to the mile. St. Johns is much larger than the Animas, but its ability to do erosive work is very much less because of its different physical environment.

Again, by way of contrast, let us choose the Big Horn River of north-central Wyoming and the Connecticut of New England. The two rivers are of about the same length and size, and they rise in regions of somewhat similar relief, but there their similarity ends. The Big Horn flows through relatively soft rocks in a semi-arid region. It is fed by numerous tributaries, all of which are actively eroding the land. The Connecticut and most of its tributaries either rise in or flow through lakes, which collect the sediment carried into them. The region drained by the Connecticut is humid and for the most part well forested. The rocks in general are much more resistant to erosion than are those of the Big Horn drainage basin. The work being done by the Big Horn River is much greater than that being done by the Connecticut.

Valley Development

There are three important types of valleys, (1) glacial, (2) structural, and (3) those formed by streams. The latter start as gullies which grow to ravines, and the ravines develop into valleys. This process can be illustrated by supposing that part of the continental shelf of humid eastern North America be gently uplifted above sea level. Assume two slight depressions on the newly formed coastal plain: (a) just above the ocean water, and (b) in the middle of an otherwise smooth slope. Both of these depressions will concentrate the runoff from the land, and tiny streams will be formed. The streams will immediately cut the depressions deeper, allowing more water to accumulate. Soon distinct gullies will appear. The water in gully (a) flows directly into the sea; therefore, the gully cannot be lengthened in that direction, but as time goes on, it will lengthen headward due to downward cutting and to continued accumulation of water. Gully (b) will lengthen toward the mouth, for the stream will be forced to cut a channel down the slope below the original depression. It also will lengthen headward just as in the case of (a). Later both ravines have been still further deepened. Due to weathering and to inequalities of the rocks, the slope wash from the sides has been concentrated and tributaries have started to form. These gradually grow headward exactly as do the original gullies. After erosion has gone on for some time, a network of valleys will cover the plain.

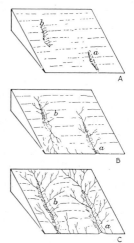

Fig. 104. — A diagram to illustrate the development of valleys.

Valley Profiles. — By the time the last stage has been reached, both transverse and longitudinal valley profiles will be distinct (Fig. 105). The transverse profile is V-shaped at the head and U-shaped at the mouth, for the stream is still deepening the valley. The longitudinal profile is steep at the head and assumes a rather uniform gentle gradient toward the mouth.

The Limits of a Valley

Obviously all valleys are limited in the length, width and depth to which they can grow. Many factors are involved in the determination of these limits. Again illustrations will help us to under-

Fig. 105. — Longitudinal and transverse valley profiles.

stand the various possibilities. Assume that a volcanic island has recently been raised above sea level. Let the island be perfectly symmetrical in form and absolutely uniform in composition. Also let the rainfall be exactly the same over the whole island. Now let four depressions, equally spaced and exactly alike, be formed on four sides of the island immediately above the sea, and assume that these initial depressions grow into gullies, ravines, and valleys, as described in the preceding section.

The Depth. — The depth to which the valleys can be cut in the case under consideration is sea level, for the ocean water breaks up the stream's current and prevents it from eroding the valley deeper.

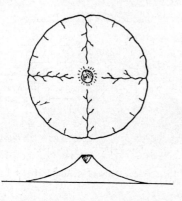

Sea level in this case is _baselevel, which is the lowest level to which a stream can cut its valley._

The Length. — None of the valleys can be lengthened toward their mouths, for all open into the sea, but if all the conditions prescribed above are fulfilled, each valley can be cut headward until all meet at the top of the island. The meeting place is the _headward divide._ As the streams cut deeper into the island, the headward divide will be lowered, but will always remain a _permanent divide_ as long as the conditions of uniformity described above apply.

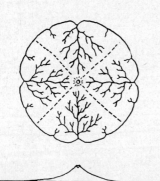

Fig. 106. — An hypothetical diagram to illustrate the development of permanent divides. See the text for details.

The Width. — Continuing to use our hypothetical island and assuming only four master valleys (something entirely improbable in reality), each valley could grow until it covered nearly one-fourth of the island. The width of each would be limited by _lateral divides_ separating one from another. As the island is worn down lower and lower by stream erosion, the lateral divides would become lower and narrower until in the last stage of erosion they would be negligible.

Summary. — There is some danger that the hypothetical illustration of valley limits just used may become confusing when applied to actual valleys scattered widely over the earth. The principles do not change, but conditions under which they are to be applied will be very different in different places.

Considering, first, the *depth of valleys,* it is evident that sea level is a controlling factor for streams that flow directly into the sea. But what about streams that do not reach the sea? The surface elevation of Yellowstone Lake in Yellowstone National Park is 7,741 feet above sea level. Many streams flow into this lake, but none can cut their valleys below the lake level, which in this case is a *local or temporary baselevel.* The surface of the Dead Sea, which lies in a great structural depression, is 1,268 feet *below* mean sea level; therefore, streams which flow into it can cut their valleys to this depth. The Platte River empties into the Missouri at Plattsmouth,

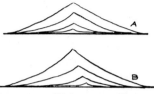

FIG. 107. — Diagrams to illustrate (A), a permanent divide, and (B), a shifting divide.

A. J. Eardley.

FIG. 108. — A lateral divide, nearly removed, between the Anvik River and the Yukon. The bluffs are about 75 feet high.

Nebraska. Naturally the depth of the Platte Valley is limited by the Missouri Valley. It is evident from these examples that *the depth of any stream-cut valley is limited by the body of water into which the stream flows.*

Turning to the *headward divides of streams,* it is most unusual to find permanent divides on a land surface. In most cases the rocks differ in composition and resistance, and the rainfall varies on the two sides of a divide. As a result, streams will cut faster on one side of the divide than on the other, and the divide at the head of the streams will shift *away* from the valley that is being lowered most rapidly (Fig. 107).

Lateral divides are usually much more complicated than is indicated in the simple statement above. Due to inequalities in the rocks, structure or drainage, the divides shift one way or another. This is particularly true in the late stages of a stream's history. In the early stages, downward cutting is predominant, while later, after streams have become graded or have reached baselevel, they tend to cut laterally, thus widening their valleys and shifting the lateral divides. If two adjacent streams are at the same elevation, as the valleys widen, the divide between them may be worn away, allowing the streams to unite. Or, if one stream is at a lower elevation than the other and both are cutting laterally, the lower stream may undercut and capture the higher one.

Baselevel. — Streams that flow to the oceans can deepen their valleys until they reach sea level. Except for a few very large streams whose currents are strong enough to push the ocean water aside, all valley deepening ceases at sea level; therefore, *sea level is the baselevel of erosion.* If an imaginary curved plane at sea level elevation be projected beneath all lands (see Fig. 1), it represents the downward limit of stream erosion or baselevel.

If sea level rises or falls, baselevel is correspondingly raised or lowered. Valley floors that have been cut down to sea level are said to be *baseleveled.* After a stream has reached baselevel, if it cuts laterally and brings large areas down to the level of the valley floor, the whole region is said to be baseleveled. In reality very few *large* areas of land are completely baseleveled. A stream requires some gradient in order to flow. Assume a stream 1,000 miles long with a gradient of 6 inches to the mile. With its tributaries it might reduce a large area to *approximate* baselevel, but only the lower part of the area near the sea could be at *actual* baselevel.

Temporary or Local Baselevels. — The surface of any body of water other than the ocean into which a stream flows constitutes a *local baselevel* for that stream. If it is a large, relatively permanent lake, the streams that reach it may reduce their valleys to this local baselevel. Later, if the lake is drained, the streams can cut their valleys deeper, and the local baselevel will prove to be only a temporary one.

The Profile of Equilibrium. — As streams continue to erode their valleys and as the surrounding higher land is worn down, there is a tendency to reach a balance between the streams' ability to do work and the work they have to do. The stream, under normal conditions, establishes its grade near its mouth and gradually carries it headward. This may be brought about by erosion alone or erosion in some places and deposition in others. In its early stages the stream may have a very uneven longitudinal profile, very steep in some places and gentle in others. As time goes on these irregularities are removed. Eventually the profile is a smooth curve, concave upward, steepest toward the head, and with gentle slope toward the mouth (Fig. 105). The adjacent slopes are more or less rounded and graded. There is a nice adjustment between the streams' ability to erode the land and the amount of erosion yet to be done. *In this condition the stream has reached its profile of equilibrium.*

THE GEOMORPHIC CYCLE — THE CYCLE OF EROSION [1]

Through our studies up to this point, it is evident that land surfaces have not always been what they are now. On the contrary, they have been and still are undergoing definite and constant changes. Broad valleys were once gullies; low, gently sloping ridges were once higher, wider and steeper. If we examine several similar regions, it becomes evident that

FIG. 109. — A diagram to show transverse profiles of youthful, mature and old valleys.

each has had a somewhat systematic topographic history. Finally we are forced to conclude that the topography produced by

[1] The broad conception of cyclic development of land surfaces is the result of the work and writings of W. M. Davis.

streams has had a cyclic development. Moreover, as we study the relief of the land, we find definite relationship between different types of topography and the streams that are associated with those types. Swift-flowing streams usually are found in gorges, canyons, or V-shaped valleys. Divides between them are high and wide. Slow sluggish streams usually occur in broad valleys. Between these valleys the divides are apt to be low and narrow.

Definitions. — *The cycle of erosion is the time required for streams to reduce a newly formed land mass to baselevel. The geomorphic cycle is the topography developed during the various stages of a cycle of erosion.*

Outline of the Cycles. — As a definite example, suppose that in a humid region some large area which has been under the sea for a long time be bowed high above the sea by diastrophism. As soon as the region is above water, erosion will begin. But assume that *the rate of uplift is much greater than the rate of erosion.* Eventually most of the land will be well above the sea. Now assume that all diastrophism ceases and that the highland is reduced by stream erosion to baselevel. The topography will at first be *youthful;* gradually, it will attain *maturity;* finally, as the relief is diminished and baselevel is approached, the land surfaces will have become *old.* The same terms, youth, mature and old, apply to streams, which with their tributaries constitute a *drainage or river system.* The chief function of a river system is to reduce the land of its drainage basin to baselevel. When this task is only well started, the river system and most of its constituent streams are *youthful.* After about half the work has been accomplished, the river system is *mature.* It is *old* when nearly all the land has been worn down to baselevel.

The terms youth, maturity and old age are entirely relative and *cannot be converted into years.* Two cycles of erosion might start at the same time, yet one be completed while the other was still in a youthful stage. The height and breadth of the newly formed land, its structure, composition and distance from the sea and the amount of rainfall are important factors in determining the length of a cycle of erosion. However, the development of topography by streams in humid regions is so systematic that the relief may be classified in terms of the geomorphic cycle no matter where the region occurs.

The following discussion of stages in an erosional cycle must, for lack of space, be generalized. Not all specific cases can be described and only typical topography of each stage will be mentioned. It should be noted at the outset that a blending of types is the rule rather than the exception. In a region of general youthful characteristics, some master streams and valleys may be mature. In a maturely dissected plain or plateau, there will be some recently formed, youthful streams actively engaged in deepening their valleys. Even in a region of typical old age it is possible to have some youthful or mature streams and valleys.

Youthful Topography

Youthful topography is characterized by comparatively few streams, but usually they have high gradients. The drainage may be poor with lakes and swamps on the divides between the streams. Divides are wide and may be high. The streams flow in steep-walled canyons, gorges or V-shaped valleys. Waterfalls and rapids are numerous. Usually the streams are actively engaged in cutting their valleys deeper, although some streams in youthful regions may be so overloaded with debris brought in by swift-flowing tributaries that they expend all their energy in removing it, and actually allow their valley floors to be built up. In youthful regions the work so far done toward reducing the land to baselevel is much less than the work that remains to be done. In other words, the bottoms of most of the valleys and the surrounding land are well above base-level.

Canyons and Gorges. — These are valleys whose walls are very steep and high in proportion to their width. They represent the results of stream erosion in which the streams have cut downward more rapidly than weathering and slope wash have reduced the slope of the upper walls of the valley. In many cases the steep walls of canyons are composed of rocks, such as quartzites (Fig. 110), that are resistant to chemical weathering. In some cases faults or great joints aid in the rapid downward cutting by the streams and in the preservation of the steep walls. The rapid recession of a waterfalls may form a gorge.

E. G. Fine.

Fig. 110. — Big Thompson Canyon, Colorado. The rock of the nearly vertical left wall is quartzite. There is very little chemical weathering but considerable mechanical weathering of this material.

The Grand Canyon of the Colorado River. — This is one of the most magnificent canyons in existence. It is of relatively recent origin, having been cut since the Late Pliocene uplift of the Colorado Plateau. In its deepest place the bottom of the canyon is 6,250 feet below the surrounding plateau. The upper walls are composed

James Johnson.

FIG. 111. — The Yellowstone Canyon with the Great Falls in the background.

of nearly horizontal beds of vari-colored sandstone, shale and limestone, while the lower walls are chiefly Pre-Cambrian slates, schists, quartzites and granites. The upper (outer) part of the canyon is wide. Within its walls are terraces, benches, spires and pillars due to the unequal erosion of the sedimentary rocks. The lower (inner) gorge is steep-walled and more uniform in slope due to the erosion of more homogeneous rocks (Fig. 83). The Colorado River is full of rapids and is actively cutting the canyon deeper. However, Lake Mead, an artificial lake behind the Boulder dam (Fig. 241), will from now on prevent erosion of the bottom of the canyon throughout the whole length of the lake, and by collecting the silt and sand reduce the rate of erosion below the dam.

The Yellowstone Canyon. — This canyon, although much

Fig. 112. — The Missouri River, a youthful stream, south of the Little Rockies, Montana. The bluffs are about 200 feet high.

smaller than the Grand Canyon of the Colorado, is noted for its beautiful clear water, waterfalls and rapids, and for the marvelous coloring of its walls. It is being cut through a great lava plateau by the Yellowstone River, which rises in Yellowstone Lake. According to Howard,[1] the river started to cut the canyon in about Middle Pleistocene time. Later the head of the canyon was filled by a greater glacier and was choked with glacial debris when the ice melted. Now the river has removed the debris and is actively deepening the canyon. The head of the canyon is only 13 miles from Yellowstone Lake. Eventually, through recession, it will drain

[1] Arthur D. Howard: "History of the Grand Canyon of the Yellowstone." Geol. Soc. Am., Special Paper No. 6, 1937.

much of the lake. The canyon walls are largely extrusive volcanic rocks which have been altered by hydrothermal action and weathering. The resulting colors are an indescribable blending of yellow, orange, red and brown.

The Royal Gorge of the Arkansas. — This gorge, situated a few miles west of Canon City, Colorado, is another fine example of youthful topography. Through recent rejuvenation of the Arkansas River, a gorge, in some places with vertical walls 1,100 feet high, has been cut in Pre-Cambrian granite, quarzites and schists. Although the river is more or less blocked by great boulders that have tumbled down from the sides, deepening of the gorge is still going on. The contrast between the swift-flowing stream, filled with rapids, in the gorge and the same stream a few miles east on the great plains where the stream is slow and sluggish is very striking.

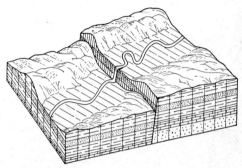

FIG. 113. — A waterfall caused by faulting.

Youthful Valleys on Plains. — Not all youthful streams and valleys are in mountains and plateaus; *they are quite as numerous on plains.* Wherever it may be found, any newly formed stream is youthful and the valley is, of course, also youthful.

Reference already has been made to the diversion of the Missouri River by continental glaciers. North and east of Great Falls, Montana, the river is now vigorously deepening its post-glacial valley. The Niagara River between Lake Erie and the end of the Niagara Gorge is doing the same thing. Hundreds of other youthful streams are scattered over the plains of all the continents. The general elevation of the plains is too low to allow the development of deep canyons, but the valleys and surrounding topography will eventually go through all the cyclic changes from youth to old age.

Waterfalls and Rapids. — Waterfalls are found on all continents, particularly in mountain and plateau regions. Rapids are almost always found immediately above or below waterfalls, but they also occur in many streams where there are no falls.

FIG. 114. — Seven Falls, near Colorado Springs, Colorado. The effects of inequalities of the rocks are clearly shown.

Many different geologic conditions are responsible for waterfalls. A fault scarp may make a cliff over which a stream flows.

Or the cliff may be due to some very resistant rock which the stream encounters while deepening its valley. It frequently happens that a large stream deepens its valley rapidly, while a smaller tributary cuts downward more slowly. Eventually, the main stream is much lower

R. H. Anderson, Courtesy U. S. Dept. of the Interior.

FIG. 115. — Yosemite Falls, Yosemite National Park. The upper fall has a sheer drop of 1,430 feet; the lower 320, which is twice that of Niagara. The water falls from the mouth of a hanging valley.

than the tributary, and if a resistant rock occurs where the side stream comes into the main valley, a waterfall will be formed. Such a region is in _topographic unconformity_ and the tributary valley is a _hanging valley_.

Many great plateaus are built up by successive lava flows which vary much in their composition, jointing and thickness. Streams cutting through these layers of lava are very apt to develop waterfalls. Famous examples of this type are the Shoshone, Twin and American falls on the Snake River in Idaho, and the world-renowned Victoria Falls on the Zambezi River in South Africa.

Waterfalls vary so greatly in height, form and volume of water that it is impossible to describe them adequately in a few words. On the one hand, in Yosemite National Park, we have Yosemite Creek, only 35 feet wide, but with a vertical drop of 1,430 feet; in contrast, there is the Iguazu Falls in South America, which really is a whole series of waterfalls in one great panorama. This marvelous waterfall has a total breadth, including several islands, of nearly two miles and a height of about 230 feet, which is somewhat greater than that of Niagara. The Iguazu Falls are on the boundary line between Argentina and Brazil where the river of the same name goes over the edge of the Plateau of Brazil.

The table opposite lists (A) some of the highest of the world's waterfalls, and (B) some that have the greatest volume. The examples are largely from Noyes.[1] Doubtless there are many other undescribed waterfalls of even greater height.

Rapids which occur on steep but not vertical slopes of a stream bed are due in many cases to recession of waterfalls. The beautiful rapids below Niagara Falls are a good example of this type. Other rapids occur where streams are eroding rocks of very unequal hardness. These are illustrated by the famous Lachine Rapids in the St. Lawrence River, just above Montreal, Quebec, or by the great series of rapids in the Grand Canyon of the Colorado.

Rapids and waterfalls are obstructions to navigation. Where they occur between waterways that are navigable below and above the falls, canals may be built around them. Naturally such canals require locks to raise and lower the boats from one level to another.

Potholes. — In rapids and at the foot of waterfalls, *potholes* are formed in solid rock through the grinding action of sand and peb-

[1] Theodore W. Noyes: *The World's Great Waterfalls.* Nat. Geog. Mag., Vol. 50, pp. 29-59, 1926.

GREAT WATERFALLS

A

Name	Height in feet	Country or State
Yosemite	2,555 (in three cataracts)	California
Sutherland	1,904 (in three cataracts)	New Zealand
Roraima	1,500	British Guiana
Kalambo	1,400 (in two sections)	South Africa
Takkakau	1,346	British Columbia
Multnomah	823	Oregon
Bridalveil	620	Yosemite, California

B

Name	Height in feet	Country or State
Niagara	167	United States and Canada
Victoria	400	South Africa
Iguazu	230	Brazil
Kaieteur	800	British Guiana
Lower Yellowstone	308	Wyoming
Grand	316	Labrador

bles which lodge in slight initial depressions and are swirled around by the swift water (Fig. 99). Some of these holes attain a diameter

E. G. Fine.

FIG. 116. — A valley in late youth, Red Mountain Park, Colorado.

and a depth of many feet. The occurrence of potholes in cliffs high above present streams is good evidence of the stream-cut origin of the valley.

Mature Topography

By the time a region has advanced from youth to typical maturity in a cycle of erosion, many changes have taken place in the topography. In the first place, the drainage is better developed. Instead of a few streams, many drain the region. The main streams may or may not have cut their valleys to baselevel, but many will be at grade. Tributaries are well established. Lakes, swamps, waterfalls and rapids have largely disappeared. Valley flats have been formed by lateral erosion of the larger streams. Divides are nar-

FIG. 117. — Little Snake River Valley, Colorado, a valley approaching maturity.

rower. Hills and ridges are lower and less steep. A good test of maturity is found in the areas of valleys and intervening hills and ridges; if the areas are about equal, maturity has been reached (see Fig. 364).

There are, of course, all gradations in types of topography between youth and maturity. One physiographer may designate a region as in late youth, while another calls it early mature. Similar transitions occur between mature and old topography, but typical regions are easily recognized.

In maturity one finds a marked difference in the patterns of drainage developed (a) in regions of homogeneous rocks without important structural features, and (b) in folded heterogeneous rocks. The folded and highly eroded rocks are so clearly indicated by the topography that the structures and even the composition of many of the rocks can be determined with considerable accuracy from good topographic maps.

Influence of Homogeneous or Non-folded Rocks. — Mature topography developed in such homogeneous rocks as granites and gneisses, or even in horizontally bedded sedimentary rocks of varying composition, tends to flow in smooth curves. On the slopes of hills and ridges already smoothed by erosion, weathering decomposes the rocks faster than the material is washed away. This material slumps, creeps or slides, covering the sides of valleys, and thus smoothing the contact between valley floor and valley wall.

The steep cliffs caused by horizontally bedded, massive resistant sandstones or limestones which are so characteristic of youthful topography (Fig. 83) largely disappear and tend to blend into the broad sweeping curves of well matured regions.

Dendritic Drainage. — Due to uniformity of rock composition where strong structural trends are absent, a dendritic (tree-like) drainage pattern is developed by the time that maturity is reached in the geomorphic cycle. In the normal development of tributaries, they meet the main stream with acute (up-stream) angles (Fig. 223). Such a well established drainage pattern insures rather uniform and relatively rapid erosion of the homogeneous rocks of the region. Slope wash almost immediately is directed into a stream channel and the divides between streams are constantly lowered.

Influence of Folded Rocks. — The drainage pattern developed in a matured region on folded beds is rectangular. Tributaries meet their main streams at right angles. Tributaries to tributaries also come in at right angles due to the controlling influence of rock structures. Consequent, subsequent and obsequent streams combine to give a trellis drainage pattern. Where the streams are equally spaced on rocks of relatively uniform composition, remarkably well rounded hills may be formed.

Cuestas and Hogbacks. — In folded mountain regions, or even on plains or plateaus, when large folds have been formed in sedimentary rocks, after considerable erosion, long narrow ridges are conspicuous topographic features. These are called *cuestas* or hogbacks. Many geologists and geomorphologists have attempted to distinguish between cuestas and hogbacks. Cuestas are supposed to be developed on rocks of low dip and to have unsymmetrical cross-sections, while hogbacks are supposed to have been formed on rocks of high dip and to have nearly or quite symmetrical cross-sections. After examining scores of ridges that have been called "hogbacks"

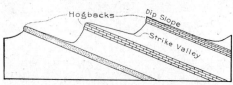

by prominent geologists and finding them almost invariably unsymmetrical in cross-section, the writer believes that attempted distinctions between cuestas and hog-backs are both unnecessary

FIG. 118. — Dip slopes, cuestas, or hogbacks, and strike valleys.

and misleading, and that the word hogback should be dropped from geomorphic literature. Symmetrical ridges may well be called, simply, ridges. If the resistant layers of rock that underlie the cuestas do not dip at angles of more than 60 or 70 degrees, the

W. O. Thompson.

FIG. 119. — Cuestas, strike valleys and wind gaps, northern Colorado.

cuestas are almost always unsymmetrical in transverse profile (Fig. 118). The gentler slope is down the dip. In many cases the angle of dip of the underlying rocks is the same as the slope of the land surface. Such slopes are called _dip slopes_. Although dip slopes are particularly common to cuestas, they are found under other topographic conditions, _but they always indicate a definite_ *control of land slopes through the composition and structure of the underlying rocks.*

Strike (Subsequent) Valleys. — The development of strike valleys between cuestas brings out interesting details of both rock structure and composition. Usually these valleys are cut in such rocks as shales and poorly cemented sandstones through the headward erosion of subsequent streams. As they are cut deeper, the cuestas between them become higher. Stream piracy is of common occurrence. Due to the dip of the underlying beds, the valley bottoms migrate down dip, and the valley profiles become decidedly unsymmetrical in cross-section (Fig. 118).

Old Topography

In typical old topographic regions all the main streams are graded and are meandering back and forth over their flood-plains. Their currents are slow and their carrying power is limited. The divides between the streams are low and narrow. Some divides may have been entirely removed by lateral erosion. The whole landscape is subdued. It may be gently rolling or monotonously flat. Occasional erosion remnants stand above the general land surface. The streams have nearly completed their work of reducing the land to baselevel. Because of the gentle slopes of the land and the low gradients of the streams, *mechanical erosion is very slow*. However, chemical weathering in humid regions is very active. Thus, the inter-stream areas gradually are covered to great depths with residual soil.

Structural control of drainage, so definite in topographic maturity, loses much of its importance in old age. Low ridges or swells cored with resistant rocks may persist, but they have been subdued by erosion, and the streams tend to cut flat plains across uptilted beds of varying resistance.

The Peneplain. — The peneplain, originally defined by Davis as *almost a plain* (also spelled by some writers *peneplane*), designates the ultimate stage reached in a normal cycle of erosion. It represents a large land area that has been reduced nearly to baselevel by streams. In reality peneplains may be *not "almost plains,"*

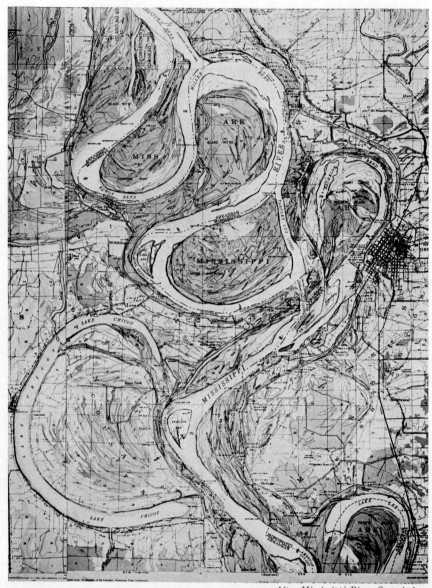

FIG. 120. — The flood-plain of the Mississippi River near Greenville, Miss. Note the ox-bow lakes and abandoned channels.

but *actual plains* in the true topographic sense of the word. Some may approach the quality of a geometric plane, therefore, may be properly designated *peneplanes* (almost planes). The final process by which a land mass composed of rocks of varying structure and composition is reduced to a peneplain is *planation* brought about by the lateral erosion of streams; therefore, it is appropriate to use the verb *to plane* in connection with the formation of a peneplain. As

Photo by U. S. Army Air Corps. Pub. by authority Miss. River Commission.

FIG. 121. — The flood-plain of the Mississippi River and man-made cut-offs of the meander necks, near Greenville, Mississippi.

a rule the surfaces of peneplains are not flat but gently rolling. Hills or even mountains (*monadnocks*) stand as erosion remnants well above the general faint relief of a peneplain.

The length of time required to wear down a mountainous region to a peneplain must be very great, yet there is good evidence that many such regions have been so reduced. The essential requirement is that the *lands stand still,* for if the region is uplifted, it will be rejuvenated and the ultimate stage of erosion, the formation of the peneplain, will be deferred.

In the development of a peneplain, the softer rocks will be worn away first. Resistant rocks will continue to form ridges or low swells, hills or mounds, long after the general land surface has wasted away to a plain. When the final peneplain has been formed, it will bevel all rocks of whatever composition and structure that may lie under the region.

Present peneplains at baselevel are scarce, due apparently to recent diastrophism on all the continents. Perhaps the best modern example is in Siberia, east of the Ural and north of the Tian Shan

T. S. Lovering.

FIG. 122. — The uplifted and eroded Rocky Mountain peneplain northwest of Colorado Springs. Pikes Peak stands as a great monadnock above the peneplaned surface.

mountains. Here a large region drained by the rivers Irtish and Ob still stands at baselevel. In the Mississippi Valley many regions are approaching the peneplain stage. Central-western Missouri and southeastern Kansas are good examples.

Uplifted peneplains which have suffered varying amounts of dissection during and subsequent to the uplift have been widely recognized. The Tian Shan Mountains of Asia, the Tanganyika Plateau of southeastern Africa, the Highlands of Scotland, the Plateau of Quebec, the great Schooley Peneplain of the Appalachian Mountains, and the Rocky Mountain Peneplain of Colorado are good examples. The Tanganyika Peneplain has been uplifted some 4,700

feet [1] since it was completed in the Miocene Epoch.   The borders of
the plateau, outlined on the south by great fault scarps, are deeply
notched by gorges and canyons, but in the interior the surface has
been little eroded and is still a great, remarkably level plain, except
for remnants of a still older peneplain which stands upon it.   The
surface of the Plateau of Quebec exhibits remarkable uniformity of
relief over wide areas; however, this surface has been recently
glaciated, thus partially obscuring the old erosional surface.   The
Rocky Mountain Peneplain, uplifted in Pliocene and Pleistocene
times is now dissected by canyons from 1,000 to more than 1,500
feet in depth.   Thus a new cycle of erosion is well under way.   *The
altitude of the present surfaces of uplifted peneplain remnants seldom, if ever, represents the height to which the peneplain was
raised.*   Even on very wide, flat surfaces, erosion goes on and the
original surface may be lowered hundreds of feet, thus leaving a new
surface essentially parallel with the original one.   It is very unusual
to find a thick layer of residual soil on an uplifted peneplain.   Where
it does occur the height of the present surface *may* agree, approximately, with that of the original one.   Where there is no thick
residual soil cover, it is safe to assume either very recent uplift or
considerable erosion.   Each suspected uplifted peneplain must be
studied individually in order to be sure of its history.

Resurrected Peneplains. — Peneplains may be submerged, covered with sedimentary rocks, uplifted and resurrected.   That is,
the sediments may be removed by erosion, disclosing the ancient
peneplain.   Resurrected peneplains have been described by several
writers, and an example, according to some authorities, is the Sher-
man Plain of southern Wyoming which lies between the Laramie
Basin and the Great Plains.   If this is a resurrected plain, the
cycle of erosion in which the original peneplain was formed was
very much older than the one that existed when the peneplain was
uncovered.   Another perhaps better example is the Pre-Cretaceous
or Early Cretaceous peneplain, cut on folded Paleozoic rocks, that
is now being exhumed and dissected on the inner part of the Gulf
of Mexico coastal plain.   Further north the same or another res-

[1] Bailey Willis: *East African Plateaus and Rift Valleys.*   Carnegie Institution of Washington, 1936.

urrected Pre-Cretaceous peneplain is widely recognized. The complete exhuming of these old plains, however, is just as delicate a task as the development of the original surface, and represents in itself the completion of a second cycle of erosion. While the recognition of buried and resurrected erosional surfaces is important in determining the complete physiographic history of a region, such plains probably have played a very small part in the topography developed in a later erosional cycle.

U. S. Geol. Survey.

FIG. 123. — A stripped plain near Lees Ferry, Arizona. The Colorado River canyon has been cut below the plain (now really plateau) surface.

Stripped Plains. — There has been considerable confusion in literature regarding the discrimination of stripped plains and peneplains. A *stripped plain* is usually one composed of flat-lying or gently tilted sedimentary rocks from which sediments have been removed down to some resistant bed which seems to have controlled the depth of erosion. It has been argued that such resistant beds control erosion and allow the formation of a stripped plain *at elevations high above baselevel*. While small mesas undoubtedly have been formed in this way, the production of a broad plain under such conditions may seriously be questioned. Fenneman [1] in discus-

---

[1] N. M. Fenneman: *Cyclic and Non-Cyclic Aspects of Erosion.* Bull. Geol. Soc. Am., Vol. 47, pp. 173–186, 1936.

sing this subject says: "To do a clean job of stripping a horizontal bed is just as difficult as to make a perfect peneplain. The processes are the same, and in its last stages are just as slow in one case as in the other if equal areas are assumed. . . . The stripping is not denied; only the altitude at which it is done."

Following this idea, with which the writer is in full accord, large stripped plains now high above baselevel should not be regarded as plains formed at that elevation but rather as plains that were stripped while at baselevel, then uplifted.

Interrupted Cycles of Erosion — Rejuvenation

At any stage in a cycle of erosion, the processes may be interrupted. In fact, due to the instability of the earth, interrupted cycles are much more common than are completed cycles.

The most common causes of rejuvenation are uplifts or downwarps of the land, lowering of stream outlets, and changes of climate. Usually the rejuvenated topography is distinctive and is an important aid in determining the complete physiographic history of a region.

Uplift. — Suppose that streams in a large drainage basin have cut their valleys deeply and have developed

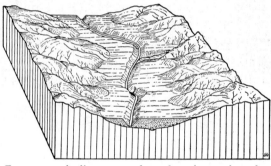

FIG. 124. — A diagram to show the rejuvenation of a stream and its valley through uplift.

valley flats (Fig. 124). Then let the whole region be uplifted by continental or mountain-making movements. The streams at once will begin to cut their valleys deeper, forming new valleys below the old valley floors. Both the streams and the topography are *rejuvenated* for they have acquired characteristics of *youth*.

Lowering of Outlets. — Lowering the outlets of streams also may cause rejuvenation. For example: the water level of Lake Erie is the local baselevel for streams that flow into it. Niagara

Falls is receding at the rate of 3.5 feet a year. If conditions remain as they are now, the Niagara River eventually will drain most of Lake Erie. The breaking of the falls into the lake will come suddenly, the lake will be quickly drained, and all the streams flowing into the lake will find themselves tumbling over steep slopes some 150 feet high. They will immediately be rejuvenated, and will start notching their valley floors. Such a condition with youthful topography near the lake and older topography higher up in the valleys gives rise to a type of *topographic unconformity*.

Lowering of Sea Level. — It is evident that changes in sea level will immediately affect the work of streams that are at baselevel

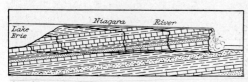

FIG. 125. — A diagram to show that eventually most of Lake Erie will be drained through the recession of Niagara Falls. Due to the horizontal scale of the diagram, 1 inch equals 10 miles, the rocks appear to dip much more steeply upstream than they do in reality. The actual dip is only 35 feet to the mile.

when those changes begin to take place. If sea level is lowered, the streams will be rejuvenated and erosion will begin. Later, if the level rises, the streams will stop eroding and begin to build new flood-plains.

During the Pleistocene Epoch there were four widespread glaciations of North America and Europe (See Chapter X). Each great accumulation of glacial ice resulted in a worldwide lowering of sea level. When the ice melted, the oceans rose to their former height. This principle, although long recognized, has been applied to the development of land forms to a very limited extent. (See submarine canyons, Chapter XII, and the coral reef problem, Chapter XV.)

Recently Fisk [1] has described what he believes to be a remarkable correlation in the development of terraces along the Red River and the changes in sea level due to glaciation. During the Pleistocene the Red River united with the Mississippi in central Louisiana. When the first (Nebraskan) glacial age came on, the rivers were rejuvenated as sea level was lowered, and slowly cut their valleys

[1] H. N. Fisk: *Geology of Grant and LaSalle Parishes.* La. Geol. Survey, Geol. Bull. 10, 1938.

deeper. Later, when the ice melted and the ocean level rose in the (Aftonian) interglacial age, the streams deposited a thick cover of alluvium over their valley floors. The second (Kansan) glaciation again lowered sea level, rejuvenated the streams, and much of the alluvium was eroded away; but some material was left in the form of terraces on the side of the newly made valley. This process was repeated until four distinct terrace levels were produced. Each terrace is composed of material deposited by the streams dur-

Geological Survey of Canada.

FIG. 126. — An uplifted peneplain with a newly cut youthful valley. Looking down Darcy Creek toward Porcupine River, British Columbia.

ing an interglacial epoch which was not removed during the following period of rejuvenation.

Changes of Climate. — It is a well known fact that climates have changed repeatedly all over the earth. Humid regions have become arid, warm regions have become cold, then warm again. If precipitation is greatly increased in any region, obviously the volume of water in the streams will also increase; but volume is a factor in the cutting and transporting power of a stream. It, therefore, follows that streams in mid-continental regions far from and at a considerable height above the sea may be *somewhat* rejuvenated

by receiving an increased supply of water.   This principle is believed by the author to be a relatively unimportant factor in causing
rejuvenation, for the total results could not be great.   Some writers,
however, have attached considerable significance to the idea.

Topography Due to Rejuvenation. — If a region has been
rejuvenated recently, so that evidence still remains, one should find
topography showing youthful characteristics superimposed on ma-

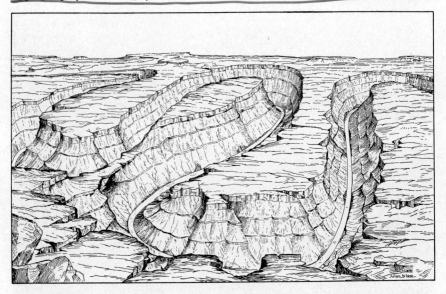

Fig. 127. — Entrenched meanders of the Dolores River.   From the Paradox Valley
topographic map, Colorado.

ture or old topography.   Or mature and old topographic forms
may be so related as to indicate ancient rejuvenation.

An Uplifted Peneplain. — No better evidence of rejuvenation
could be found than a peneplain high above *present* baselevel now
entering a second cycle of erosion.   Examples are known on nearly
all the continents.   Some uplifted peneplains, such as the older ones
of the Appalachian Mountains, are now greatly dissected; others
have broad, little-eroded surfaces.

Entrenched Meanders. — If a stream that is meandering widely
over its flood-plain, as most old streams do, is rejuvenated, it may
proceed to cut a deep canyon or gorge into the old meanders (Fig.

127). After streams cut the gorges deeply, they may widen the curves of the entrenched meanders and by undercutting a neck of land from two sides make great natural bridges like those of southeastern Utah in the Bridges National Monument.

Stream Terraces.— In many regions a series of stream terraces rise like a gigantic flight of stairs above a stream. The individual terraces may be narrow or they may be several miles in width.

E. G. Fine.

FIG. 128.— The Edwin Bridge, Bridges National Monument, Utah. Due to undercutting on opposite bends of an entrenched meander the stream finally cut a channel through the neck, which now makes the arch of the bridge.

The height between successive terraces may be a few feet or a few hundred feet. Usually the terraces are carved out of solid rock, although their surfaces may be covered to a depth of several feet with stream boulders and gravels. Some, however, are formed in the alluvium that covers old valley floors. Terrace development is simple. A stream becomes graded or it may reach baselevel, then it proceeds to form a wide valley flat. Later the stream is rejuvenated and cuts downward through the first valley flat to a new grade or to baselevel, where it may develop a second valley flat *inside* and *below* the first one. In cutting the valley after rejuvenation, if all the old valley flat is removed, there will be no trace of the rejuvenation; but if the new valley is formed in the middle of the old one, paired terraces will result. Repeated rejuvenation allows the development of successive terraces at lower levels (Fig. 130).

Spurs and Benches. — In mountain and plateau regions, uplifts are of common occurrence. Mature valleys are cut deeper after

Richard Ragle.

FIG. 129. — Entrenched meanders on the left side of the view, near Manhattan, Kansas.

rejuvenation, as described in the preceding paragraph. If it were not for erosion by tributary streams, well-defined terraces might be formed on the sides of the rejuvenated valleys. But due to the work of tributaries, instead of terraces, one usually finds a series of spurs or benches (Fig. 131), the tops of which represent the old valley floor. In regions of repeated uplifts, there may be several benches at descending levels.

Hanging Valleys. — In recently uplifted mountains, hanging valleys due to faulting are common. Figure 371 is a photograph of

the west side of the north end of the Sangre de Cristo Range in
Colorado. The triangular-shaped ends of the ridges show the posi-

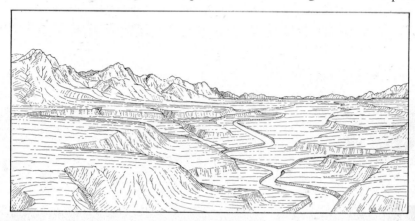

FIG. 130. — The development of terraces through rejuvenation and stream erosion.
Paired or single terraces may be formed depending on the positions of the stream
after rejuvenation.

tion of a great fault that either uplifted the range or possibly
depressed San Luis Valley which appears in the foreground. Before

FIG. 131. — Spurs and benches due to rejuvenation.

the uplift the valleys on the side of the range opened into San
Luis Valley at grade; now they are high above the main valley.
Such a condition is another type of *topographic unconformity*.

Waterfalls are characteristic of youthful topography, but if a mature or old valley be faulted, as described in the preceding paragraph, so that a stream falls over a fault scarp, we have good evidence of rejuvenation and again a topographic unconformity (Fig. 113).

TOPOGRAPHY RESULTING FROM STREAM DEPOSITION

Flood-plains. — Flood-plains which are formed by deposition of alluvium on valley flats by meandering streams, are always of

Photograph by U. S. Army Air Corps.
Pub. by authority of the Miss. River Commission, Vicksburg, Miss.

FIG. 132. — The Vicksburg, Mississippi, region. The hills on which the city stands rise 200 feet above the flood-plain of the river.

low relief. On them may be found flat or gently sloping plains, stream meanders, *ox-bow lakes,* marshes, irregular temporary lakes which occupy small depressions, sand bars, natural levees, and other

minor relief features due to the flooding of streams or the shifting
of stream channels.

Meanders. — Both streams that have cut their valleys nearly
to baselevel and graded streams at any altitude above sea level
tend to flow in broad sweeping curves. This is due to the low
velocity of the current and to deposits of alluvium which divert the
stream courses. As the current is directed against the outer bank

Courtesy U. S. War Department.

FIG. 133. — "Passes" on the Mississippi Delta. Only south and southwest passes are
navigable for ocean-going ships. Both of these passes are jettied near their
mouths.

of a meander (Fig. 121), it cuts further in this direction and at
the same time builds up a bar of sand or silt on the inner side.
After the current swings around one curve, it tends to cross the
channel and develop a curve in the opposite bank. Thus meanders
grow and shift *down stream*. The development of meanders greatly
lengthens a stream. The Mississippi River Commission, between
the years 1929 and 1937, made 13 cut-offs through meander necks
of the Mississippi River. The total length of the cut-offs is 40.7

miles as against 156.5 miles around the bends. The total shortening is 115.8 miles in 330.6 miles of river.

Ox-bow Lakes and Bayous. — As meanders grow, it frequently
happens that a narrow neck of land is cut through from two sides
(Fig. 108), thus allowing the stream to straighten its course. The
ends of the meander that has been cut off soon are likely to be
choked with sand and silt, forming a *bayou,* but water seeping into
the cut-off meandering channel from the stream or through run-off
from the surrounding land forms an *ox-bow lake.*

Marshes. — The abandoned channel of a stream on a flood-
plain may become partially filled with vegetation, thus forming a
marsh or swamp. Also swamps may form in any low place on the
flood-plain regardless of the origin of the depression.

Natural Levees. — These already have been described. They
are not of common occurrence, therefore, present decidedly unusual
topographic features where they are found. Due to the growth of
levees and to filling of the channel with alluvium, a stream may be
raised so that it flows in *normal conditions well above its flood-
plain.* If such a stream in flood overflows or bursts through its
levees, the damage may be very great, for the water flows *down* the
outside of the levee onto the flood-plain.

Deltas. — A delta is an alluvial tract of land at the mouth of
a river enclosed by its spreading branches. The name was first
applied to such an area at the mouth of the Nile, which resembles
the *Greek* letter *delta.* When streams enter a sea, bay, lake, or,
much less commonly, another river, they tend to deposit their load.
If waves and currents are unable to remove the material as fast
as it comes in, an alluvial deposit is built up at the mouth of the
stream. As the deposit grows, the river tends to fork upstream.
The divided water has less carrying power than before, its channels
become clogged, more distributaries are formed, and more material
is deposited.

Most deltas grow seaward or lakeward, some very rapidly, some
slowly; therefore, delta successions are common with a new one
growing out beyond an old delta plain, the new ones being characterized by long finger-like channels, enclosing alluvium, that extend well
out into the water. Old deltaic plains are much like large flood-

plains in their surface topography. Both have distributary streams, meander loops, ox-bow lakes, natural levees, swamps, etc.

Due to up-stream accidents, many deltas have been cut off from the streams that formed them. Perhaps the most notable example is the Hwang Ho (River) in China, which changed its course in 1892 and now reaches the sea some 350 miles north of its old delta.

Depressions on the sides of deltas, due apparently to subsidence and compaction of the alluvium, give rise to lake basins if they are enclosed, or to bays if they are open to the sea. The tremendous weight of the sediment brought to the sea by large streams over a long period of time tends to depress the shores. Russell has shown

D. F. Higgins.

FIG. 134. — An alluvial fan. This type, which extends well up the valley, has been called a "bay fan" by Davis.

that there has been great subsidence of the north side of the Gulf of Mexico due to the accumulation of the old and present Mississippi deltas.

Many of the great rivers of the world have formed large deltas. The Orinoco in Venezuela has built an enormous delta over which 36 distributary streams carry the water of the mighty river to the sea. The old delta of the Yellow River (Hwang-Ho) in China is even larger than that of the Orinoco. It is one of the most fertile and thickly populated in the world. The Nile delta of Egypt, the Ganges of India, the Rhone of France, the Mississippi, and the Colorado in the United States and Mexico are notable examples.

The Colorado River has had much to do with the development

of local topography in southern California and Mexico. At one time a long narrow structural depression extended southward from the present Imperial Valley to the Gulf of California. The river coming in from the east gradually built up a great delta in this depression, completely blocking it, and leaving on the north in the Imperial Valley a land-locked basin whose bottom is 275 feet below sea level. The river, throughout its older history seems to have more or less impartially deposited its sediment, first, on the Gulf side, then on the Imperial Valley side of its axis. The last great discharge into the Imperial Valley came in the years 1905 to 1907 when the river, whose channels had been raised by silting, burst its banks and, for a time, carried all its water to the Salton Sea. The break was not controlled by engineers until February, 1907. Since that date the regular flow has been to the Gulf, although much water is diverted by canals to the Imperial Valley for irrigation. Control of flood-water by the Boulder dam should prevent any such catastrophe as occurred in 1905 when thousands of acres of the fertile land of Imperial Valley were ruined.

Alluvial Fans. — The origin of these alluvial deposits has already been described. Fans vary greatly in size and composition. Small fans occur at the mouths of gullies and of streams which come down steep slopes into mountain and plateau valleys. Very large fans are formed where larger streams merge from highlands and spread out on plains. These are *piedmont* (foot of the mountain) alluvial fans. Piedmont fans formed by adjacent

Fig. 135. — Longitudinal profile (above) and transverse profile (below) of alluvial fans.

streams may unite to form broad *alluvial plains*. Both piedmont alluvial fans and alluvial plains flank nearly the whole east side of the Rocky Mountains. Other fine examples occur in the Basin Range Province of western North America.

The longitudinal profile of an alluvial fan is concave upward. The transverse profile of a piedmont alluvial fan, parallel with the mountain front, is convex over the individual fans with concave forms in the inter-fan areas (Fig. 136).

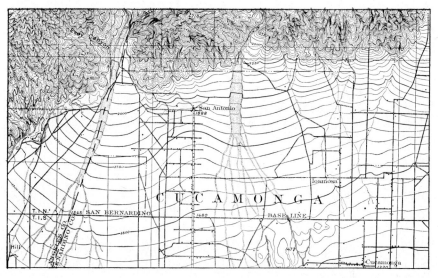

U. S. Geol. Survey.

FIG. 136. — Alluvial fans spreading at the bottom into a piedmont alluvial fan or alluvial plain, Cucamonga, California, topographic map.

Alluvial Terraces. — Streams which have deposited thick alluvium on flood-plains, or streams whose valleys have become partially filled with alluvium may be rejuvenated, thus giving rise to terraces. These terraces differ from normal ones in that they are carved out of alluvium instead of solid rock.

Fertility of Alluvial Deposits. — Flood-plains, deltaic plains and alluvial terraces are noted for the fertility of their soils. In many cases periodic floods bring in new fresh silt to enrich soils

R. D. Crawford.

FIG. 137. — A gently sloping mesa on the front of the Sawatch Range, Colorado. It is covered with alluvium washed down from the mountains and has been dissected by the Arkansas River and its tributaries. Note the flat alluvial terrace in the center of the valley.

whose plant foods have been depleted by constant crop growth. The high fertility combined with the fine texture of the soil and low relief makes flood-plains and deltas favorable places for agriculture, if the climate is suitable, and causes them to be thickly populated.

Alluvial fans and plains may or may not have fertile soils. Usually the soil is good, but the alluvium may be so filled with large boulders that agriculture is impossible.

Unusual Topographic Features Made by Streams

Under this heading are grouped a number of unusual land forms which are not produced through the ordinary or normal processes of stream work. They are the results of unusual stream action or are due to peculiarities of rock composition or structure. Other agents than streams, such as atmospheric weathering and wind erosion, may have played a subordinate part in their development.

Scablands. — "The terms 'scabland' and 'scabrock' are used in the Pacific northwest to describe areas where denudation has removed or prevented the accumulation of a mantle of soil, and the underlying bare rock is exposed or is covered largely with its own coarse angular debris." [1]

Probably the most unusual stream-developed topography ever described is the channeled scablands area [2] which is situated west and southwest of Spokane, Washington, between the Columbia and Snake Rivers. Before Pleistocene glaciation the topography of this region was mature. Dendritic drainage was well established south to the Snake and west to the Columbia River. Streams had cut broad valleys through some 200 feet of loessial soil and poorly consolidated sedimentary rocks barely into the underlying solid basalt of the plateau.

Now, due to streams formed in some way as a result of glaciation, the soil and mantle rocks have been swept away over an area of some 2,000 square miles and thousands of abandoned channels varying in depth from a few feet to 1,000 feet have been carved out of the basalt. These channels are "gorges, canyons or elongated basins" in the scabland tracts. While these tracts still are surrounded by the *maturely eroded* pre-glacial topography, within the

[1] J Harlen Bretz: *The Channeled Scablands of the Columbia River Plateau.* Jour. Geol., Vol. 31, p. 617, 1923.

[2] Bretz: Idem, pp. 617–649. And:
Alternative Hypotheses for Channeled Scablands. Jour. Geol., Vol. 36, pp. 193–223, 312–341, 1928.
Grand Coulee. Am. Geog. Soc., Special Pub. 15, 1932.
Ira S. Allison: *New Version of the Spokane Flood.* Bull. Geol. Soc. Am., Vol. 44, pp. 675–722, 1933.
R. F. Flint: *Origin of the Cheney-Palouse Scabland Tract.* Bull. Geol. Soc. Am., Vol. 49, pp. 461–524, 1938.

tracts the topography is *youthful*.   All the tracts are elongated;
nearly all are developed along the pre-glacial drainage lines.   All
open upstream on a basaltic plain near Spokane, and all are traceable downstream to either the Columbia or Snake Rivers.

Some of the canyons and gorges which lie in the scabland tracts
are continuous for long distances parallel to the trend of the tracts,
but many of the elongated basins are shorter and are discontinuous

Junius Henderson.

Fig. 138. — A general view of one of the scabland valleys, Washington. Note the
height of the basalt walls in the background and the basalt remnants in the
foreground.

although they also are parallel to the trend of the tracts in which
they are situated.

The whole scabland area suggests great anastomosing streams
which rose from a rapidly melting glacier north of or on the basaltic
plain near Spokane.   According to Bretz, streams of great volume
and velocity swept with incredible violence down the dip slope of
the plateau, following, in general, the pre-glacial drainage lines.
They not only removed all the soil from the basalt, but cut the canyons and plucked out great masses of columnar-jointed basalt to
form the basins.

Grand Coulee. — This represents an outstanding topographic
and scenic feature of the scablands.   It is described by Bretz as a
tandem canyon 50 miles long and 1,000 feet in maximum depth.

The lower coulee is separated from the upper larger one by a structural basin 5 miles long. The upper gorge is believed to have been formed by a receding cataract. This waterfall was 800 or 900 feet high, and during its retreat was from 1¼ to 5 miles in width. Through its recession it cut a gorge 25 miles long. The lower gorge also is believed to have been formed in part through a recession of a cataract.

Alternative Hypotheses. — Allison questions the sudden liberation of large quantities of glacial water to produce the catastrophic Spokane flood. Instead he believes that the Columbia River was blocked in the gorge, where it goes through the Cascade Mountains. The blockade advanced eastward (headward) until finally the water level rose high enough to cover the scablands of eastern Washington. Then the waters were diverted, now into one channel, later into another, and the scablands were formed through a "moderate flow of water now here, now there, over an extended period of time."

Junius Henderson.

FIG. 139. — Dry Falls and plunge basins in Grand Coulee, Washington. In places the falls were as much as 900 feet high.

Flint accepts the idea of a blockade in the Columbia gorge and assumes that the water was backed up into the Pasco Basin where a large lake (Lake Lewis) was formed. The order of events according to his thesis are: (1) Streams originating in glaciers near Spokane scoured the basalt on steep gradients, mainly along preglacial drainage lines. (2) Rising ponded water in the Pasco Basin reduced the stream gradients to one-third their former amounts and caused the streams to fill their valleys with sediment. (3) As the ponded waters were drained away, the streams, still fed by glaciers, removed the greater part of the fill and extensively channeled the basalt, forming the scablands much as they are now.

All these events occurred during the Wisconsin stage of glaciation, although similar erosion and fill may have accompanied at least one earlier glaciation.

Summary. — These brief outlines give three different explanations for the origin of this region. The first requires the catastrophic liberation of glacial water. The second and third invoke normal stream erosion that was brought about by an unusual event, that is, the blocking of a great stream. This was by no means impossible through lava flows, landslides, ice jams, earth movements or combinations of these. While most physiographers seem to prefer to accept the more normal erosion by glacial meltwater, the scouring of deep discontinuous basins and the lifting out of great blocks of basalt certainly strongly imply torrents of water.

E. G. Fine.

FIG. 140. — Raton Mesa, southern Colorado. A lava-capped mesa that now stands high above the adjacent plains.

Mesas. — Mesas or tablelands abound in many parts of the earth. They are particularly common in plains and plateaus. They differ greatly in size and in height above the surrounding land. Some are nearly flat on top, while others have very gentle but uniform slopes. They are erosion remnants left by streams which have worn away the land from around them. Some mesas are capped by hard layers of rock, such as conglomerates or lava flows which preserve their surfaces from rapid erosion; others, particularly those situated near the flanks of mountains, are covered by great boulders that preserve their tops.

Lava-capped Mesas. — These are of widespread occurrence in western North America where Tertiary vulcanism was particularly active. In these regions fissure flows spread over large areas covering sedimentary rocks of many different ages. Later, through erosion, vast quantities of the land were removed, leaving more or less completely isolated mesas. Some in New Mexico and Colorado are so large that they might equally correctly be called plateaus.

Sandstone-capped Mesas. — These are of even more common occurrence than are the lava-covered mesas. Throughout much of the Great Plains and Colorado Plateau physiographic provinces

Junius Henderson.

FIG. 141. — East Pawnee Butte. An erosion remnant that was once part of the High Plains, northeastern Colorado.

(Fig. 336), much of the land was once higher than it is now. Streams have eroded broad valleys leaving erosion remnants capped with resistant sandstone or conglomerate, which have protected the surfaces of the original plains or plateaus.

Boulder-covered Mesas. — As has already been noted, on the flanks of most of the great mountain ranges of western United States there are large alluvial fans and plains. In a great many cases both are covered deeply with large stream-worn boulders. As streams have dissected the land after rejuvenation, boulder-covered mesas have been left standing high above the present valleys.

Buttes. — Buttes are erosion remnants of small but flattish summit area that stand conspicuously above their surroundings. Their origin is the same as that of mesas, and they occur in similar localities.

Minor Erosion Remnants. — Scores of minor erosional forms originally blocked out by streams but later shaped by wind or other erosive agents are of very common occurrence. In many cases the unequal resistance of the rocks that compose these remnants is responsible for their peculiar forms.

Erosional Forms of Arid Regions. — *Pediments, bajadas* and other forms more characteristic of arid than humid regions are discussed in Chapter IX.

REFERENCES

1. W. C. Alden: *Physiography and Glacial Geology of Eastern Montana and Adjacent Areas.* U. S. Geol. Survey, Prof. Paper 174, 1932.

2. I. S. Allison: *New Version of the Spokane Flood.* Bull. Geol. Soc. Am., Vol. 44, pp. 675–722, 1933.

3. Isaiah Bowman: *The Analysis of Land Forms.* Geog. Rev. Vol. 16, pp. 122–132, 1926.

4. J. Harlen Bretz: *The Channeled Scablands of the Columbia River Plateau.* Jour. Geol., Vol. 31, pp. 617–649, 1923.

5. ———: *Alternative Hypotheses for Channeled Scablands.* Jour. Geol. Vol. 36, pp. 193–223 and 312–341, 1928.

6. ———: *Grand Coulee.* Am. Geog. Soc. Sp. Pub. 15, 1932.

7. W. M. Davis: *Geographical Essays.* Ginn and Co., 1909.

8. N. M. Fenneman: *Cyclic and Non-Cyclic Aspects of Erosion.* Bull. Geol. Soc. Am., Vol. 47, pp. 173–186, 1936.

9. H. N. Fisk: *Geology of Grand and LaSalle Parishes.* La. Geol. Survey, Geol. Bull. 10, 1938.

10. R. F. Flint: *Origin of the Cheney-Palouse Scabland Tract, Washington.* Bull. Geol. Soc. Am., Vol. 49, pp. 461–524, 1938.

11. G. K. Gilbert: *The Transportation of Debris by Running Water.* U. S. Geol. Survey, Prof. Paper 86, 1914.

12. A. D. Howard: *History of the Grand Canyon of the Yellowstone.* Geol. Soc. Am., Sp. Paper 6, 1937.

13. D. W. Johnson: *Plains, Planes and Peneplanes.* Geog. Rev., Vol. 1, pp. 443–447, 1916.

14. T. W. Noyes: *The World's Greatest Waterfalls.* Nat. Geog. Mag., Vol. 50, pp. 29–59, 1926.

15. R. J. Russell and H. V. Howe: *The Lower Mississippi Delta.* La. Geol. Survey, Geol. Bull. No. 8, 1936.

16. Godfrey Sykes: *The Colorado Delta.* Carnegie Inst. Wash. Pub. 460, 1937.

17. A. C. Waters: *Terraces and Coulees along the Columbia River near Lake Chelan, Wash.* Bull. Geol. Soc. Am., Vol. 44, pp. 783–820, 1933.

CHAPTER IX

TOPOGRAPHY OF SEMI-ARID AND DESERT REGIONS

There are no sharp boundaries either in climate or topography between humid and semi-arid regions. Neither are the boundaries definite between semi-arid regions and deserts. However, the contrasts between *typical* landscapes of humid regions and deserts are clear-cut. In general, we shall consider as *semi-arid*, regions that have between 10 and 20 inches of annual precipitation, and as *deserts* those regions having less — in many cases *much less* — than 10 inches of rainfall a year. Many writers characterize as deserts only those parts of the earth that have no exterior drainage to the oceans. Such a classification is not strictly a correct one; although *it is a notable fact that most of the large deserts of the earth have interior drainage only, with no streams flowing from them to the sea.*

In humid regions streams are the dominant agents of erosion. In arid regions streams become less important and *wind* assumes increasing importance. Permanent streams are rare in deserts. If present, usually they rise in regions of greater humidity and flow across the deserts. Intermittent and ephemeral streams formed by heavy rains or melting snows, flood at the slightest provocation. Mechanical weathering is more important than chemical weathering in most arid regions. Vegetation is scanty and in many places *entirely* absent.

The topography of arid regions is produced largely through the combined activities of weathering, running water and wind. It is, therefore, a curious mixture of types dependent upon the amount of work accomplished by each agent.

THE WORK OF WIND

The wind has much in common with other erosive agents. It wears away the land, carries the material from one place to another, and finally deposits it. Like running water, wind erodes faster when it has cutting tools, such as fine sand or dust, to work with. Vegetation and standing water in lakes and marshes greatly retard wind erosion.

Wind Corrasion

Very little mechanical abrasion is accomplished by light winds, but strong winds, which are characteristic of deserts, pick up dust and sand and drive them with tremendous force against the rocks, thus acting like a sand blast. Very resistant rocks are polished and smoothed to a remarkable degree. Less resistant rocks are etched, and, in time, completely worn away. Chemical weathering, which loosens the cementing material of sedimentary rocks, or disintegrates the surfaces of igneous and metamorphic rocks, is a great aid in this process. The joints of rocks and all types of mechanical weathering also are helpful.. Naturally, shales and poorly cemented sandstones are most susceptible to the attack of the wind. In regions where winds prevail from one direction, the amount of corrasive

W. O. Thompson.

FIG. 142. — Wind polishing and erosion, near Muroc Lake, California.

work is surprisingly great. Telegraph wires along the Trans-Caspian Railway in eleven years were eroded to one-half their original diameter. Wooden telegraph poles in southwestern United States have been so badly cut by wind-blown sand that it has been necessary to protect them with rock or concrete. Usually the sand blast effect is greatest within 4 feet of the ground. Wind or sand fences are built in many places to prevent sand from drifting into road cuts and onto railroad tracks. Cavernous forms made by solution and wind abound in desert regions.

Deflation. — The complete blowing away of fine dust, leaving coarser and heavier materials, is the process of *deflation*. It is in evidence in all types of regions, humid as well as semi-arid and desert, but it becomes of outstanding significance in all arid regions. Petrie estimates that at least 8 feet has been removed by the wind from part of the Nile Delta in 2,600 years. Rock plains, due to wind erosion, have been recognized in South Africa, India, Central Asia and southwestern United States. On the semi-arid plains of Colorado, Wyoming, Montana and western Nebraska, there are hundreds of shallow lake basins which have been scooped out of easily eroded rocks by the wind. Near Laramie, Wyoming, many enormous depressions have been carved out of the plains in a similar way; from one of these depressions, Big Hollow, which is 9 miles long, 3 miles wide, and 300 feet deep, more than *10 billion tons of dust and sand* have been removed by the wind.

Eliot Blackwelder.

Fig. 143. — Cavernous weathering of pumice agglomerate about 30 miles southwest of Battle Mountain, Nevada.

Deflation is particularly active on plowed fields, alluvial plains and similar regions, where, from time to time, loose, fine-grained soil and silt are exposed. Even in humid regions, soil losses due to the wind are great; in semi-arid regions often they are tremendous. The so-called "dust bowl" of western Kansas, southeastern Colorado, and adjacent areas has lost billions of tons of soil, which has been blown away during *the recent* drought. Throughout great areas of farm lands in the semi-arid, wheat-growing belt, which extends from northern Texas to central Saskatchewan, it frequently happens that the fall plantings of winter wheat are entirely lost.

The wheat is said to be blown out of the ground; what actually happens is that the soil is blown away from the wheat! Not infrequently the soil from these farms is drifted into road cuts in such amounts that it is necessary to use graders to open the roads.

These illustrations, which could be multiplied many times, are from *semi-arid regions*. In *deserts*, where winds are more continuous and stronger, erosion is much greater. There the wind, regardless of elevation, searches out and moves all fine-grained materials.

Courtesy Farm Security Administration.

FIG. 144. — A dust storm, Cimmarron Co., Oklahoma.

To be sure, deflation is limited by the size of available materials; for wind cannot move great quantities of coarse debris. But as the rocks are broken into finer and finer grains by weathering, they are carried away by the persistent winds.

The comparative amounts of erosion by wind and streams has long been a controversial subject. Some writers insist that streams are more powerful erosive agents, even in deserts. In regions of high relief, this probably is true, but in areas of low relief, the wind is the more powerful of the two.

Dust. — Dust is very finely divided, solid material. It is universally present in the atmosphere. This is proven in many cases by direct observation. It also is indicated by "red snow" or "black snow," which is, of course, snow colored by the dust washed out of the atmosphere. Rain water, when caught in a clean container and evaporated, leaves a trace of sediment which is dust. Even in polar regions and in the interior of Greenland, far from any sources of dust, it is present in the atmosphere.

Sources of Dust. — Dust is derived from burning fuels, volcanoes, dry land surfaces, such as plowed fields, bare slopes, floodplains, desert basins, pollen from flowers, decayed wood, and even salt which has evaporated from saline waters. Little dust is obtained from wet or snow-covered surfaces.

Sand. — Although quartz grains predominate, sand may consist of any fine-grained mineral or rock material somewhat coarser than dust. There are many sources of sand: lake and sea shores, river flood-plains, desert basins, dry, poorly cemented sandstones, and bare rocks that are being broken down by weathering agencies — all furnish sand, which is transported from one place to another by the wind. Quartz sand grains that have been carried far by the wind exhibit a definite frosting when viewed under a microscope.

Wind Transportation

Wind moves dust and sand in several ways. The fine, light materials are picked up, suspended in the air, and carried away. Heavy or large sand grains are rolled along the surface of the ground. Grains of intermediate size and weight may be carried at one time and rolled at another. Sudden, severe gusts of wind are capable of picking up and carrying for short distances larger materials than can be consistently held in the air; therefore, some grains are carried and dropped innumerable times in the course of their history.

No one yet has been able to estimate accurately the amount of material eroded by the wind in any year. That the amount is stupendous is unquestioned. Accounts of desert travel are full of descriptions of dust or sand storms. Recent events in the "dust bowl" of the United States confirm even the most startling tales of wind erosion in deserts. One dust storm, in November, 1933, starting in Nebraska and the Dakotas, traveled to New York State at an average rate of 43 miles an hour. Some 600,000 square miles was covered by the storm. When it crossed Omaha, Nebraska, the height (or depth as it is usually called) of the storm was 9,000 feet. Visibility at the ground surface was very poor. Another dust storm of short duration deposited 35 tons of dust per square mile over large areas in eastern Nebraska. The dust came from the southwest. In a single 30-minute snow storm a few years ago at Boulder, Colorado, dust was brought down from the atmosphere in amounts that equalled 30 tons per square mile.

In China there are loess deposits that cover 300,000 square miles to a depth of several hundred feet. Most of this dust came from the deserts of central Asia hundreds of miles away. After the great eruption of the volcano Krakatoa in the East Indies in 1883, dust which had been shot high into the air by the force of the explosion was carried completely around the earth by the wind. Some of the dust remained in the atmosphere for as much as three years. Dust, usually called sirocco dust, from the Sahara Desert has fallen on the Atlantic Ocean, Mediterranean Sea, and as far north as central Europe since earliest recorded times, which date back to at least 300 B.C. In one storm, March 9th to 12th, 1901, which covered at least 300,000 square miles of land and 170,000 square miles of ocean, an estimated amount of 1,960,420 tons was deposited over an area of 168,500 square miles, which equals 12.3 tons per square mile. Similar accounts of dust storms are recorded for Australia, Argentina, eastern Asia, and many other desert regions; although usually estimates of the amount of dust deposited are lacking. Vast quantities of dust often are carried tremendous distances. Australia dust storms reach New Zealand 1,500 miles away. The Saharan storms travel 2,000 miles to north central Europe. Udden,[1] in an examination of western dust storms, estimated that in *one year* there was a total movement of 850 million tons of dust for a distance of 1,440 miles. This, of course, represents many storms.

[1] J. A. Udden: *Dust and Sand Storms in the West.* Pop. Sci. Monthly, Volume 49, pp. 655–664, 1896.

Wind Deposition

The fine material carried in direct suspension by the wind and the heavier materials that are carried for short distances or rolled along eventually are deposited, due to reduction in the velocity of the wind.

Loess. — Loess, which is wind-deposited dust, usually tan or buff in color, is found widely spread over the earth. The largest known deposits are in China. There caves and houses are carved out of the thick deposits. In the Mississippi Valley, loess in the form of more or less rounded ridges or bluffs is abundant on the

D. F. Higgins.

FIG. 145. — The hills are loess as is the material underlying the plain, China.

banks of many large streams. The bluffs from which the Town Council Bluffs, Iowa, derived its name are a good example. Loess has the unusual property of standing in vertical cliffs where it has been cut through by streams or by man during road building. Loess deposits have been described in the valleys of the Rhine and Rhone in Europe, in Austria, Argentina, Asia Minor, Australia, and many other parts of the earth. Each deposit is a reminder of the transporting and depositional work of wind.

Dunes. — Dunes are hills of wind-blown sand. Although they are typical of deserts and certainly are more numerous there than elsewhere, they are by no means confined to deserts or even to semi-arid regions. They are formed wherever there is a source of dry

sand and where winds are of sufficient strength to move the sand.
Notable dunes may be seen on both the Atlantic and Pacific coasts
of the United States, at the south end of Lake Michigan (Dune
Park), in San Luis Valley, Colorado, and throughout the Basin
Range Province in western United States. Also along the larger
streams in Kansas, Idaho and Oregon, and in the great valleys of

Milwaukee Public Museum Photo.

FIG. 146. — A conflict between wind and vegetation. The grass and shrubs are trying
to hold the dune in place, Terry Andrae State Park, near Sheboygan, Wisconsin.

California, such as Death and Imperial valleys, there are many
dunes.

The Formation of Dunes. — It is surprising to see how little
excuse it takes for a dune to form. If wind, blowing sand along
just above-ground, meets an obstruction, such as a fence post, bush
or large rock, the force of the wind is checked and sand is deposited
on the *leeward* side of the obstruction. The initial deposit of sand
thus forms a further obstruction, causing more sand to be deposited
and so on. Soon a dune may be formed. Dunes vary in size from a
few feet to at least 500 feet in height and correspondingly in length.
(Dunes as great as 1,000 feet in height have been reported in some

G. W. Johnson. From "Peru from the Air." Am. Geog. Society, N. Y.

FIG. 147. — Air view of dunes near Ancon, Peru.

deserts.)   In regions, such as the San Luis Valley, Colorado, where dunes are piled up against the side of a mountain range, the total height of the sand above the valley floor may be even greater than 1,000 feet, but this is a special type of formation.

Migration of Dunes. — Where they are not held in place by vegetation, dunes almost invariably migrate in the direction of the prevailing wind.   This is accomplished by the wind blowing sand grains up the gentle windward face of the dune and letting them

D. F. Higgins.

FIG. 148. — Dunes covering hills in Egypt.

fall down the steeper leeward face (Fig. 147).   The rate of migration varies greatly with different conditions.   In regions where the sand is very dry and the wind is very strong, migration is rapid. Even in humid regions forests and cultivated land have been completely overwhelmed by migrating dunes.   In the drier parts of the world, villages and cities have been buried.   Pumpelly [1] has described graphically buried cities of Turkestan.   Such phenomena

[1] Raphael Pumpelly, Wm. M. Davies and Ellsworth Huntington: *Explorations in Turkestan.* Carnegie Institution, Washington, 1905.

U. S. Dept. of Agriculture, Bureau of Chemistry and Soils.
FIG. 149. — A barchan. A typical dune with crescent-shaped front.

well illustrate the shifting scenes that have taken place and are now taking place in the great deserts of the earth. Anyone who

H. E. Gregory, U. S. Geol. Survey.
FIG. 150. — A canyon in Arizona being filled with wind-blown sand.

has watched the movement of sand in large dune areas must be impressed with the *rapidity* of the changes in topography that take place.   Walther states that in the Kizyl-kum Desert dunes have migrated as much as 65 feet in one day, but the average is 20 feet a year.   Cobb reports that a large crescentic dune in North Carolina moved at an average rate of 200 feet a year for 20 years. Other records of movement range from a few feet to one-third of a mile a year.

Canyon Filling. — In the dry plateau regions of southwestern United States and doubtless in similar regions in all deserts, migrat-

Courtesy New Mexico State Tourist Bureau.

FIG. 151. — "White sands" composed of gypsum.   The whole area covers 270 square miles and has been set aside as a National Monument, west of Alamogordo, New Mexico.

ing sands have filled or partially filled valleys and canyons. Gregory [1] has described canyons in Arizona as much as 150 feet deep (Fig. 150) that have been partially filled by migrating dunes.   The intervening spaces of the canyon floors between the sand "are occupied by lakes and marshes, singular features in a region of less than 6 inches of rainfall a year."

[1] H. E. Gregory: *Geology of the Navajo Country.*   U. S. Geol. Survey, Prof. Paper 93, p. 137, 1917.

Streams of Arid Regions

There are two principal types of streams in arid regions. They are through streams which rise in humid regions and flow across the arid lands, and temporary streams which rise in highlands within or on the borders of deserts, flow for short distances, only to lose themselves in the desert sands. Although many large streams flow across *semi-arid* regions, it is a notable fact that there are few permanent streams in true deserts; of the many that flow *into* deserts

U. S. Geol. Survey.

FIG. 152. — The San Juan River and Canyon near Honaker Trail, Utah. The aridity is indicated by the lack of slope wash on the canyon walls. The river rises in the San Juan Mountains where precipitation is heavy.

only a few come out alive. The Nile is probably the most remarkable example of a stream that survives desert conditions. It rises in east-central Africa, where there is abundant moisture, and flows for 900 miles across the Sahara, which is the largest desert on earth.

The Rio Grande, Colorado, Arkansas, Platte, Missouri, North and South Saskatchewan, and many others rise in regions of abundant rain and snow fall in the Rocky Mountains and flow for many miles through the semi-arid regions of western North America. Every such stream which flows in a broad, open valley loses much water through evaporation. The loss is less from streams like the Colorado River which flows throughout most of its course in deep narrow canyons.

Through Streams. — The streams which have sufficient volume of water to carry them across arid regions differ little in their major characteristics from streams of humid regions. The processes of erosion and valley development, being similar, need not be repeated here (see Chapter VIII). In general, due to less vegetation, the streams of arid regions erode the land more rapidly. Due to their own corrasion and to large quantities of silt and sand contributed by tributaries, they soon become overloaded. This condition is augmented by the loss of water due to evaporation. As a result, the streams that are not confined in canyons tend to become anastomosing relatively early in their history.

Eliot Blackwelder.

Fig. 153. — Exfoliation of granite on the inside of a niche, east side of Rogers Dry Lake, Mohave Desert.

Intermittent Streams. — Rain in and on the borders of deserts is exceedingly variable. Some regions go for years without a drop of rain; others have occasional, exceedingly heavy rains of the "cloud burst" type. Melting snows on highlands in and near deserts contribute much water in the spring and early summer, but little or none the rest of the year. For these reasons desert streams are notably irregular both in their time of flow and in the amount of water that they carry. A stream bed is dry today and filled by a raging torrent tomorrow! This torrent may rush down the steep slopes of some rocky highland, scouring its channel and flooding its valley as it goes, only to lose itself in the sand and gravel of the desert basin into which it flows.

Naturally, the carrying power of such streams is great while it lasts, and the stream does much work in a short time. Since weathering is rapid on bare slopes, much material is prepared dur-

ing dry stages for removal during floods. On this account, intermittent desert streams often are highly overloaded.

Mudflows. — Mudflows are of rather frequent occurrence under a considerable variety of conditions in semi-arid regions; they
occur less commonly and under more restricted conditions in very
arid or in humid regions. Favorable situations are bare steep slopes
covered with loose shale, volcanic ash, or with residual clays formed
from the chemical disintegration of igneous rocks. Heavy rains

Eliot Blackwelder.

FIG. 154. — A recent mudflow on an old alluvial fan north of Bishop, California.

falling on such regions lubricate the clays, causing them to swell and
become slippery. With the addition of sufficient water the mud
begins to move either in a sheet-flow or, if confined in channels, *as
usually is the case,* something like a stream flood. Under the latter
condition the velocity may be great enough to snap off trees and
move boulders weighing many tons.

Small, thin, sheet-like mudflows may be seen in many of the
"bad-land" areas of western United States and Canada. Larger,

more concentrated flows have been observed in Colorado, Utah and other semi-arid regions of this and other countries. Blackwelder,[1] who has described several types of flows, states that "the mudflow of the semi-arid mountain canyon is intermediate between the better known landslide and the ordinary stream-flood. There are, in fact, all gradations between them; but the mudflow is more closely akin to the landslide than to the stream-flood." Some flows consist almost entirely of mud; others have gathered up quantities of rock debris of all shapes and sizes from sand grains to boulders many tons in weight. Blackwelder attributes the occurrence of boulders weighing hundreds of tons far from the mouths of semi-arid mountain can-

Eliot Blackwelder.

FIG. 155. — The margin of a dry mud-flow on the east side of the Stillwater Mountains, Nevada.

yons to great mudflows. He also calls attention to the fact that many alluvial fans of semi-arid regions have been built up in layers consisting of mudflows and stream gravels. It is apparent that mudflows are of importance in transporting large boulders; therefore, they play a definite part in producing the present erosional and depositional topography of semi-arid regions.

Mudflows in Humid Regions. — Mudflows are not at all uncommon in humid regions. For example, in the San Juan Mountains of Colorado and on the west slope of the Wasatch Mountains of Utah, there have been many notable flows. One in Colorado in 1914 overwhelmed part of the mining town Telluride. The flow, caused by exceptionally heavy rains on steep slopes littered with decomposed shales and volcanic rocks, rushed into the town, blocked the streets, and completely filled the basements and first story rooms of several houses.

Mudflows also are frequent in connection with eruptions of explosive volcanoes (Chapter XIV). The rain that forms from

[1] Eliot Blackwelder: *Mudflow as a Geologic Agent in Semi-arid Mountains.* Bull. Geol. Soc. Am., Vol. 39, pp. 465–484, 1928.

the condensed steam mingles with the dust thrown from the volcano, resulting in a rain of mud which, after it reaches the ground, may flow over the land surface overwhelming everything in its path.

THE ARID GEOMORPHIC CYCLE

Many years ago Wm. M. Davis,[1] the greatest writer on physiographic subjects of all time, in a brilliant example of deductive reasoning, supplemented by the then known facts, outlined the stages of a geomorphic cycle in an arid region. Most of his deductions have since been proven true, and his outline has become the standard for subsequent writings and field work on this subject. The

Eliot Blackwelder.

FIG. 156. — Typical forms of mudflows in mill tailings of coarse wet sand.

following discussion is based on Davis' work with certain modifications and enlargements of topics gained through field observations of other physiographers since Davis' article was written.

General Conditions. — As opposed to a humid region, an arid region is deficient in rainfall, hence also in vegetation. Bare slopes or those sparsely covered with arid types of plants and shrubs offer little obstruction to mechanical weathering and to erosion. The ground-water surface is low; therefore, deep subsurface chemical weathering is slight. Surface chemical weathering is much slower than in humid regions, but, since there is some moisture in the air even in deserts, it is an active process. Wind, which blows *up slopes*

[1] Wm. M. Davis: *The Geographical Cycle in an Arid Climate.* Jour. Geol., Vol. 13, pp. 381–407, 1905.

quite as much as down slopes, searches out and removes dust wherever it is found. Desert streams fed by melting snows or rains, frequently of the cloud burst type, do a tremendous amount of work during their temporary existence.

Interior Drainage. — It is a notable fact that large areas in many different deserts *do not* have streams flowing out to the oceans. Instead, the drainage is centralized in *interior basins* (*bolsons*) of which there are many *separate ones at different elevations* in most deserts. Figure 158 shows a small interior basin in the western

D. F. Higgins.

FIG. 157. — A youthful desert basin, probably formed by block-faulting, Egypt.

part of the United States. Somewhat similar conditions exist in most great arid regions of the world, including major parts of the deserts of Atacama, Arabia, Sahara, western Australia, Gobi, Takla Makan and Kalahari. In all these cases the streams, many of which are very large, lose themselves in the deserts. Some of the streams flow into lakes. Examples are Owens River, which empties into Owens Lake in eastern California, and Shari River, which flows into Lake Chad in Africa. Others simply disappear through evaporation and seepage into the sand.

Torrential Storms. — Deserts are deserts because they receive little precipitation. It follows then that storms which reach them usually are severe. Torrents of water may fall during a short-lived storm, causing excessive slopewash, gullying, scouring of stream channels, and even severe floods. Stream erosion, although limited in time, may be excessively great while it lasts.

The Beginning of the Cycle

No special conditions, except aridity, are required at the beginning of a cycle. It may be assumed that the land has been uplifted by either folding or faulting, and that there may be any structure or composition of the underlying rocks. Mountain ranges of various heights are separated by valleys of varying depth. The bottoms of some of the valleys may even be below sea level. All the streams

Eliot Blackwelder.

FIG. 158.—A desert basin near Las Vegas, Nevada, showing a small playa.

will be consequent. Each basin will receive the drainage of only the local streams. There is no through drainage from one basin to another. There are as many drainage systems as there are separate basins. The individual streams will vary greatly in length; many will disappear through evaporation or by sinking into the sandy slopes; some may reach the bottoms of the valleys, each of which is the local baselevel for its own system of streams. *It is understood that there is not enough rainfall to fill any of the valleys and cause an overflow.*

Topographic Youth

In the early stages of erosion, short, consequent, intermittent streams cut ravines and V-shaped valleys in the mountain slopes. The debris is washed down the slopes to the valley floor, where valley filling begins. Alluvial fans appear at the mouths of the valleys, and most of the streams disappear in the sands. Seepage water collects in the bottoms of the valleys, forming *playa lakes*. (*Playas are the flat, silt- or salt-covered valley floors.*) If streams reach these lakes, their silt is deposited on the playas. The lake waters soon become salty, due to the minerals carried in solution by the streams and by seepage waters. As the temporary lake waters evaporate, salts are deposited around the margins of the lakes. If the whole lake disappears periodically through evaporation, it leaves a playa composed of a mixture of silt and salt. Deflation is active. The wind blows away the dry dust that forms anywhere in the region. Its sand blast effect aids in direct erosion. The salt formed in the playas *may* prevent deflation, if it accumulates in thick continuous layers. *Otherwise*, hollows will be formed in the silt-covered playas as the water is evaporated. Dunes are formed here and there on the valley floors from the sand that has been washed down by the intermittent streams.

The relief of the region, instead of being increased as in the youthful stage of a normal humid cycle, is *reduced*, for the highlands are being *worn down* at the same time that the adjacent valleys are *being filled*. Each valley is still the local baselevel for all the streams tributary to it. The stream-cut valleys expose bare rocks to the chemical and mechanical attack of weathering; thus the rocks are prepared for removal by slopewash and streams during and following the next rainfall.

Mature Topography

On account of the limited rainfall, the progress from youth to maturity is slow. However, as time goes on, the drainage lines on the upland slopes become more firmly established. The mountain fronts are cut back by erosion; the divides are narrowed, and the intervening basins become wider and *higher* due to valley filling.

Spence Air Photos.

FIG. 159.—The Avawatz Mountains, California. Note the valley filling back of the first ridge and the narrowing of divides due to erosion and to burial by alluvium. The integration of drainage is well underway.

The receding mountain fronts may be separated from the alluvium in the valleys by narrow, rock-cut plains (*pediments*). The alluvial fans have coalesced to form broad alluvial plains (*bajadas*) whose outer margins interfinger with the silt and salt of the playas. Large alluvial fans from the two sides may meet and divide the main valley into smaller enclosed basins.

If headward erosion by the consequent streams has gone far enough, valleys may be cut clear through some of the ranges, so that streams drain parts of the upper valleys into the lower ones, thus marking the beginning of an *integrated* drainage system (Figures 159 and 160). If there is considerable difference between the heights of the upper and lower valleys, there will be active headward cutting in the alluvial fill of the upper valley by the streams that flow from it into the lower one. The material so derived will be spread over the lower valley floor.

It is a function of highlands to cool the moisture-laden winds, and thus induce precipitation; evidently, then, rainfall will decrease as the highlands are lowered, and erosion and deposition by streams, also will decrease. Deflation, however, may increase, due to the widening of the basins, which allows a broader sweep of the wind, and due to a greater proportion of fine material brought into the valleys as the gradients of the streams are decreased.

Old Topography

In extreme old age the highlands will be largely worn away. Island-like mountains or hills (*inselberge*), because of their superior resistance to weathering, will stand above the surrounding pediments or bajadas. The streams have nearly completed their work of reducing the land to the level of the lowest basin, which, because of its interior drainage, has no reference to sea level. Wind-scoured hollows, and dunes become more numerous. If not held in place by salt crusts, the silt of the playas has been largely blown away by the wind. The wind-blown hollows and wind-swept plains have no common baselevel.

"At last, as the waste is more completely exported, the desert plain may be reduced to a lower level than that of the lowest initial

FIG. 160. — Avawatz Mountains, California. Bajadas, inselberge, and integrated drainage between basins are well shown. Note also the structures of the mountains as indicated by the etching.

basin; and then a rock-floor, thinly veneered with waste, unrelated to normal baselevel, will prevail throughout — except where monadnocks still survive." (Davis.)

This condition persists without marked changes in topography until a new cycle of erosion is started either through uplift or through a change to a more humid climate. Wind erosion continues indefinitely, wearing the land lower until it may be brought to an elevation far below sea level. The only limiting factor, apparently, is the ground-water table. Below permanent ground-water, the rocks and soil are moist. *Wind cannot erode wet ground; therefore, the water table is the baselevel for the arid cycle of erosion.*

LAND FORMS PECULIAR TO ARID REGIONS

The discussion so far in this chapter has mentioned several land forms that are found chiefly in semi-arid and desert regions. Further descriptions of these and certain others that have not been discussed will help us to appreciate the differences that exist between the topography of humid and dry regions.

Badlands

One of the most striking features of semi-arid and desert regions is badland topography (Fig. 161). In areas underlain by thin alternating beds of sedimentary rocks, slopewash following occasional rains starts little channels that later are occupied by small streams which cut innumerable small ravines and valleys, leaving between them irregular ridges, ledges and erosion remnants of varied shapes and sizes. These peculiar forms are found in regions both of low and high relief. The drainage patterns suggest topographic maturity, but often the high relief is direct evidence of youth.

In North America badlands are widely scattered over Alberta, Montana, Wyoming, North and South Dakota, Colorado, New Mexico, Utah, Arizona, Nevada and California. They are equally well developed under characteristic conditions all over the world. No two regions are alike; yet all share certain similarities in topog-

D. F. Higgins.

FIG. 161. — Badlands, southern Wyoming.

Copyrighted by Spence Air Photos.

FIG. 162. — Erosion of the Painted Desert, Arizona, with the development of typical badlands.

raphy. Wind, chemical weathering and frost action augment the work of slopewash and temporary streams.

Bryce National Park. — Nearly every one of our National Parks is noted for some peculiar topographic features: Bryce is no exception. Here one finds one of the most remarkable badlands in North America. The general region is a plateau out of which has been carved a great bowl-shaped valley (incorrectly called a canyon). The rocks are chiefly limy shales and sandstones which vary greatly in color, but are predominately red, pink, gray, yellow and

Fig. 163. — Bryce Canyon National Park, Utah.

white. The lime dissolves readily under atmospheric weathering, and the loosened grains of sand and clay are easily washed away by rain and streams which are gradually cutting back into the plateau. The whole region is a maze of amphitheatres, small canyons, narrow ridges, spires, pedestals and pinnacles, many of most grotesque form. Few other regions have such a marvelous variety and blending of colors in the rocks. The colors, combined with the fantastic erosion, make Bryce one of our most beautiful and interesting parks.

Playas

Playas are the beds of ephemeral desert lakes. They are very flat plains in the bottoms of bolsons, made by the clay, silt and salts deposited in temporary lakes. At the present time playas can be

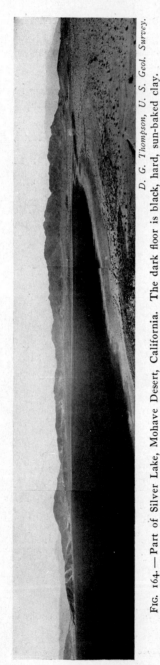

FIG. 164.— Part of Silver Lake, Mohave Desert, California. The dark floor is black, hard, sun-baked clay. *D. G. Thompson, U. S. Geol. Survey.*

found in nearly all the individual basins of the Basin and Range Province of southwestern United States. They are typical of all deserts. The extreme *flatness* of the playa is a striking topographic feature. After infrequent rains, water only a few inches deep may cover scores of square miles of a playa. Some surfaces are covered with salts of various kinds that have been precipitated as the lake waters were evaporated. These surfaces may be hard and firm, or, if ground water is near the surface, soft and spongy. The soft salt-covered playas are sometimes called *salinas*. Many are marshy. The most typical playa is composed of alternating layers of silt and salt, which, soon after the intermittent lake has disappeared, present a hard buff or white surface. The size naturally varies greatly, depending on the extent of the desert basin, the amount of water that collects in temporary lakes, etc. Some playas cover hundreds of square miles.

Ancient playas which have not been covered with water for many years are likely to have quite irregular surfaces. Wind scoops out hollows in some places and builds dunes in others. Ground water dissolves salts, leaving solution depressions. If, through drainage changes, streams dissect playas, badland topography may result. The Salt Lake Desert, with a total area of 3,000 square miles, lying south and west of Great Salt Lake, Utah, is a good example of a playa recently abandoned by the lake. Here one may find all types of playa surfaces, including salt beds on which the world's record automobile races have been run, solution depressions, dunes, silt beds from which violent dust storms arise, and hard surfaces as flat as a floor.

Bajadas

Two types of sloping plains usually connect the borders of desert basins with the flat central playa plains. These are *bajadas* and *pediments*. Bajadas are compound alluvial fans which, in many deserts, make continuous sheets of

*U. S. Dept. of Agriculture,
Bureau of Chemistry and Soils.*
Fig. 165. — Playa, with solution cavities in salt, Death Valley, California.

alluvium, miles in length, at the border zone between the basin floors and the surrounding highlands. They are composed of poorly assorted layers of coarse and fine debris which is the product of mudflows and stream floods. Each component fan is formed by a single stream; yet in old fans the individual characteristics largely yield to the composite form of the bajada. A profile across a bajada parallel to and near the mountain front will be an undulating one (Fig. 135), each fan at the mouth of a canyon having a convex surface, while concavities exist between the canyons. Some distance away from the mountains, the component fans may have so completely coalesced that a transverse profile shows few or no undulations. This is particularly true of gently sloping fans (Fig. 160), which grade basinward into playas. The surfaces of bajadas are cut by the radiating, shallow channels of intermittent streams. These channels are likely to shift during each stream flood. After the streams disappear there may be seepage of water in gravel-filled channels, or underground flow throughout the whole bajada, which finally reaches the playas, or furnishes a source of water for artesian wells.

The slopes of bajadas vary greatly. Near the mountains they may be 8 or 10 degrees or, in exceptional cases, even more; yet, in the bottoms of the basins, they usually flatten out to considerably less than 1 degree. Individual fans which coalesce basinward may grade insensibly headward into alluvial cones which form on the mountain borders at the foot of steep cliffs. The declivity of the cones may be as great as 30 degrees. The variable slopes, composition, and convex profiles are important criteria in differentiating bajadas and pediments. Many bajadas are tremendously thick at their lower ends. Borings in desert basins of southwestern United States have reached depths of more than 800 feet without passing through the alluvium. Doubtless many are much thicker.

Pediments

In many arid and semi-arid regions, long, smooth rock-cut plains extend out varying distances up to several miles from mountain fronts. *These plains are pediments.* They are cut by streams across rocks of varying composition and structure. From a distance it may

FIG. 166.—A pediment surface beveling uptilted sedimentary rocks of varying hardness, west of Berthoud, Colorado.

be difficult to distinguish them from bajadas, but close examination reveals the difference in their origin. *Bajadas, as we have just learned, are plains of aggradation,* built up by the detritus deposited by intermittent streams; while *pediments are plains of degradation.* In many cases, perhaps always, pediments represent the recession of mountain fronts due to weathering and stream erosion (Fig. 170). According to some views, as a region attains greater topographic age the width of pediments increases mountainward. It follows, then, that ultimately either isolated mountains or mountain ranges may be so thoroughly worn away that pediments will converge at the top of the eroded mountains.

In all stages of pediment development, except the last, there is an abrupt change in slope between the mountain front and the pediment surface. The profile of a pediment parallel to the mountain front is flat, not undulating, as in case of a bajada. Moreover, the whole surface of an undissected pediment, except for the re-

Fig. 167.—A pediment north of Golden, Colorado. Note the abrupt contact of the pediment and the mountain front.

gional slope, is relatively smooth. Most surfaces are slightly concave upward both in longitudinal and transverse profile. Blackwelder [1] states that the declivities of pediments in the southwestern deserts of the United States range from one-half of 1 degree to 7 degrees, with an average of about 2½ degrees. Few exceed 3½ degrees. The average slope of 2½ degrees is greater than that of many pediments in New Mexico and Arizona that have recently been described.

[1] Eliot Blackwelder: *Desert Plains*. Jour. Geol., Vol. XXXIX, p. 137, 1931.

Typical pediments have only a thin covering of alluvium except on their lower margins. However, as the pediment widens mountainward, the alluvial cover may advance in the same direction. Many pediments advance up valleys well into the mountains, where they merge into *rock-fans*. After pediments are formed, it is entirely possible that either a change in climate or diastrophism will cause different stream conditions, such that alluvial fans are deposited completely over the pediments, giving *fan-topped pediments.*

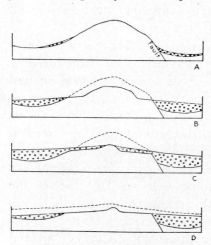

FIG. 168. — A diagram to show the development of pediments and pan fans. Small pediments are shown in (B), with fan-topped pediments and a pan fan in (C). In (D) due to erosion, well-defined pediments exist between the alluvium-filled bolsons and the highland.

On the other hand, after fans or bajadas have been formed, their surfaces may be altered through the normal processes of pedimentation to true pediments. In another place the writer has described pediments in the Front Range of Colorado, which have had the following interesting history: first, pediments were formed on uptilted sediments of very diverse composition; second, apparently due to a more humid climate which increased stream flow, coarse alluvium was deposited on the pediments; third, a new pediment surface was developed on the fan, thus giving a pediment-topped, fan-topped pediment.

It is evident that late in the cycle of desert erosion pediments and playas will attain their greatest development. Thus, broad plains, sloping gently from the greatly eroded highlands, will meet the flat plains of the desert valleys.

The Origin of Pediments. — Pediments have been widely recognized in both semi-arid and desert regions; yet their mode of origin has not been definitely established. Several questions remain unsettled. First, there is the question of the climatic conditions under which they were formed. Although they have almost univer-

sally been considered as products of *arid erosion*, many fine examples
are found in the present *semi-arid* belt along the front of the Rocky
Mountains all the way from New Mexico to Alberta. If they are
always products of arid climates, it is evident that the climate of
the Rocky Mountain front has changed since the pediments were
formed. While this is quite possible, not enough work has been
done yet to demonstrate such a change.

A more important question arises as to the exact mode of origin
of the rock-cut plains.[1] The views of different investigators fall
into three general groups.

Resurrected Surfaces. — The first group holds that a pediment
is a resurrected surface, the normal product of the recession of a
mountain front in an arid region. Assume a mountain composed
of homogeneous rock with steep slopes due to crustal movement
facing an enclosed basin. The weathering processes of the desert
proceed to break up the rocks, and the resulting debris is washed
into the basin below forming an alluvial fan. As weathering continues, the mountain front recedes and the fan rises in wedge-like
form with the edge on the degrading slope and the butt in the
valley. If weathering and removal of the material are nicely balanced, the inner thin edges of the fan will always meet the retreating face of the mountain; thus the rock-cut slope is always covered
with alluvium. The process continues with lowering of the mountain by erosion and upbuilding of the fan by deposition until the
fan is as high as the top of the mountain. Then, unless there is
rejuvenation, the processes of aggradation and degradation by water
practically cease, and the process of geomorphic development ends.
The resulting surface is called by Lawson a *pan fan* (Fig. 168).

But before this stage is reached, yet after the mountain front
has retreated some distance, suppose that, due to some diastrophic
or climatic change, part of the fan be stripped from the rock-cut
surface by streams. There would then be a mountain separated
from the alluvial fan by a pediment. According, then, to this mode

---

[1] For detailed discussions of this problem consult the following references
at the end of this chapter; the number after each name corresponds to the
numbers in the list of references: Blackwelder (2), Bryan (4), Davis, (7, 8),
Gilluly (11), Johnson (13, 14), Lawson (15), McGee (16), and Paige (17).

DAVIS

of origin, *pediments "are resurrected surfaces due to the stripping of the alluvium which once rested upon them." Lawson.*

Pediments Formed by Sheetfloods. — A second group of investigators hold that pediments are the result of sheetfloods. Attention is called to the great eroding and transporting power of the occasional desert sheetflood and to the fact that the surfaces of most pediments that have been described are dissected by rills and shallow braided stream channels. Low, broad, exceedingly symmetrical, unchanneled domes, in form similar to pan fans, but eroded to bedrock not covered by alluvium as are pan fans, are described, and their origin is attributed to sheetfloods. Lateral erosion by streamfloods is challenged because steepened basal slopes of ridges and mountains are not evident in desert topography now.[1] The slopes are concave, which flatly contradicts the theory of lateral erosion by swinging streams. Davis also states that no unconsumed residual rock knobs should stand above the general surface in front of the steepened bases of the mountain ridges if lateral erosion by streams had formed a pediment at the mountain front. (However, this statement must also be challenged, for erosion remnants on peneplains are of common occurence.) The conclusion reached by this group of physiographers is that rock plains are not formed by lateral erosion, but are due to normal desert weathering, the back-wearing of the mountain slopes and sheetfloods which strip the debris from the rock floor of the retreating mountain front.

Pediments formed through Lateral Erosion by Streams. — Johnson[2] has given a clear exposition of this process. He visualizes: "(1) An inner zone, the *zone of degradation*, corresponding closely to the mountain highland, in which vertical down-cutting of streams

---

[1] In an article published after his death, Davis (reference 8, p. 1380 at the end of this chapter) states: "In any case, the bay (alluvial fans that extend up mountain valleys) sides are not steepened at their base; and no channels are seen in the much larger fans of the high Avawatz Mountains." This author dislikes to contradict a man who cannot reply, but desires to call attention to Fig. 160, an air photograph of the Avawatz Mountains. In the lower half of this view, in an enlarged photograph, not less than a score of steepened sides and ends of ridges, and fans can be seen that are clearly the result of lateral erosion by streams.

[2] References (13) and (14) at the end of this chapter. See also Blackwelder (2).

reaches its maximum relative importance; (2) an intermediate zone, *the zone of lateral corrasion*, surrounding the mountain base, in which lateral cutting by streams attains its maximum relative im-

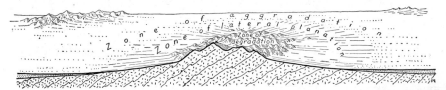

D. W. Johnson, courtesy Geographical Review.

FIG. 169. — Concentric zones of the ideal desert range.

portance. This is the zone of pedimentation. (3) An outer zone, *the zone of aggradation*, where upbuilding by deposition of alluvium has its maximum relative importance."

Weathering of the rocks is accorded its proper place in the process, and possible modifications by wind are recognized. In the early stages of erosion the streams are chiefly transporting agents carrying material from the mountain to the neighboring valleys and depositing it on the valley floors. Soon (Fig. 170 B) the streams become graded at their lower ends and begin to cut laterally, forming the piedmont rock benches or pediments, the playa floor with its alluvial deposits being the local base-level of the stream. Inselberge (unreduced rock islands) may stand out on the pediment or be partially buried by the alluvium. Eventually the mountain slope is

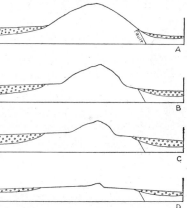

FIG. 170. — Normal pediment development due to lateral erosion by streams. Note that in (D) the whole region has been greatly reduced in elevation by erosion.

actively cut back by the lateral erosion of the heavily loaded streams which emerge from the mountains. As they reach the pediment surface, they are unable to cut vertically downward, but continually change their courses due to blocking of their own distributary channels by their load, which is scattered over an ever-widening surface beyond the mountain front. Ridges between the streams are removed, and a sharp, concave profile (Fig. 170 C, D) is developed at the junction of the pediment and retreating mountain front.

Johnson, Blackwelder and others, have emphasized strongly the fact that wide pediments at the foot of retreating mountains are the normal result of desert erosion. In the last stages of the geomorphic cycle, the mountains are largely worn away, and broad pediments nearly surround the gently sloping remnants that remain. The outer edges of the pediments grade gradually into the alluvial plains which surround them.

Many pediments are dissected after they are formed, leaving terraces or other fragments of older, higher ones above newer ones. This implies crustal disturbances which raise the highlands, lowering of the surrounding basins or climatic changes, any one of which may change the old baselevel.

Also, as the alluvial covering of the adjacent basins is removed by stream or wind erosion, the pediments may be regraded and lowered (Fig. 170 E). Many other details could be added to support this hypothesis: for example, in the Rocky Mountain region uptilted sedimentary rocks differing greatly in hardness have been completely truncated to a smooth, gently sloping plain (Fig. 166) by pedimentation. Also, streams that come out of canyons upon their alluvial fans, descending first in one channel, then in another, frequently are found in depressions on edges of the fans, where they can cut back the edges of the mountain front (Fig. 160).

In conclusion, the writer concurs with Johnson, Blackwelder and many others in the view that lateral planation by streams is the dominant process in forming pediments.

Rock Fans

Through fine deductive reasoning, Johnson [1] concluded that rock fans should project mountainward into canyons from the upper sides of pediments. *A rock fan is defined as a partial cone or fan-shaped bed-rock surface apexing in the mouth of a canyon.* From a distance rock fans and alluvial fans are indistinguishable. Many rock fans

---

[1] Reference (13) at the end of this chapter.

are covered or partially covered with alluvium, which prevents or hinders their detection. Particularly fine examples have been found in the Sierrita Mountains of Arizona. In all cases the fans, where there has not been down slope dissection, merge imperceptibly into pediments.

Canyons

Where rainfall is light, slopewash is held to a minimum; therefore, gorges and steep-walled canyons abound in mountains and plateaus of arid regions. Naturally, they remain *youthful* much longer than they would in humid areas. The occasional torrential storms give rise to flooded streams which sweep away all the loose material that they can carry, often clearing their channels down to bed rock. Near their mouths canyons are likely to be widened by lateral corrasion of streams which are caused to swing from one side to the other due to blocking of their channels by debris.

Box Canyons. — These peculiar canyons are most commonly found in regions of horizontally bedded sedimentary rocks, but they may be formed in rocks of any composition. Because of inequalities in the resistance of the rocks and the inability of temporary streams to reduce their channels to a uniform grade, the floors of box canyons often consist of a series of benches separated by vertical or even overhanging cliffs. Streams enter these canyons over waterfalls that are dry most of the year. Each abrupt descent from one bench to the next lower one gives rise to another waterfall or rapids. As the waterfalls recede, gorges are perpetuated.

REJUVENATION IN ARID REGIONS

From the preceding discussion it is evident that the normal processes of erosion and deposition in an arid region are delicately balanced. The topography of such regions is particularly sensitive to any change in the physical conditions. For example, pediments indicate stability of the earth's crust for a time long enough to allow ephemeral streams to form these rock-cut plains; but pediments channeled deeply by streams indicate some sort of rejuvenation. Playas now covered by migrating dunes are good evidence of important diminution in the water supply of the region. Great allu-

Lowell Stagner.

FIG. 171. — Canyon of the Little Colorado River, Arizona. Weathering and slope wash in this arid climate are very slight.

vial fans built entirely across desert valleys that are floored by playas indicate at least a local increase in rainfall with consequent increased volume of the streams.   Lake terraces high above the present lakes or playas are definite proof of former greater humidity.

The most important ways in which rejuvenation in arid regions is brought about are through (1) diastrophism, (2) increased precipitation, (3) decreased rainfall, (4) the lowering of valley floors through (a) overflow, (b) the headward cutting of streams from lower basins.   Diastrophism already has been discussed (Chapter VI), and we are familiar with the fact that upward and downward movements of the earth's surface are of common occurrence.   Variations in climate of both long and short duration have been amply proven by geologic and human history.   (For a good summary of climatic changes see Brooks' "Climate Through the Ages.")   The possibility of lowering desert basins through stream erosion already has been suggested in this chapter.   The following examples indicate typical topographic features produced through the various processes of rejuvenation.

Rejuvenation due to Diastrophism. — In the early stages of an arid cycle of erosion the effects of diastrophism may not be easily recognized.   If it occurs late in the cycle it is reflected by the resulting topography.   Renewed uplift of mountains increases the gradient of the streams and allows them to dissect pediments, channel bajadas, build deltas in playa lakes, and deposit new alluvial fans and cones on old fans and pediments.   Streams that wander aimlessly over desert valleys may be rejuvenated so that they deepen their valleys, leaving terraces cut out of alluvium or solid rock.

Rejuvenation due to Climatic Changes. — This is probably one of the most important causes of rejuvenation in arid regions. Records based on tree-rings, sediments and the fragmentary history of people in many parts of the earth, plainly indicate wide fluctuations in rainfall during the last 5,000 years. Similar variations are believed to have existed all through earth history.

Results of Increased Rainfall. — In many arid basins the great aprons of alluvium (bajadas) that lie at the base of the mountains are deeply channeled by streams.   Where there is no evidence of diastrophism, it is evident that the channels are due to streams re-vived by heavy rainfall. Dissected pediments may be due to the same cause. In the Libyan Desert ancient stream channels have be-come deeply filled with alluvium. Later, due to greater stream flow, the channels were reopened and terraces were formed.

In southwestern United States and in Asia well-developed lake terraces stand high above the floors of desert basins, some of which contain no lakes at the present time. These terraces show the water

D. F. Higgins.

Fig. 172. — A dissected pediment and rock fan, Egypt. Before rejuvenation the rock fan in the center of the view extended well into the mouth of the valley.

level of the ancient lakes which must have been fed by greater streams than now exist in the region. Valleys that have been cut through the terraces are much smaller and younger than those above the terraces, thus giving an interesting type of topographic uncon-formity. In the Carson-Humboldt Basin of western Nevada, a playa now 500 square miles in area attests the former size of the lake which occupied that valley. Thick deposits of alluvium containing large boulders on pediments may indicate either increased rainfall or diastrophism.

Results due to Decreased Rainfall. — Abandoned channels of streams (not anastomosing), sand-filled, stream-cut canyons, dunes on playas, pediment surfaces carved on alluvial fans are typical examples of topographic forms due to decreased rainfall.

Results of Integrated Drainage. — If streams from a lower val-

H. E. Gregory, U. S. Geol. Survey.

FIG. 173. — Hope Window, Arizona. A typical desert window formed by wind erosion and the solvent action of ground-water.

ley cut headward into a higher one, drainage in the latter will be rejuvenated; lakes will be drained, playas will be dissected, bajadas will be channeled, and the material from the higher valley will ultimately be carried to the lower one. The net results will be to drain the upper valley and to fill more completely the lower one. In the lower basin, alluvial fans and playas will increase in size.

Minor Erosional Features of Arid Regions

Just as in humid regions, many minor topographic forms are found in arid regions. They are products of weathering, wind or running water acting on rocks of peculiar structure or composition.

Windows and Arches. — Remarkable examples of these structures are found throughout the drier regions of western United States. They are the results of chemical and mechanical weather-

Lowell Stagner.

FIG. 174. — An erosion remnant, Petrified National Forest, Arizona.

ing, aided by wind and in some cases by running water. The Rainbow Bridge of southeastern Utah is a magnificent arch 309 feet high with a span of 278 feet. According to Gregory, it was carved out of cross-bedded sandstone much as the arch is being formed as shown in Figure 65. Ground-water dissolves out the cementing material of the sandstone, allowing scales to form and blocks to drop. Where the attack takes place on both sides of a narrow ridge or spur, as in the case of the Rainbow Bridge, perforation soon occurs, and then the arch or window grows rapidly in size. In many cases strong winds aid in the process by driving sand against the weakened rocks. After perforation, streams may widen the openings.

Pedestals and Pinnacles. — Usually these weird forms are blocked out by stream erosion. Their present forms, however, are the products of chemical and mechanical weathering and of wind. The weathering processes in most cases are necessary to disintegrate the rock so that it may be removed by the wind, but in certain situations (Fig. 174) the wind is chiefly responsible for the final results. Many towers, buttes and pinnacles still stand only slightly separated from the sides of mesas or plateaus of which

H. G. Rodeck.

FIG. 175. — Animal trap. A wind-formed bowl in cross-bedded sandstone, southern Wyoming.

they were once a part. No streams exist in the valleys that separate them, and it is evident that wind is directly responsible for the removal of the vast quantities of material.

U. S. Dept. of Agriculture, Bureau of Chemistry and Soils.

FIG. 176. — Desert pavement, Death Valley, California.

Bowls and Caves. — Depressions and caves are formed through the combined work of chemical weathering and wind. Usually they are formed in massive sandstones whose cementing material is calcium carbonate. This cement is easily dissolved by carbonic acid of the air or of groundwater. The sand grains thus freed are blown away by the wind. Near Laramie, Wyoming, there are several bowl-shaped depressions, locally called "animal traps", that have been carved out of *massive sandstone* through the processes just indicated. The largest "trap" is 20 feet deep and more than 30 feet in diameter. It is nearly circular in form with symmetrical overhanging sides. It is evident that eddies and gusts of wind have removed all the material.

Caves are formed in a manner similar to that described above, except that it is easier for the wind to remove the material from caves than from bowls. In all cases the rocks are first disintegrated by weathering, then removed by the wind. Caves of varying size, from tiny, drill-like holes to those large enough to shelter many people are found, particularly in massive sandstones and volcanic tuffs, on canyon walls and beneath the rims of buttes and mesas in many arid regions.

Desert Pavement. — Where mountain wash containing pebbles, gravels and sand is exposed to the wind, the fine material is soon removed, leaving a *mosaic of pebbles which has been fittingly called desert pavement*. After long exposure to the wind, the pebbles become highly polished. The pavement is common to deserts everywhere and is a most important factor in protecting the underlying fine-grained material from deflation. This protection is not complete, for the material between the pebbles is susceptible to the wind attack, also the pebbles may be moved by running water or soil creep; however, wind degradation of desert surfaces is greatly reduced where the pavement exists.

REFERENCES

1. Eliot Blackwelder: *Mudflow as a Geologic Agent in Semi-arid Mountains.* Bull. Geol. Soc. Am., Vol. 39, pp. 465–484, 1928.
2. ———: *Desert Plains.* Jour. Geol., Vol. 39, pp. 133–140, 1931.
3. Isaiah Bowman: *Desert Trails of Atacama.* Am. Geog. Soc. Sp. Pub. No. 5, 1924.
4. Kirk Bryan: *Erosion and Sedimentation in the Papago Country, Arizona.* U. S. Geol. Survey Bull. 730, 1922.
5. C. E. P. Brooks: *Climate through the Ages.* Coleman, 1926.
6. Wm. M. Davis: *The Geographical Cycle in Arid Regions.* Jour. Geol., Vol. 13, pp. 381–407, 1905.
7. ———: *Rock Floors in Arid and Humid Climates.* Jour. Geol., Vol. 38, pp. 1–27, 136–158, 1930.

8. ———: *Sheetfloods and Streamfloods.* Bull. Geol. Soc. Am., Vol. 49, pp. 1337–1416, 1938.

9. E. E. Free: *The Movement of Soil Material by the Wind.* U. S. Dept. Agr. Bureau of Soils, Bull. No. 68, 1911.

10. James Gilluly: *Possible Desert Integration in Utah.* Jour. Geol., Vol. 37, pp. 672–682, 1929.

11. ———: *Physiography of the Ajo Region, Ariz.* Bull. Geol. Soc. Am., Vol. 48, pp. 323–348, 1937.

12. H. E. Gregory and R. C. Moore: *The Kaiparowitz Region.* U. S. Geol. Survey, Prof. Paper No. 164, 1931.

13. D. W. Johnson: *Rock Fans of Arid Regions.* Am. Jour. Sci., 5th Ser., Vol. 23, pp. 389–416, 1932.

14. ———: *Rock Planes in Arid Regions.* Geog. Rev., Vol. 22, pp. 656–665, 1932.

15. A. C. Lawson: *The Epigene Profiles of the Desert.* Univ. Calif. Pub. Dept. Geol., Vol. 9, pp. 23–48, 1915.

16. W. J. McGee: *Sheetflood Erosion.* Bull. Geol. Soc. Am., Vol. 8, pp. 87–112, 1897.

17. Sydney Paige: *Rock-cut Surfaces in the Desert Ranges.* Jour. Geol., Vol. 20, pp. 422–450, 1912.

18. Caton Thompson and E. W. Gardner: *The Prehistoric Geography of Kharga Oasis.* Geog. Jour., Vol. 80, pp. 369–409, 1932.

CHAPTER X

GLACIERS AND GLACIAL TOPOGRAPHY

Late in the Pleistocene Epoch, some 30,000 or 40,000 years ago, nearly half of North America, all of northern Europe, Greenland and Antarctica, and much of Patagonia and northern Asia were covered with great blankets of snow and ice called continental glaciers. At the same time valley glaciers in all the high mountain regions of the earth were much larger than the present ones, and thousands were in existence where none are now. It is estimated that more than one-fifth of the whole land surface, about 12,000,000 square miles, was covered with ice during this time!

The earth has not recovered from the effects of this "Great Ice Age." Even now 5,000,000 square miles of Antarctica and 600,000 square miles of Greenland are covered with glacial ice. In addition, there are hundreds of valley glaciers in the high mountains of western North America, the Alps, Caucasus, Andes, Himalayas, New Zealand, and many other mountainous regions of the earth. Nearly all present glaciers are believed to be remnants of the much greater ones of Pleistocene times. *Our studies of present glaciers, which are in themselves important topographic features, help us to understand the Pleistocene glaciation which occurred so recently that it is in a large measure responsible for the topography of several million square miles of the earth's surface.*

During the last century, following studies of Pleistocene and recent glaciation, it was believed by many scientists that the earth was growing progressively cooler. Dire predictions were made to the effect that the end of the world was rapidly approaching, or at least that our planet would soon be too cold for human habitation. However, these gloomy forebodings were soon dispelled by discoveries of ancient glaciation in many earlier geologic periods. Without going into detail it may be stated definitely that there was extensive glaciation in North America in the Proterozoic Era; in China, in late Proterozoic or early Cambrian times; in Africa, Australia, India and South America, and possibly in North America in late Pennsylvanian or Permian times. Less well authenticated evidence indicates glaciation in several other periods. *There is now sufficient information at hand to warrant the statement that glaciation is a normal event in earth history.* On account of its recency and the size of its glaciers, the Pleistocene Epoch has been called, deservedly, *The Great Ice Age*; yet, as a matter of fact, it was but one of many great ice ages.

Types of Glaciers

Glaciers may be divided into four principal types: continental glaciers, ice caps, valley glaciers and piedmont glaciers. All have certain characteristics in common, but they differ in size, position and in their origin.

Definition. — *A glacier is a mass of snow and ice that moves slowly over the land away from its place of accumulation.*

Continental Glaciers. — These are the largest of all glaciers. There are good examples today in Antarctica and Greenland. The Keewatin and Labrador ice sheets in Pleistocene times (Fig. 178) together covered more than 3,500,000 square miles of north central North America. The Labrador glacier was at least 10,000 feet thick in the neighborhood of James Bay and was about 6,000 feet thick in New England, where it completely covered all the White and Green Mountains. The Scandinavian, or Baltic, glacier of similar age, must have had approximately as great a thickness as that of the Labrador ice. Although definite figures are lacking, it is probable that the present Greenland and Antarctic continental glaciers are less than half as thick as was the Pleistocene Labrador ice sheet. Continental glaciers may form, regardless of topography, on plains, plateaus or mountains. From the center of accumulation, the ice moves slowly outward in all directions.

Ice Caps. — Unfortunately, the term ice cap has been used in two quite different senses. Some writers define it simply as a small

Byron Harmon.

FIG. 177. — Mount Robson, elevation 13,500, the highest peak in the Canadian Rockies. A cascading glacier descends into Berg Lake.

continental glacier. Others regard an ice cap as the covering of snow and ice on mountains from which alpine glaciers *spring and move in different directions.* In the author's opinion, the latter definition is the correct one.

Using the second definition, ice caps accumulate either on a single mountain (example: Mount Ranier, Washington) or on a range of mountains. Directed by gravity, the ice moves down the slopes; tongues of ice entering valleys become *alpine or valley glaciers*.

Modified after U. S. Geol. Survey.

Fig. 178. — Map of North America showing the extent and great centers of Pleistocene glaciation.

Valley Glaciers. — These are glaciers which rise in ice caps or single snowfields and occupy mountain valleys. They are sometimes called *alpine* because this type of glacier was first studied in the

Alps. There is a great difference in the size of these glaciers. Some are many miles long and hundreds of feet thick near their heads. Others are only a fraction of a mile in length, nearly as wide as they are long and only a few score of feet thick. Many modern valley glaciers are but tiny remnants of their former size. Where

Courtesy French Government Tourist Bureau.
FIG. 179. — La Mer de Glace, the Alps.

they hang precariously on steep mountain slopes, they may be called *cliff, or cascade, glaciers*.

Piedmont Glaciers. — Two or more valley glaciers that combine on a plain or in a broad intermontane valley *at the foot of a mountain* constitute a piedmont glacier. There were many glaciers of this type on the plains which border the Northern Rocky Mountains during the Pleistocene ice age, and there are fine examples in Alaska at the present time.

The Growth of a Glacier

Three conditions are necessary to the formation of a glacier: first, abundant snowfall; second, cool or cold temperatures; and,

James Johnson.

FIG. 180. — The Arapaho Glacier, Colorado. The glacier is less than a mile long and about three-fourths of a mile wide. During the Pleistocene it was 10 miles long.

third, a sufficiently low rate of summer melting and evaporation, so that snow fields endure and increase in size through a long period of years. *Snow fields are the parents of all glaciers*.

Snow Fields. — Snow fields may accumulate on plains, plateaus or mountains. Wherever the conditions indicated in the last paragraph are favorable, the snow field grows in depth and in surface area from year to year. *The lower or outer edge of a snow field beyond which all the snow does not melt during a summer is the snow line.*

E. G. Fine.

FIG. 181. — Fair Glacier, Colorado. A small cliff glacier with morainal lake and recessional moraine.

"Snow line occurs at any altitude at sufficiently high latitude and at any latitude at sufficiently high altitude." (Salisbury.) Thus we find the snow line at 0 degree latitude on the mountains of Ecuador at an altitude of 17,000 to 18,000 feet, while in Antarctica, latitude 66.5° to 90° South, the snow line in some places is at sea level. Obviously, snow fields form at any elevation above the snow line, depending on other factors.

The Change from Snow to Ice. — The transformation of snow to glacial ice occurs chiefly in the snow field. As it falls through the air, snow consists of delicate, thin, tabular, hexagonal crystals. After the snow has lain on the ground for some time and has been covered by later falls, it gradually changes to granular ice which is called *névé*. This change is brought about by the partial melting of the snow crystals due to weight of the overlying load. *It may occur even when the temperature is constantly below 32 degrees Fahrenheit.* The water from the melting snow trickles down and almost immediately freezes, thus making grains of ice. A thick snow bank formed by the successive snowfalls of only one winter will have ice at the bottom, thoroughly granular snow in the center, and slightly altered snow at the top. After many years of accumulation, the ice at the bottom of a snow field becomes very thick, and, at last, is ready to move.

The Movement of Glaciers

The question of just how the ice of a snow field begins its movement, thus making it a glacier, is controversial.   Some authorities state that gravity alone, due to the weight of the ice and snow, is responsible for glacial movement.   Others call attention to the expansive force (about 2,000 pounds per square inch) of freezing water and believe that in the growth of ice crystals at the bottom

E. G. Fine.

FIG. 182. — The front of the Columbia Glacier, Alaska.   The glacier is 50 miles long, 4 miles wide and 360 feet thick where it enters the ocean.   At times great icebergs break off.

of the snow field a stage is finally reached when the ice is so compact that further freezing of water between the grains causes expansion and movement of the ice.   *The repeated processes of melting and freezing both in the snow field and the glacial ice, aided by gravity, probably cause the movement of glaciers.*

Nature of Glacial Motion. — Many things need to be considered in a discussion of glacial motion.   The rate of movement varies greatly in different glaciers and in the same glacier at different seasons.   All glaciers move faster in the summer than in the winter.   Arapaho, a small glacier in Colorado, moves only 27 feet a year; yet in the summer some Greenland and Alaskan glaciers move as much as 60 feet a day. Long glaciers move more rapidly than do short ones. The center and top of a glacier, where friction is less, move more rapidly than do the bottom and sides. Glaciers are capable of carrying great loads of rock debris. Boulders as large as a small house may be carried long distances. Rocks in the bottom of a glacier are held in one position so that the bottom face of the rock is smoothed and polished or striated with grooves parallel to the direction of glacial movement.

The ice itself is a brittle solid, as is shown by faults, folds and shear zones, and by crevasses (Fig. 180) which remain open long after they are formed. Yet a glacier which is highly fractured, due to movement over steep slopes, soon becomes welded together at the bottom, like a plastic substance, after it resumes its normal course. Unlike streams which move around obstacles, glaciers tend to overwhelm them or erode them away. This is well illustrated by the straight smooth walls of mountain valleys from which spurs and minor projections have been removed. *Glacial boulders are carried up-hill.* In Montana, Alberta and Saskatchewan there are boulders which were picked up by a continental glacier a short distance west of Hudson Bay at an elevation of 1,000 feet or less above sea level. The boulders have been transported several hundred miles and are now 3,000 to 4,000 feet above sea level. At first thought this suggests that glaciers move for long distances up-hill. This is possible, but not probable. The boulders probably were carried up from the bottom of the glacier into higher ice through shearing of fresh ice over stagnant ice.

Many writers speak of glaciers as streams or rivers of ice "that flow through their valleys." But, as a matter of fact, they are very unlike rivers, and they do not flow like a liquid. If the word flow is used in connection with glaciers, it should be thought of as a *solid flow whereby the movement is due to orderly molecular rearrangement and not as liquid flow whereby the molecules move in pell-mell fashion without order.*

With these features of glaciers in mind, we may now examine more critically the nature of glacial motion. If gravity were the only factor involved, glaciers should move faster in the winter than in the summer, for the weight of ice and snow is much greater in the winter; yet they move faster in the summer. If glaciers flowed like water, they should break away from their parent snow fields and flow down their valleys like water which flows out of a reservoir through a headgate or broken dam; *but this is exactly what glaciers do not do.* In a normal alpine glacier there is a continuous sheet of ice from the snow field to the lower end, where melting and evaporation terminate the glacier. The reason for more rapid summer than winter movement clearly is due to summer melting of the ice. The water trickles down into the ice, refreezes and expands; also it lubricates the ice as it moves over the rock floor. The shear of ice over stagnant non-moving ice that has been noted in many modern glaciers and which is believed to have caused drumlins definitely indicates a rigid thrust which is most easily explained by granular growth of the ice with consequent expansion.

Wastage of Glaciers

All glaciers waste away at their lower ends and at their margins. This is accomplished through melting and evaporation, which are greatest near the lower end, but which go on to some extent the whole length of the glacier. Also, glaciers which move from the land out into the ocean finally break to pieces and float away as icebergs (Fig. 182). Many icebergs form from the ice sheets of Alaska, Greenland and Antarctica. They are gradually carried away from their sources by winds and currents, and finally melt in the ocean water. The glacial cycle is something like the river cycle in this respect. Precipitation feeds both glaciers and rivers, and the moisture which falls as rain or snow eventually is returned to the atmosphere through evaporation. These processes of melting and evaporation terminate all glaciers that do not reach the oceans. If, due to climate conditions, melting and evaporation are rapid, the end of the glacier recedes; if these processes are reduced during a period of years, the glacier advances. Under delicately balanced conditions, where the rate of movement exactly equals the melting and evaporation, the end of the glacier may remain in the same position for many years. As a rule, however, glaciers periodically advance and retreat.

THE WORK OF GLACIERS

Glaciers, in common with streams and wind, are agents of gradation; they erode, transport and deposit the materials of the land. In this respect they are among the most powerful of all physiographic agents.

Erosion. — The mechanical abrasion of clear, pure ice is probably very slight. This, however, is a negligible factor in glacial

F. Fortson.

Fig. 183. — Glacial cirques near Longs Peak, Colorado. The low ridge on the left between the two cirques has been nearly worn away by sapping and lateral erosion.

erosion, for, as the ice moves over the land, it gathers up loose boulders, mantle rock and soil, which become its cutting tools. These materials, imbedded in the ice, act as rasps or files with which the glacier, as it advances over the land, removes all loose material and wears away points and projections of the solid rocks. Most bed rocks are jointed; therefore are susceptible to the attack of the moving, debris-laden ice. Boulders are dislodged and carried away, thus deepening the bed of the glacier. The solid rocks both beneath and on the sides of the ice (in valleys) become beautifully smoothed

and striated. Limestones and other soft but compact rocks may
exhibit deep smooth grooves after the glaciers have passed over
them. Through this mechanical abrasion valley glaciers smooth
their floors and walls, gradually reshaping the valleys through which
they move from narrow, V-shaped, winding valleys to broad
U-shaped, straighter ones. At the foot of steep slopes there is a
tendency for the ice to gouge out basins in the solid rock. Some of

I. C. Russell, U. S. Geol. Survey.

FIG. 184. — Forest growth over the stagnant ice of the Malaspina Glacier, Alaska.

these basins are very deep and, after the ice has melted, become
the sites of lakes and swamps.

Continental glaciers, because of their great thickness and weight,
reshape the whole topography of the land over which they move. In
New York and New England most of the mountains were completely covered by the Labrador ice sheet. The present mountains
have relatively smooth outlines (Fig. 207) and are devoid of ridges
and spurs characteristic of non-glaciated highlands.

Plucking and Sapping. — A remarkable feature of valley glaciers
is their ability to *erode headward.* Water from rain and melting

snow gets into the joints of the rocks, freezes and expands. The boulders loosened in this way are plucked out by the glacier and carried away. This process (*sapping*) results in great amphitheater-like depressions (cirques, Fig. 183) being formed at the heads of the glaciers.

Transportation. — The tremendous power of a glacier is well illustrated by the load it is able to carry. Every imaginable size of material from fine rock flour to boulders as large as a house is carried on and in the ice. Continental glaciers get this load from the land over which they move. The load of alpine glaciers is derived in part from erosion of the bed and sides of their valleys, and in part from the slopes above the glacier. There boulders are detached by frost action and gravity, and roll down onto the ice. Also snow slides, avalanches and streams bring material from the mountain sides to the surface of the glacier. All

U. S. Geol. Survey.

FIG. 185. — Drift of Wisconsin stage overlying Patrician drift, Mesabi Iron Range, Minnesota.

this debris is carried from its source by the moving ice to the place where it is finally deposited. Doubtless some rocks and soil are pushed along in front of the ice, but most of the material is carried in or on the glacier.

Stagnant Ice. — If there is much loose material in the path of a glacier, the lower part of the ice becomes more and more filled with debris; motion becomes increasingly sluggish and finally ceases. Then the upper layers shear over the stagnant ice which protects the land from further erosion. This explains the stretches of unpolished rocks in glaciated valleys that lie between well-polished regions.

Ice also becomes stagnant through excessive melting near the lower end or margin. In this situation the ice may melt away from around the rocks and dirt carried by the glacier. The effect is to so overload the remaining ice that it is unable to move. Such stagnant ice may lie buried by its own debris for many years. The great Malaspina glacier in Alaska is, in part, of this type; forests and thick underbrush are now growing on the soil that covers the stagnant ice. The lower part of the Asulkan glacier, British Columbia, became stagnant in this way many years ago. Now a new advance is taking place over the old stagnant ice.

Deposition. — When the ice melts, all the material it has been carrying is dropped, leaving a mixture of unassorted coarse and fine debris without stratification (Fig. 185) called *glacial drift* or *till.* The resulting deposits exhibit characteristic topographic forms

E. G. Fine.

Fig. 186. — Tunnel in the Mendenhall Glacier, Alaska.

that are described in a later section of this chapter. Typical drift is angular or subangular in form, for the rocks are held in a relatively fixed position while carried by the ice and have no chance to become rounded as are stream pebbles and boulders. Many boulders are smoothed and striated on one face that was dragged along the ground.

Glacio-fluvial Deposits. — Streams formed by melting ice occur on, beneath, on the sides of, and at the lower ends of all glaciers. Debris of a size that can be transported by the streams is washed away, and soon much of it is deposited. If it comes from a valley glacier and is spread out in a thick sheet in the valley below the ice, it is called a *valley train.* Material washed out from and deposited near the margin of a continental glacier is an *outwash plain*.   In some glaciers, tunnels are formed beneath the ice by running water (Fig. 186).   Obstructions in the tunnels cause the streams to deposit their load.   After the ice melts, long narrow ridges, *eskers,* are left. All glacio-fluvial deposits are roughly stratified and assorted. Debris carried far by glacial streams is rounded.

CHARACTERISTICS OF MODERN GLACIERS

There is no good reason to believe that our modern glaciers differ from those of past ages except in size. The continental glaciers of Antarctica and Greenland are relatively inaccessible, and have not been thoroughly studied, although a tremendous amount of research has been accomplished. It may seem invidious to mention only a few names when so many investigators have worked in these regions,[1] but T. C. Chamberlin, Hobbs, Nansen, Nordenskjold, Peary, Stefansson and Wilkins are noted for their work in Greenland or other northern polar regions; while Mawson, Scott and Byrd, to mention only a few of many illustrious names, have contributed much to our knowledge of Antarctica.

Valley glaciers were first described in the Alps more than a century ago. Now they are being studied intensively wherever they occur, all over the earth. There are more than 2,000 glaciers in the Alps. Hundreds occur in the mountains of south central Asia, and other hundreds in Alaska. Many are found in the Scandinavian highlands, the Andes, Pyrenees, Carpathians, Rockies, Coast ranges, and other highlands the world over. In Alaska one finds some of the largest and most accessible glaciers known. There may be found all types of valley glaciers from small cascading ice sheets to great trunk glaciers which are fed by many smaller tributaries. These glaciers deserve more recognition than they have received, for they are not only of outstanding interest in themselves, but they are situated midst some of the most magnificent scenery on the North American continent. The following discussion deals particularly with valley glaciers which embody most of the characteristics, except size, of all other types.

[1] For a good bibliography see reference (14) at the end of this chapter.

Dimensions. — The largest valley glaciers now known are in the Pamir region of west central Asia, where one, the Fedtschenko, is 44 miles in length. The Aletsch, one of the finest in the Swiss Alps, is 10 miles long; while the Susitna in Alaska has a length of 25 miles, and the Seward, also in Alaska, is about 40 miles long. The *lower* ends of many of the Alaskan glaciers, where they enter the ocean, are from 200 to 900 feet thick. We know little about the thickness of glaciers at their heads. Crevasses more than 150 feet deep are of common occurrence, and, judging by the surrounding topography, there is good reason to believe that the ice may be at least 2,000 feet thick. Estimates based on very insecure data place the thickness of the Greenland and Antarctica ice sheets at from 2,000 to 5,000 feet. The width of the Hubbard glacier, one of the finest in southern Alaska, where it enters Disenchantment Bay, is 3.5 miles. These figures suggest the great dimensions of some of our modern glaciers. They may not represent maximum conditions, for details of many great ice sheets are lacking. The smallest known valley and cliff glaciers are scarcely more than snow banks with a surface area of only a small fraction of a square mile and a thickness of only a few feet.

Advance and Retreat. — Most of the glaciers studied during the past fifty years show remarkable fluctuations in the positions of their lower ends. After a few years of unusually heavy snowfall and lower than normal summer temperatures, the glaciers advance. After periods of lighter snowfall and warmer temperatures, they retreat. The response of the glacier to fluctuation in climate is not immediate but lags somewhat. Glaciers whose lower ends are practically stationary in position represent a definite balance between rate of movement and rate of wastage. An advance indicates that the equilibrium has been upset, so that forward movement exceeds melting and evaporation. A retreat shows that wastage is greater than the forward movement. *In this case it is important to note that the ice has a forward movement, although the lower end retreats up the valley.* In the early part of the present century, many Alaskan glaciers were retreating. Nunatak glacier retreated about a *mile between 1899 and 1905.* Curiously, at the same time, some adjacent ones were advancing. Climatic change could not very well explain such opposed phenomena. It was finally determined that the *advancing* glaciers had been fed by avalanches which carried enormous amounts of snow from the steep mountain slopes to the heads of the glaciers. In some cases the avalanches appear to be due to earthquakes.

Most of the glaciers of the earth have been retreating during the past 50 or 75 years. Many small ones have retired to their parent snow fields, where practically all movement has ceased. If this condition persists through the present century, hundreds of small glaciers in the mountains of mid-temperate latitudes will, undoubtedly, disappear.

Surface Features. — In the winter, when glaciers are covered deeply with snow, their surfaces are smooth or rolling and offer little difficulty to properly equipped exploration parties, but in the late summer everything may be changed. Crevasses and surface drainage make travel difficult, dangerous, and often impossible over very large glaciers.

Crevasses. — The floors of most glaciers are irregular; therefore, when the ice moves over a cliff or any projection that develops tension (Fig. 180), it cracks open. Also tension is developed through differential movement causing the ice to crack. These cracks or crevasses may be parallel, transverse or, less frequently, diagonal to the course of the glacier. Apparently, the cracks rarely extend to the bottom of the ice. If they do they soon are closed. In the upper part they not only remain open, but are enlarged by summer melting. In the winter they may be partially or completely filled with snow, which, being less compact than the glacial ice, usually melts the following summer. Objects and even people lost in crevasses have appeared in due time at the end of the glacier.

Faults, Folds and Shears. — Where glacial ice is well exposed, thrust faults, folds and shear planes are of common occurrence. They are easily recognized in ice that is distinctly layered due to seasonal accumulations of debris. Some shear planes are marked by pebbles or fine debris; others are paralleled by layers of air bubbles in the ice. Intersecting shears that show more than one period of deformation are not uncommon. High angle faults and

shear planes with dips of from 45 to 90 degrees are characteristic
of the lower ends of large glaciers.

Seracs. — At the lower ends of thick, highly crevassed glaciers,
the surface topography becomes a complex jumble of ice cliffs, irregular ridges and valleys. Many of the ice cliffs are in the form of
irregular pinnacles called *seracs*.

Bergschsund. — At the head of a valley glacier, where the top
of the ice pulls away from the snow field, a great irregular crevasse
called the *bergschsund* is likely to develop. This is always closed
by snow in the winter, but in the summer it may be open so that
it can be explored. Then one may see the beautiful blue ice at its
best.

Ice Pedestals. — On many glaciers, great boulders protect the
underlying ice from summer melting. As the surrounding ice disappears, the boulders stand on ice pedestals higher and higher above
the general surface of the ice. Eventually the pedestals melt and
the boulders fall.

Dust Wells. — Dust and thin pieces of rock absorb heat from
the sun and melt the underlying ice, thus developing cylindrical holes
several inches to many feet in depth. Other wells of smaller diameter, but much deeper, without dirt or rocks at the bottom, apparently are formed through melting along small vertical crevasses.

Slope. — The surface slope varies tremendously with different
glaciers. Some small cliff glaciers have slopes as steep as 25 to 30
degrees. Cascade glaciers locally may be even steeper. Many of
the long Swiss and Alaskan glaciers slope footward approximately
100 feet to the mile. However, *for short distances,* where the ice
is riding over obstructions, the *slope may be headward*.

Drainage. — In warm weather the surfaces of glaciers are channeled by many small streams which remove much dust and dirt from
the ice. The streams either flow off the end or sides of the glacier,
or empty into crevasses, where much of the water soon freezes.
On Alaskan glaciers great rivers of water issue from tunnels in the
ice, flow on the surface of the glacier, and eventually disappear in
other tunnels. In many places small lakes stand on the glacier,
hemmed in by ice or by morainal debris. At the lower ends of great

valley glaciers, tunnels may be found which extend far back under the ice. These tunnels sometimes are dry, but usually in the summer strong streams of water carrying rock flour and other fine debris issue from them.

Where glaciers have receded recently, it is quite common to find small lakes between the terminal moraine and the ice. The turbidity of the water of these lakes is good evidence of the movement of glaciers that lie above them. The rock flour ground by the moving glacier from its floor and washed out from beneath the ice by streams gives an almost milk-white color to the lake water.

Junius Henderson.

FIG. 187. — A lake between a terminal moraine and the glacier, Colorado.

Surface Debris. — Large alpine glaciers carry tremendous quantities of debris on and near their surfaces. Except at their lower ends most of this is near the sides of the glaciers.

Lateral Moraines. — As the ice erodes the valley walls, it accumulates rocks and dirt, which form well-defined ridges or *lateral* moraines. Also much debris is added to these moraines from frost action, snow slides and avalanches.

Medial Moraines. — Many alpine glaciers are of the trunk type that receive large additions of ice through tributary glaciers. The lateral moraines of these tributaries become *medial moraines* of the main glacier after the two have united. In some of the large Alaskan glaciers, there are as many as six well-defined medial moraines. Advances of the small glaciers, shown in Fig. 188, until they unite with the main glacier would give similar results.

Near the lower ends, where melting is great, the morainal debris is spread by surface streams over the glacier. It has been reported

Byron Harmon.

FIG. 188. — The Athabaska Glacier, Alberta, one of the sources of the river of the same name. Part of the Columbia Ice Cap, 180 square miles in area, is shown in the background. Note the irregular front of the ice and the long lateral moraine on the left side of the glacier.

that such a mantle of debris completely covers more than a square mile of ice of some Alaskan glaciers.

Piedmont Glaciers

The Malaspina glacier in Alaska is probably the most typical and certainly is the most interesting piedmont glacier known. Situated immediately west of Yakutat Bay and southeast of Mount St. Elias, it is fed by numerous alpine glaciers, some of which are very large. The total area of this great ice sheet is about 1,500 square miles. Its central portion is a great plateau of clear white ice cut by thousands of shallow crevasses. Its margins, except where the larger glaciers come in, are covered with a thick mantle of morainal debris. Proceeding from the clear ice toward the sea, on the outer margin of this belt of morainal material there are, first, scattered flowers, then clumps of alders, and, finally, thick forests of large spruces. *Yet the whole area is underlain by glacial ice, stagnant in some places, but moving in many others.* The movement is plainly shown by new crevasses and great trees that have been overturned in the forested areas. The surface slope from the mountain front to the outer margin is about 70 feet to the mile. The morainal belt shows characteristic kettle and hummock topography. Crevasses are numerous, as are small lakes of peculiar hour-glass shape formed in the underlying ice. Beneath the marginal ice are subglacial streams of large size. Hundreds of such streams, all loaded with silt, pour out from the south margin of the glacier. One, the Yahtre, flows through a tunnel 6 or 8 miles long.

Ice Caps

Two short quotations will help us to understand the nature of ice caps as defined in this book. In 1891, on his second expedition to Mount St. Elias, I. C. Russell [1] described the region north of the great mountain in the following words:

"What met my astonished gaze was a vast snow-covered region, limitless in expanse, through which hundreds and perhaps thousands of barren angular mountain peaks projected. There was not a stream, not a lake, and not a vestige of vegetation of any kind in sight. A more desolate or more utterly lifeless land one never beheld. Vast, smooth snow surfaces, without crevasses, stretched away to limitless distances, broken only by jagged and angular mountain peaks."

In his description of the glaciers of the Yakutat Bay Region, Alaska, R. S. Tarr [2] used the term "through glacier" to designate

[1] I. C. Russell: *Second Expedition to Mount St. Elias.* U. S. Geol. Surv., Thirteenth An. Rept., Pt. 2, p. 47, 1892.

[2] R. S. Tarr: *The Yakutat Bay Region, Alaska.* U. S. Geol. Surv., Prof. Paper 64, pp. 34–36, 1909.

glaciers of that region, which are so different from normal valley glaciers as to require a special name. His definition follows:

"By 'through glacier' is meant a continuous ice-filled valley from the terminus of one glacier to that of another, across a flat divide from which, in some area of indefinite location and extent, ice drainage flows in both directions. Where well developed, as it is east of Russel Fiord, the through-glacier condition forms an intricate maze of broad rather flat-topped glaciers of moderate slope, which so submerge the mountains as to give them the appearance of a drowned mountainous land, like the island-skirted coast of southeastern Alaska."

These snow and ice fields, the common source of many valley glaciers, which move away in various directions, are typical *ice caps* as this author would use the term. The movement of these broad flattish ice sheets evidently is slow, but in case of the valley glaciers which emanate from them, it is much more rapid. Because movement is slow, crevassing is slight. Rock debris, so apparent on the lower parts of wasting valley glaciers, is less abundant on ice caps. Where present, it is largely buried by snow, *for ice caps form in regions of accumulation rather than wastage of snow and ice.*

VALLEY GLACIAL TOPOGRAPHY

The magnificent scenery of high mountains the world over is largely the result of sculpturing by valley glaciers. *Matterhorns,* serrated ridges, waterfalls, lakes nestling in glacial meadows or occupying deep-forested valleys, hanging valleys, gigantic gorges with broad floors and over-steepened sides are but a few of the many indications of glaciation. Just as do streams and wind, glaciers develop characteristic types of topography through (a) erosion and (b) deposition. We now are ready to examine the results of the work of the glaciers of Pleistocene and Recent ages that covered hundreds of thousands of square miles of the land surface in the high mountain regions of the earth. A single example will serve to show the importance of glaciers in the development of mountain topography. Colorado is situated well toward the southern end of the Rocky Mountain system, and was not as extensively glaciated as were the regions farther north; yet, in this one state, during

Pleistocene times, not less than 10,000 square miles of the mountains and valleys above 8,000 feet in elevation were covered by valley glaciers.

Erosional Topography

Valley glaciers are powerful erosive agents. There is abundant evidence that many of them were at least 2,000 to 3,000 feet thick during the Pleistocene Epoch. The great weight of the moving ice,

FIG. 189. — U-shaped glacial valleys, Teton Mountains, Wyoming. Many glacial valley floors have gentle rather than such steep slopes.

together with the abundant abrasive tools, allowed these glaciers to do a tremendous amount of work.

Glaciated Valleys. — Unlike youthful, stream-cut valleys, glaciated valleys have broad floors and relatively smooth, over-steepened sides (Fig. 189). The valley floors and lower borders were smoothed and polished, although now they may be littered with debris deposited during the last retreat of the ice. The ends of ridges and spurs between tributaries of the main valley are usually triangular in shape, and are said to be *faceted*. In most glacial valleys there are swamps and lakes whose basins were gouged out of the bed rock or were formed by moraines. Highly glaciated valleys 20 to 40 miles in length are of common occurrence.

Hanging Valleys. — Where great trunk valley glaciers are fed by tributary glaciers, the latter usually come in well above the main valley floors. After the ice of both valleys melts, the tributary valleys (Fig. 188) hang high above the main ones. Often steep cliffs, which separate the mouth of the tributary from the main valley floor, give rise to beautiful waterfalls (Fig. 115). In a large drainage basin, the hanging valleys may occur at any elevation, from a few feet to more than a thousand feet above the main valley.

Cirques. — All glaciated valleys open *at their heads* into amphitheater - shaped depressions called cirques. These are among the most typical of all glacial features. Gilbert, in describing the crest of the Sierra Nevadas, said that the sides of the range were scalloped as if cut out by a gigantic biscuit cutter (Fig. 183). The walls of cirques are steep, in many cases nearly perpendicular. The floors are sometimes well-polished and are likely to contain gouged lake basins up to a hundred feet or more in

FIG. 190. — A sketch of a hanging valley tributary to a main glaciated valley.

depth. The areas of cirques vary greatly, depending on the size of the snow banks that fed the original glaciers. Some embrace only a few acres; others cover many square miles. Cirques often are mistaken for eroded volcanic craters. However, a careful examination reveals the polished and striated rocks on the floor and lower walls which are clear evidence of glacial erosion.

Matterhorns. — Through headward erosion of the cirque walls, glaciers tend to remove divides. If three or more glaciers cut headward until their cirques meet or almost meet, it often happens that high, sharp-pointed, steep-sided peaks called *horns*, or matterhorns, after the famous Matterhorn in the southern Alps, remain as the only remnants of original broad highlands. Many such peaks

F. Fortson.

FIG. 191. — A large cirque and glacial lake below the east face of Longs Peak, Colorado.

still have glaciers at their base, which remove the debris loosened and dropped onto them by frost action, and thus perpetuate the steep cliffs.

Serrated Ridges. — Another typical feature of glaciated regions is the _serrated, or saw-toothed, ridge,_ which stands between the heads of present glaciers or between the heads of cirques once occupied by valley glaciers. These ridges, in many cases only two or three feet wide at the top and of extremely irregular surface, are all that remains of broad pre-glacial divides. Due to headward sapping of their cirque walls, the glaciers have nearly removed their divides. The narrow ridges continually lose boulders through frost action and gravity. Many ridges, undoubtedly, have been reduced greatly in altitude since the Pleistocene Epoch. The degree of irregularity of

FIG. 192. — A small cirque, Mount Adubon, Colorado.

the crest line varies somewhat with the composition of the rock. Uptilted sedimentary and metamorphic rocks may be so greatly eroded that it is impossible for a person to travel over the ridge.

Nunataks. — A nunatak is rock mass surrounded by ice. It may separate two valley glaciers or two lobes of ice sheets. It stands out as an island in the ice. Through lateral erosion by the glaciers, accompanied by frost action, avalanches, etc., the nunatak is soon worn away until a very narrow ridge, merely a remnant of its former size, remains (Fig. 194).

Shifting of Divides. — When there is greater precipitation on one side of a mountain range than on the other, or due to less melt-ing and evaporation on the side that receives heat from the *morning* sun, or due to snow blown from the windward to the leeward side of a range, a large number of glaciers may form on one side, with few or none on the other. Where this condition exists, divides will shift through headward erosion toward the side of the range where there are the fewest numbers of glaciers. In some of the north-south trend-ing ranges of the Rocky Moun-tains, notably the Front Range, the Continental Divide has been

Courtesy W. Stzygowski.

FIG. 193. — The Matterhorn, Alps.

shifted at least two miles to the west. The crest of the Sierra Nevada Range has been shifted to the east. Lateral, as well as headward divides may be shifted in similar fashion, especially by the sideward sapping of cirque walls.

Cyclopean Stairs. — One of the most puzzling topographic features commonly found in valley-glaciated regions is a succession of glaciated benches, separated by nearly vertical cliffs, all well within typically glaciated valleys (Fig. 196). The benches, which may be from a few hundred yards to several miles in length, have the full width of the valley in which they lie. The cliffs separating the benches usually range in height from 100 to 1,000 feet. Gouged basins or irregular depressions are likely to occur on the heads of the benches at the foot of the cliffs. To this whole assemblance of topographic forms, the names *Cyclopean stairs,* or *giant's stairways,* are singularly appropriate.

The origin of these great staircases is not always clear. Some are due to faults which leave scarps over which the glaciers descend from one level to another. Others appear to be due to differences

Courtesy Canadian Pacific Railroad.

Fig. 194. — Franz Joseph Glacier, New Zealand. Note the serrated divide with matterhorns in the making, also the nunataks sticking up through the ice.

in composition or structure, or both, of the bed rocks. Where the rocks are soft or highly jointed, they are plucked and quarried by the glacier, and, of course, are carried away. As soon as *slight variations* in the gradient of the valley floor are established, the glacier, through selective erosion, tends to increase cutting at the base of the cliff, until, finally, the new stair-like profile has been made.

Tandem Cirques. — In highly glaciated mountain regions, it is not unusual to find two or more well-defined cirques connected by a glaciated valley (Fig. 198). These easily may be confused with the Cyclopean stairs just described, for the cirque floors are bench-like, and are separated from one another by steep cliffs. In some cases the walls of the lower cirques are well polished and striated, showing that they have been overwhelmed by moving ice. Lakes usually occur on the cirque floors. The position of the cirques indicates that the lower ones are older, thus representing an earlier stage of glaciation than do the higher ones.

Fiords. — Among the most beautiful of all glacial features are the drowned glaciated valleys, fiords, that occur so extensively in such regions as New Zealand, Norway, Chile, Labrador, Greenland, British Columbia and Alaska. These long, straight or broadly curved valleys are now filled with sea water, in some cases as much as 5,000 or 6,000 feet deep. Their glacial origin is plainly indicated by the polished and striated, over-steepened walls, hanging tributary valleys, and other characteristic

F. A. Melton.

Fig. 195. — An irregular "knife edge" mountain crest formed by the headward cutting of glaciers, Sangre de Cristo Range, Colorado.

topography. At present some of the so-called inlets, such as the Taku, Reid, and others in Alaska show fiords in the making. The great alpine glaciers that occupy the heads of these inlets are actively eroding the floors of their valleys, which are now in some cases nearly a thousand feet below sea level. When the glaciers retreat, naturally the sea water follows the ice headward. The great depth of water in some fiords that now are without glaciers indicates possible subsidence of land since the ice melted from the valleys.

Roches Moutonnées. — In all well-glaciated regions where the debris deposited by the retreating ice has not completely covered the floor of the valley, rounded, highly polished knolls and hum-

mocks of solid rock are distinctive features. Where they occur
in profusion, because of their slight resemblance to herds of sheep
they have been called *roches moutonnées*. Striae on the rocks show
plainly the direction of glacial motion. The unsymmetrical profile
of a roche moutonnée, usually steeper to-
ward the head of the glacier, also is typical
of irregularities of the land that have been
smoothed by moving ice.

Topography due to Deposition

Glacial deposits are distinctive and seldom need be confused with other types.
The debris is usually a mixture of dirt,
rock flour and subangular boulders, unassorted and without stratification. Where
well exposed, the topography of glacial
deposits is quite as distinctive as are the
materials.

FIG. 196.—A sketch show-
ing Cyclopean stairs.

Terminal Moraines. — Under rather
specialized conditions, huge ridges or belts
of debris (*drift*) are deposited at the ends
of valley glaciers. Let us suppose that near the lower end the ice
moves forward 500 feet a year. Also suppose that melting and
evaporation at the end amount to 500 feet a year. This means that
each year 500 feet of new ice will deposit its load at the end of the
glacier. In a few years a great ridge (Fig. 187) will be built up.
Now suppose that the glacier advances with the usual irregular
frontal lobes pushing into the moraine. The initial ridge will be
distorted and small hummocks and depressions will be left. Continued oscillations with slight advances and retreats will cause a
large irregular belt of morainal material to form across the valley.
Nearly all terminal moraines exhibit a characteristic "kettle and
hummock" topography. Lakes and marshes are likely to occupy
the depressions (kettles). Large angular boulders are almost always present. Many terminal moraines are partially destroyed by
streams that rise within or near the end of the glacier and cut

through a low place in the moraine. Some moraines contain a considerable amount of stream-worn material washed out from the glacier and caught by the embankment.

Lateral Moraines. — The origin of these moraines as they exist on moving glaciers has already been described. When the ice

Don Kemp.

FIG. 197. — A series of glaciated benches and lakes separated by steep cliffs, Rocky Mountain National Park, Colorado.

melts, all this material and, in addition, debris washed to the sides of the glacier by small streams is deposited in the form of narrow steep ridges which parallel the valley walls. The slopes toward the valley often are remarkably smooth and uniform. In Alaska

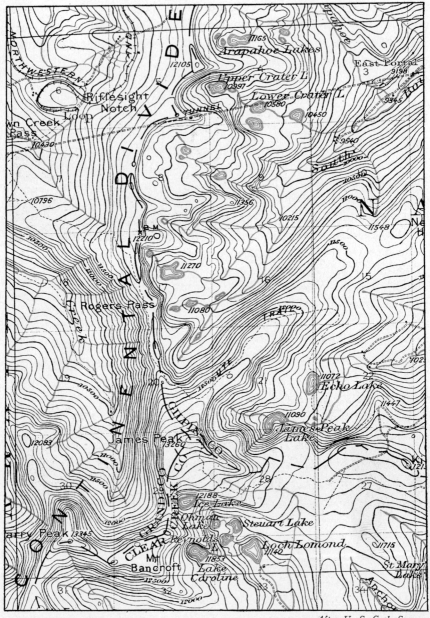

After U. S. Geol. Survey.

Fig. 198. — A section from the Central City, Colorado, topographic map. Upper and Lower Crater lakes are in tandem cirques. Note the Cyclopean stairs. The scale is about 1 inch to the mile. Contour interval, 100 feet.

lateral moraines 1,000 feet high show the great thickness of the ice that formed them. In many places well-developed lateral moraines join a terminal moraine, thus forming a huge horseshoe-shaped ridge (Fig. 232). It is not un-usual to find as many as three lateral moraines, all essentially parallel, on the side of a gla-ciated valley. Each may rep-resent a separate advance of the ice or under certain con-ditions they may represent halts in the retreat of the ice. The composition and structure of the drift is essentially the same as in terminal moraines.

F. A. Melton.

FIG. 199. — Gouged lake basins in an oversteepened glacial valley that now is being filled rapidly with debris from the high cliffs. Sangre de Cristo Range, Colorado.

Medial Moraines. — Usu-ally medial moraines are diffi-cult to recognize on the ground. When the ice wastes away the moraines are deposited, but are so mixed with ground morainal debris or with outwash that they

John W. Vanderwilt.

FIG. 200. — A fine glaciated bench on the right. There is another beyond the lake. Two cycles of valley glaciation are indicated, Snow Mass Mountains, Colorado.

rarely are distinguishable. Where they occur, they are imperfectly developed ridges that stand out in the middle of a valley.

Ground Moraines. — Many valley glaciers retreat rapidly after their last advance, leaving an irregular sheet of drift over their valley floors. This debris varies greatly in thickness and in surface

Royal Canadian Air Force Photo.

FIG. 201. — Khutze Inlet, a typical British Columbia fiord.

R. L. Ives, courtesy Am. Phil. Society.

FIG. 202. — Roches Moutonnées, Colorado.

R. L. Ives, courtesy Am. Phil. Society.

FIG. 203. — A pair of long, lateral moraines, Rocky Mountain National Park, Colorado. The light-colored foliage of the aspens shows the position of the moraines. Between the nearest moraine and the observer is a long narrow valley, Hidden Valley, with lakes and swamps without outlets.

James Johnson.

FIG. 204. — An esker near Alma, Colorado.

topography. Small depressions and knolls, wavy thick belts interspersed with scattered boulders, and alluvium deposited by glacial
streams are typical features.

Glacio-fluvial Deposits. — Certain deposits characteristic of
alpine glaciated regions are due to the combined action of streams
and glaciers.

Eskers. — These are long, low, narrow ridges composed of
stratified sand, silt and gravel that occasionally are found parallel

Byron Harmon.

FIG. 205. — Bow River Valley, Banff, Alberta. The geomorphic history of this region
is interesting. The mountains, composed of sedimentary rocks, were uplifted; a
great valley glacier occupied the present valley forming the typical U profile.
After the ice melted, the valley was choked with glacial debris and with alluvium
from the surrounding highlands. Now the river is clearing its valley, leaving a
broad glacio-fluvial terrace in the middle ground.

with the walls of glaciated valleys. They are not to be confused
with lateral moraines, which usually are much larger and always are
made up of typical drift. Since eskers are much more typical of
continental than of alpine glaciated regions, further descriptions are
deferred to the discussion of continental glaciation.

Valley Trains.—Below the ends of many valley glaciers, streams deposit thick, crudely stratified beds of alluvium washed from the glacier and from its terminal or ground moraine. The gradients of many glaciated valleys are low; therefore, the weak glacial-born, overloaded streams are unable to carry their sediment very far. As a result, the valleys are soon blocked, and the streams become braided. Much of the debris is subangular, but if carried far from the glacier, it becomes typically stream-rounded. The plain formed in this way resembles a flood-plain, but its position in a steep-walled mountain valley betrays its glacial origin.

TOPOGRAPHY PRODUCED BY CONTINENTAL GLACIERS

Very little is known about the land surfaces beneath the existing continental glaciers of Greenland and Antarctica. Much of Greenland is believed to be a plateau, and the subglacial surface of Antarctica, no doubt, is composed of plains, plateaus and mountains. In both regions the ice sheets are so great that they largely obscure the underlying land.

The areas of North America, over-run by the Pleistocene ice sheets, are well known, and much of their pre-glacial topography is helpful in appreciating the changes that were made to form the present landscape. The northern part of North America, which was almost entirely covered by continental ice sheets, furnishes striking examples of the effects of glacial erosion on many types of land surfaces. The ice completely overwhelmed all of New York (except the higher Catskills), northern Pennsylvania and New England, even covering Mount Washington. Its thickness in central New England must have been more than 6,000 feet. North of the St. Lawrence River the Plateau of Quebec was entirely covered by the Labrador ice sheet. From the Keewatin center the ice spread south, west and north, covering several hundred thousand square miles of the great Interior Plains.

Effects of Glaciation in Mountain Regions. — The White and Green mountains of New Hampshire and Vermont, respectively, are typical illustrations of the effects of continental glaciation on a

mountainous topography. Before glaciation the region apparently
was mature with well-developed drainage, the master streams flowing in broad, old valleys. The total relief was not less than 6,000
feet.

Locally, above elevations of 4,500 feet, this topography was
made more rugged by valley glaciers that existed largely if not
entirely before the last advance of the Labrador ice sheet.

The continental glacier removed sharp peaks, narrow ridges and
spurs, and smoothed and polished the rocks of the mountain slopes.

Elizabeth Worcester.

FIG. 206. — Smarts Mountain, west central New Hampshire. The whole region was
covered by the Labrador continental glacier.

Some pre-glacial valleys were deepened, and their sides were steepened by tongues of ice that moved through them. Most of the
valleys were blocked by drift scoured from the nearby highlands,
thus profoundly changing the pre-glacial drainage lines. Lakes
abound in the smaller debris-filled valleys, although many have been
drained or filled by sediment and vegetation. Thousands of huge
boulders (erratics), carried varying distances by the ice, are found
indiscriminately on valley floors and mountain slopes. Ground
moraines are widespread. Marginal moraines are present, but are
much less abundant. Kames, eskers, drumlins and outwash plains
are numerous.

Opinions differ as to the total effect of continental glaciation on

After U. S. Geol. Survey.

FIG. 207. — A section from the Paradox Lake, New York, topographic map. It shows the rounded hills, lake basins and other evidence of poor drainage. The preglacial relief was probably greater than now. Scale approximately 1 inch to the mile. Contour interval 20 feet.

the topography, but it is apparent that many lowlands were made rougher and more irregular by the glacial deposits, while the mountain slopes, in many places certainly were smoothed both by erosion and by deposits of drift. The profiles of the mountains are very different from those of the alpine glaciated regions of western North

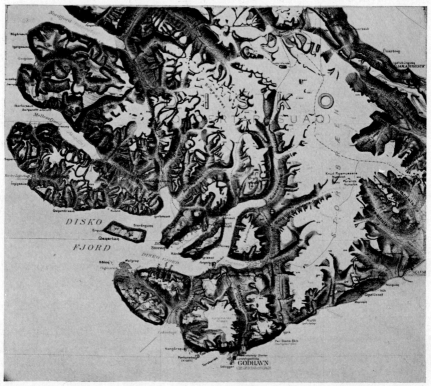

After Geodetic Institute, Denmark.

Fig. 208. — Greenland fiords. The white areas are glaciers. The width of the land area from left to right is about 60 miles. From Godhavn topographic map.

America and are relatively smooth and subdued. How much of this quality is due to pre-glacial erosion and how much is due to glacial erosion and deposition is an open question. In the author's opinion, the latter were exceedingly important.

It has been estimated that in New England the glacial drift deposited by continental glaciers averages 12 to 15 feet in thickness. In some valleys it is very much thicker and, in general, it is much thicker over the lowlands than over the highlands. In a sense, glaciation rejuvenated the region, for the lakes, marshes, and youthful streams that are now cutting on glacial debris, or glaciated surfaces have been superimposed on the well-drained, pre-glacial mature and old topography.

Continental Glacial Erosion of Plateaus.—The great Plateau of Quebec (the Laurentian Plateau) furnishes an excellent example of topography altered by a great ice sheet. The present area of more than 2,000,000 square miles is characterized by a remarkable similarity of surface relief. The pre-glacial surface was a peneplain dotted with monadnocks. The underlying rocks are largely granites and metamorphics of Pre-Cambrian age. Before glaciation these rocks were covered with a thick mantle of residual soil. The Labrador glacier almost completely removed the mantle rock, transporting it in all directions away from the parent snow field. The states bordering the Great Lakes from Illinois to New York received vast quantities, and much was deposited in New England. After removing the soil, the ice "quarried" great boulders from the highly jointed rocks of its bed and transported them far from their source. Perched boulders from Quebec may be seen today high on the slopes of New England mountains. Where quarrying was extensive or where the loose mantle rock was unusually deep, depressions were made in the surface of the plateau. The origin of these gouged basins now occupied by lakes and marshes is in marked contrast to the ground morainal lakes on the plains of western Canada. It should not be understood that there are no morainal lakes on the plateau; as a matter of fact, there are many, but rock-rimmed lakes predominate. Over wide areas the loose material was so completely removed by *early glaciers* that when the last glacier melted it contained comparatively little drift to form moraines. As a result, the present land surface consists of highly polished rocks, a thin postglacial soil, clays left by glacial lakes, and here and there a thin covering of glacial drift. This drift, however, which is quite thick in southeastern Quebec, shows the characteristic deposition of moraines and *kames,* intermingled with glacio-fluvial outwash plains.

The surface of the plateau now stands at an elevation of from 800 to 2,000 feet above sea level. Locally, on top of the plateau, the relief is monotonously low, seldom ranging more than 300 feet in elevation. In some places, however, the topography is irregular and rugged due to gorges and rapids of post-glacial origin. The broad flattish surfaces are characteristic of pre-glacial mature or old topography, while the innumerable lakes, wandering streams and local rugged relief are superimposed details typical of youthful physiographic development.

The present drainage agrees well with the radial movement

Geological Survey of Canada.

FIG. 209. — Part of the glaciated surface of the Plateau of Quebec.

of the ice from the center of the plateau. While the greater number of streams flow toward Hudson Bay, there is drainage outward in every direction from the central highland. Thousands of lakes, many of them hardly more than wide places in sluggish rivers, nestle in the depressions on the plateau surface. Drift in some places has increased the height of the rims of the basins.

Deep, steep-sided, stream-cut valleys, gorges and waterfalls of great size, both pre- and post-glacial in age, dissect the south and east margins of the plateau, giving rise to a rugged topography of magnificent scenic beauty which is entirely out of harmony with the landscape of the surface of the plateau.

Glacial Erosion on Plains. — The Pleistocene continental glaciers covered at least 1,500,000 square miles of the Interior Plains of North America. Advancing over a region of low relief, underlain by very diverse rocks, they wore out large basins in the softer rocks, enlarged river valleys that were parallel to their courses, removed low hills and ridges, and polished the more resistant rocks

Geological Survey of Canada.

FIG. 210. — Beaverlodge Lake. Typical of the region north of Lake Athabaska, Saskatchewan.

over which they moved. In general their erosive work is obscured by the great deposits of drift made when the ice melted, but detailed studies show that erosion was great. In fact, the amount of drift carried and deposited by the glaciers is the best possible evidence of their erosive work.

The Great Lakes of the United States and Canada are perhaps the best example of glacial erosion on plains that can be found. The origin of these basins is discussed in Chapter XI, and need not be described here. Hundreds of other small lakes scattered over the whole glaciated area owe the origin of their basins, in whole or in part, to the erosive power of the ice; yet the total number of gouged basins on the plains is insignificant compared to the number formed by irregular deposition of glacial drift.

Topography of Drift Areas

The variety of landscapes due directly or indirectly to deposits of drift from continental glaciers is very great. Many topographic forms are similar to those made by alpine glacial deposits, but they occur on a much grander scale.

There were four general advances and retreats of the continental ice over central and northern North America. (The last one, Wisconsin, fluctuated so much that in some places it is divided into two glaciations.) Four distinct glacial ages also are recognized in Europe. The last drift sheets were deposited so recently that in many places there have been only slight changes made in their surfaces, which are characterized by poor drainage, youthful valleys, low mounds, thick belts of moraines, kettles and hummocks, oval-shaped drumlins, irregular kames, eskers, and, in humid regions, thousands of lakes and swamps. The drift areas made by the earlier ice sheets but not covered by late drift are deeply weathered, maturely eroded, and exhibit sharp contrasts in topography to that of the most recent drift.

The thickness of the drift varies greatly, due in part to the filling of pre-glacial valleys, and in part to the variable amount of debris carried in different parts of the ice. In southern Michigan the drift in some places is as much as 1,000 feet thick; in some parts of Indiana, its thickness is more than 500 feet. Over much of Wisconsin, Minnesota and Manitoba, it averages about 300 feet. Disregarding the pre-glacial topography, the thickness of the morainic material would limit the present surface relief. But, as a general rule, pre-glacial depressions are more deeply covered than are the pre-glacial highlands; therefore, in some respects, the drift sheets tend to make the existing relief more uniform than it was before the first epoch of glaciation.

Marginal Morainal Topography. — The continental glaciers advanced, not with a smooth regular front, but, rather, in great lobes, from which the ice tended to spread outward. As a result neither lateral nor terminal moraines are distinguishable; therefore, the term marginal moraine best designates the debris deposited at the edges of these glaciers. The moraines were deposited in a highly curved, definitely lobate form. Usually the greatest advance of an ice sheet is marked by a well-defined moraine. Later, after a certain amount of retreat, if wastage of the glacier just about balanced the

FIG. 211. — The edge of a marginal moraine north of Regina, Saskatchewan.

rate of movement, another moraine was formed inside and roughly parallel to the first one. This condition in some regions was repeated several times, thus giving a concentric series of moraines which may be called *recessional moraines.* In other regions the glacial retreat was more uniform without pauses during which marginal moraines could accumulate. Under these conditions large areas were covered by *ground moraines.*

Between the well-defined marginal moraines, one now may find ground-morainal debris and usually stratified clays that were washed by glacial-born streams into lakes hemmed in between the marginal moraine and the ice. Some lakes of this type between two moraines still exist, but many of them have been drained. In other places gravel plains (outwash plains) have buried whatever ground moraine is present, leaving a relatively smooth surface between two moraines.

Individual marginal moraines are thick, wide belts of drift, in some cases traceable continuously for hundreds of miles. Their surfaces invariably are very irregular, being dotted with small depressions, hills and ridges. Where precipitation is great enough, the irregular depressions are now occupied by lakes, peat bogs and marshes in which varying proportions of water, sediment and vegetable material may be found. The surfaces of moraines are from 10 to 1,000 feet in elevation above the surrounding country. The sides may grade gradually into ground moraines or descend steeply to lacustrine flats at their base.

Structure of the Drift. — The structure and composition of dif-

Milwaukee Public Museum Photo.

FIG. 212. — Knobs and kettles near Eagle, Wisconsin.

ferent moraines and of the same moraine in different places vary greatly. In some places the drift is a firm compact clay; in others, a clay matrix is filled with boulders; in still other places, one finds sand, or sand and boulders. These materials grade into one another in all possible proportions. Some of the surfaces of the moraines in the region of the Great Lakes and in Saskatchewan and Alberta have several thousand boulders per square miles. In Michigan and adjacent regions, boulders with a diameter of 8 to 10 feet are common. These are expressions of what one would find throughout the whole thickness of a moraine. The unassorted nature of the material and lack of stratification are striking features (Fig. 185). In many places, however, especially on the morainal borders, irregular, well-stratified lacustrine beds or roughly stratified sands and gravels of outwash plains are interspersed with typical drift. Some moraines occur in well-defined, parallel ridges, but usually the outlines are very irregular, due to repeated slight advances and retreats of the ice.

Knobs and Basins.—Knobs and basins, or *hummocks* and *kettles,*

Geological Survey of Canada.

FIG. 213. — Air view of a ground moraine, southeastern Saskatchewan.

of *two* distinct types are associated with moraines. In the first type the knobs, or hummocks, are composed of *unstratified drift* and with the basins represent simply the irregular surface of a moraine. In the second type the large knobs, called *kames,* are composed of *stratified sand and gravel* of very different origin which will be described in a later section.

Ground Moraines. — A rapidly melting, retreating glacier drops its load indiscriminately over the land surface. The resulting drift constitutes a *ground* moraine. It is *not* arranged in bands or belts as are terminal moraines, but is a thin blanket of debris covering older rocks.   In composition and internal structure, there is no difference between a ground and a marginal moraine.   However, most ground moraines are thinner and their surfaces have lower relief (Fig. 213).   Due to the unequal load carried by the glacier, the ground moraine varies greatly in thickness.   Its surface usually is rough, being covered with knolls and shallow depressions.   In typical ground morainal regions, such as Wisconsin, Minnesota,

George A. Thiel, courtesy Minnesota Geol. Survey.

FIG. 214. — Surface of moraine, Dakota County, Minnesota.

Manitoba and the Northwest Territory of Canada, thousands of shallow lakes and marshes are in the depressions formed by these moraines.   The total area covered by ground moraines in the United States and Canada is far greater than that of other types of moraines and glacio-fluvial deposits combined.   The moraines are thickest far from the centers of accumulation of the continental glaciers; but near the margins of the regions covered by the ice, they are usually thin, having been more or less removed by erosion.   In many areas thick drift completely obscures the pre-glacial topography, but where it is thin, as for example over the central part of

the Laurentian Plateau, it rests as a veneer over the old land surfaces that were modified by glacial erosion.

Drumlins. — Most interesting and conspicuous of ground morainal topographic features are elongate, oval-shaped hills, called
drumlins. These drift hills usually range from 20 to 120 feet in
height; their longer axis invariably is parallel to the direction of
the moving ice. They present a modern "streamlined" appearance,
being two to five times as long as wide, and steepest on the *stoss
or struck* end — the end against which the glacier advanced. Drumlins almost always occur in groups; frequently several hundred are

Milwaukee Public Museum Photo.

FIG. 215. — Side view of a drumlin, near Sullivan, Wisconsin.

together. In southeastern Wisconsin there are at least 10,000 and
hundreds occur in western and central New York. Another large
group is just south of Charlevoix, Michigan.

The origin of drumlins is in doubt. Some glaciologists believe
that they are formed beneath the ice under special conditions, while
others think they result from the erosion of older drift much as
roches moutonnées are formed. Leverett,[1] discussing the origin of
Michigan drumlins, states that:

> "The drumlins are composed of a very evenly mixed stony till (drift),
> stones being distributed through almost every cubic inch of the deposit.

[1] Frank Leverett: *The Pleistocene of Indiana and Michigan.* U. S. Geol.
Surv., Mon. LIII, p. 311, 1915.

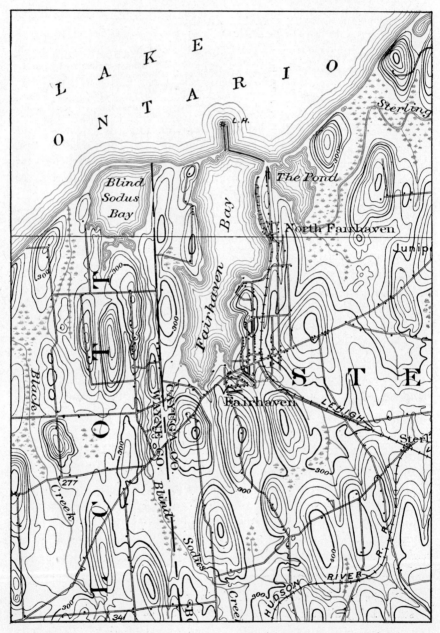

After U. S. Geol. Survey.

FIG. 216.—A section from the Oswego, N. Y., topographic map, showing drumlins, connecting bars, spits and hooks. The drumlins on shore are being cut away by the waves of Lake Ontario. Scale approx. 1 inch equals 1 mile. Contour interval 20 feet.

The majority of the stones are small but some bowlders were noted and small rock slabs are not rare. In most of the exposures the till shows indistinct partings rudely concentric with the surface. The rock slabs do not show, as in ordinary till, all sorts of deposition from vertical to horizontal, such as result from dropping into a deposit, but lie in the plane of the deposits, as if carried by the ice across the surface of the drumlin until lodged in a position that offered least resistance to the ice movement. Most of them show on both their upper and under surfaces striation whose direction generally coincides somewhat closely with the trend of the axis of the drumlin. The position of the rock slabs, the indistinct bedding of the deposit, and the thorough admixture of pebbles seem to bear evidence to the growth of the drumlins by slow accretion."

Leverett goes on to compare the shape of drumlins to shale hills that have been sculptured by glaciers. He also calls attention to furrows, grooves and flutings parallel to the direction of the movement of the ice. These descriptions apply so well to what would happen when *an active glacier shears over stagnant debris-filled ice* that the present writer accepts Leverett's explanation of the origin of drumlins and assumes that deposition starts with masses of stagnant ice over which the glacier rides.

Topography of Glacio-fluvial Deposits

These deposits are of particular importance in connection with continental glaciers. As already indicated in a previous section, small deposits are formed by waters from valley glaciers, but melting of the larger ice sheets liberated enormous quantities of water which spread silt over vast areas. Moreover, the lower portions of the great ice sheets were crevassed and tunneled in such fashion that water must have been an important factor in removing material from beneath and within the ice.

Eskers. — These are the most unusual and conspicuous of all features due to glacio-fluvial action. A typical esker is a long, narrow, rather smooth-surfaced ridge that crosses hills, valleys and marshes indiscriminately, parallel with the direction of movement of the glacier. Some in the United States are twenty miles long. Usually the sides are steep and the top is narrow and rounded. In many cases, but not always, eskers lie in valleys. The material is not typical drift as in the drumlins, but is crudely stratified gravel and silt. It is generally believed that eskers are formed through deposition of silt from streams that occupy tunnels in the ice. These streams, which are formed by the melting of the ice, wash out the fine debris from the glacier. When their channels are blocked so that velocity is reduced, deposition must necessarily follow. The shape of an esker indicates that the tunnels were completely filled with sediment. An alternate theory holds that eskers are formed in stream channels on the surface of the ice and are lowered to their

Milwaukee Public Museum Photo.

FIG. 217. — An esker, near Myra, Wisconsin.

final position when the ice melts. It should be noted that eskers are associated with typical ground morainal topography, although their lower ends may merge into terminal moraines.

Kames. — These steep-sided knobs or hills may be associated with either ground or marginal moraines; they are characteristic, however, of the latter. Their origin, which clearly involves the action of water, is believed to be as follows: The margins of glaciers were crevassed and ragged. Subglacial streams issuing from tunnels in the ice deposited their load in crevasses and in depressions between the ice and the moraines. When the ice melted, irregular mounds, hills and short ridges were left as *kames*. The basins between the present kames represent the areas occupied by blocks of glacial ice before it melted. In some places kames are so numerous and are connected in such fashion that they are called *kame ridges, kame moraines,* or *kame terraces.*

Hummocks and Kettles. — Thousands of small hummocks separated by small steep-sided depressions are scattered over the glaciated regions of North America. Many of the low mounds and

Milwaukee Public Museum Photo.

FIG. 218. — Moulin Kame, Holy Hill, Washington Co., Wisconsin.

hills are made up of typical drift and are characteristic of marginal and ground moraines. Many others, particularly those situated on the glacier side of a terminal moraine are composed of stratified silt. Their mode of formation evidently is the same as that of kames. The kettles are, of course, the depressions left when blocks of ice melted. The general lack of exterior drainage from the individual depressions indicates how recently they were formed.

Outwash Plains.—On the outside of terminal moraines (the side away from the glacier) and the outer edge of drift sheets where no well-defined terminal moraines were formed, streams from the melting ice spread vast quantities of silt in the form of aprons or plains. Where streams issued from the moraines in well-defined channels, no aprons were formed; but where there were no channels to confine them, the silt was spread by many small streams that wandered over their own deposits. The area, thickness and surface slope of the plains vary greatly, depending on the underlying topography, the thickness of glacial ice and the moraines through which the streams cut.

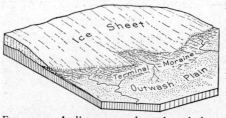

FIG. 219.—A diagram to show the relations of a glacier, the terminal, or marginal moraine and an outwash plain.

Many outwash plains are so nearly flat that they easily may be confused with lacustrine plains, but usually the steeper surface slopes, which are ten feet or more to the mile, indicate their origin. Also their position abutting a marginal moraine is distinctive. The composition of the outwash aprons indicates plainly their origin. Where they fit against

Milwaukee Public Museum Photo.

FIG. 220.—A section of an outwash plain, Sheboygan County, Wisconsin.

marginal moraines (Fig. 219), the material is a mixture of coarse and fine debris, usually the former predominating. With distance away from the moraine, the debris gets finer until at the outer edge of long flat aprons it is mostly fine sand and silt. Clays may be interbedded with sand and gravel at any horizon. The plains clearly are formed much as flood-plains are built by small individual and larger anastomosing streams.

F. B. Hanley, Minnesota Geol. Survey.
FIG. 221. — A lacustrine plain, Minnesota.

Lacustrine Plains. — When the last continental glaciers melted from North America, the discharge of glacial water must have been both long-continued and very great. This water collected in depressions of all sizes from a few square feet to hundreds of square miles. Streams brought sediment to these lakes, where it was deposited in well-stratified form. Many lakes received sediment for hundreds or thousands of years until their floors were covered with thick beds of clay and silt, which completely obscured underlying irregularities of the original floors. Finally some of the lakes were drained and their very flat floors became the lacustrine plains that we see today.

After U. S. Geol. Survey.
FIG. 222. — The former Lake Agassiz. The scale is about 1 inch equals 400 miles.

Lake Agassiz. — One of the finest examples of lacustrine plains in North America is the bed of the extinct glacial Lake Agassiz (Fig. 221). This lake was hemmed in on the west by moraines and groups of low hills, on the south in part by moraines but largely by the Lake Superior highland and by groups of low hills and on the north and east by the retreating Keewatin ice sheet. As the glacier waned, the lake followed it north. The position of the lake fluctuated somewhat, but during its whole history it embraced an area of 110,000 square miles, which is greater than that of the present combined five Great Lakes of United States and Canada. At first the outlets of the lake drained to the Mississippi River, but later, after the ice retreated far to the north, drainage was established to Hudson Bay. The Red River of the north and its tributaries now drain the southern portion of the region to Lake Winnipeg. This lake with lakes Manitoba and Winnipegosis are the largest remnants of former Lake Agassiz, but all three occupy rock or drift-rimmed basins, and, therefore, are of somewhat different origin.

Now thousands of square miles of the bed of the former lake in Minnesota, North Dakota, Manitoba and Saskatchewan constitute a remarkably level plain, which is underlain by a thick deposit of stratified clay and very fertile silt.

The Driftless Area

A region of special interest to physiographers is the driftless area of Illinois, Iowa, Wisconsin and Minnesota. Although it is entirely surrounded by characteristic glacial topography, this region, some 10,000 square miles in area, shows no evidence of ever having been glaciated. This fact is remarkable when we remember that all four advances of the great ice sheets extended farther south than this region. It might be expected that *some* of the ice lobes from the two great glaciers would fail to meet, but it is not apparent why *all* should have avoided this region, although it has been suggested that the highland south of Lake Superior diverted the flow-lines of the ice sufficiently to cause the lobes to miss the driftless area.

The topography of the driftless area is that of a well-matured, stream-eroded region in marked contrast with the youthful surrounding glaciated regions. The Mississippi River, which drains the drift-

After U. S. Geol. Survey.

FIG. 223. — Mature topography of the driftless area. From the Lancaster, Wisconsin, Iowa and Illinois topographic map. Each little square is 1 square mile. Contour interval 20 feet.

less area, flows in a deep valley in which there are wide valley flats and floodplains. Its principal tributaries have thoroughly dissected the plateau-like upland which stands some 400 feet above the river.

Milwaukee Public Museum Photo.

FIG. 224. — Mississippi River and the mature topography of the driftless area.

The drainage exhibits a definite dendritic pattern, which also is in sharp contrast to the aimlessly wandering streams a few miles to the north.

INDIRECT EFFECT OF PLEISTOCENE GLACIATION ON TOPOGRAPHY

If we assume that the Pleistocene continental glaciers of North America, Europe, Greenland, Antarctica and South America reached maximum size at about the same time, it is evident that locking up such great amounts of water in the form of ice would have several very important effects on both the land and the oceans.

Lowering of Sea Level.—It is estimated by Daly [1] that if all the present ice of Greenland and Antarctica were melted and re-

---

[1] R. A. Daly: *Glacial-Control Theory of Coral Reefs.* Proc. Am. Acad. of Arts and Sciences, Vol. 51, No. 4, p. 172, 1915.

turned to the oceans, it would raise their level between 35 and 110 feet. He also estimates that the combined area of the Pleistocene glaciers that have now disappeared was at least 6,000,000 square miles and that the average thickness was 3,600 feet. If we further assume that there is about the same amount of water from year to year in the atmosphere, the amount of water taken from the oceans to form the Pleistocene glaciers would reduce sea level by some 165 to 200 feet. It is generally believed that a maximum glacial age lasted at least 40,000 to 50,000 years; therefore, if the surface of the oceans were lowered some 200 feet, waves would have had time to cut broad shelves which would be submerged when the ice melted. Such shelves have been found in many places. Lowering of the water level also would have an important effect on the formation of coral reefs (Chap. XV).

Attraction of the Ice. — It is a well-known fact that high mountains on the borders of the present continents, through their local gravitative attraction, raise the sea level on their borders. For this reason the Pacific Ocean water is higher on the Chilean Coast than is the Atlantic Ocean on the coast of Argentina at the same latitude. The same principle applies to continents heavily loaded with ice. Since the Pleistocene glaciers were most extensive in the northern hemisphere, it follows that as glacial maxima were reached, ocean water would be drawn from the southern to the northern hemisphere, thus lowering the water level of the southern oceans an estimated 15 to 30 feet.

Depression and Re-elevation of the Land. — The weight of the amount of ice indicated above, undoubtedly, was great enough to depress the land somewhat during maximum stages of glaciation. The amount of such depression and the following re-elevation after the ice melted are impossible to determine with certainty, but several authorities have placed the depression and elevation of the land in the vicinity of Lake Superior at not less than 1,500 feet, with smaller amounts near the borders of the ice-covered areas. These movements, both downward and upward, must have been exceedingly slow. That both sorts of movements occurred is amply demonstrated by the following facts.

The Champlain Marine Stage. — Late in the Pleistocene Epoch an arm of the sea extended up the St. Lawrence River to Lake Ontario, also covering the basin of Lake Champlain. This seems to represent the results of subsidence of the land due to the weight of the Labrador ice. Later the land rose to its present height, draining the sea water back to the ocean and leaving the drainage lines as they are today.

Evidence of Marine Fossils. — Marine fossils of late Pleistocene or Recent age are now found 200 feet above sea level on the coast of Maine, 500 feet at the north end of Lake Champlain, and 600 feet in elevation near James Bay. All indicate glacial or post-glacial submergence followed by recent uplift of the land.

Effects on Present Topography. — Fluctuations in the height of land due to glacial loading and unloading affected the present topography of the land in many ways. On the plateau of Quebec many streams were so rejuvenated by recent uplifts that they have been able to cut deep post-glacial gorges. Wave-cut plains, probably formed during a glacial stage when sea level was low, now stand high above the seas. Marine beaches have been raised, submarine canyons were formed at low-water stages, coral reefs were developed to unusual thickness. Many of these conditions are discussed in detail in later chapters.

PLEISTOCENE GLACIAL AGES

In both North America and Europe four major advances and four retreats of the Pleistocene continental glaciers are recognized. It is not known with certainty that during the retreats the ice completely melted at the sites of original accumulation, but it is evident that it withdrew from very large areas on both continents. The glacial and interglacial ages as recognized in North America are shown in the following table. A fifth age, the Iowan, was once supposed to have occurred between the Illinoian and Wisconsin glaciations. It was, however, probably only a slight advance, after a partial retreat, of the Illinoian ice sheet.

Pleistocene Glacial and Interglacial Ages
in
North America

Recent (interglacial or post-glacial age)
Wisconsin (fourth glacial age)
Sangamon (interglacial age)
Illinoian (third glacial age)
Yarmouth (interglacial age)
Kansan (second glacial age)
Aftonian (interglacial age)
Jerseyan or Nebraskan (first glacial age)

Recognition of Interglacial Ages. — It is evident from the preceding discussion that each glacier deposited a layer of drift over the land when the ice melted. Thus we speak of Nebraskan, Kan-

G. M. Schwartz, courtesy Minnesota Geol. Survey.

FIG. 225. — Red drift (R) of Early Wisconsin age overlain by outwash (O) which in turn was covered by Late Wisconsin gray drift (G), Twin Cities region, Minnesota.

san, Illinoian or Wisconsin drift as the material deposited by glaciers that existed during these ages. In some places an older drift sheet is covered by a younger one. In other places the contact between two layers of drift of different ages is well exposed. In still other regions successive glaciers did not cover the same areas. Detailed work extending over a large part of the glaciated areas of North America and Europe has made possible the recognition of four distinct drift sheets. The criteria for distinguishing the different layers of drift vary from place to place. The Jerseyan drift, where exposed in New Jersey and Pennsylvania, is much eroded and *deeply weathered*. The thick residual soil indicates a very long

Milwaukee Public Museum Photo.
Fig. 226. — Loess on Sangamon soil over Illinoian drift, Peoria, Illinois.

period of chemical weathering and contrasts sharply with the relatively fresh debris of Wisconsin age. In Iowa and western Illinois the ancient Kansan drift was weathered to a depth of 10 to 20 feet, forming a sticky clayey material called *gumbotil*. Over this, *loess* (wind-blown dust) accumulated to a depth of several feet before the advance of the Illinoian glacier, which, in turn in some places was covered with soil and loess before the Wisconsin glacial stage. The great length of time of an interglacial age is indicated not only by a large amount of weathering of the older drift, but also by the presence of partially eroded peat bogs between glacial drift of two ages. It is evident that the older drift surface was pitted with kettles and lake basins similar to those we can see today on the Wisconsin moraines. The interglacial climate was warm and humid enough to permit the growth of vegetable material in quantities sufficient to make thick beds of peat before the new advance of the glacier.

Duration of the Pleistocene Glacial Epoch

Much has been written on the length of time represented by the Pleistocene Epoch. The whole question involves theoretical estimates of the time required for the accumulation of each ice sheet, the rate of movement of the ice, the melting time after a maximum advance, the duration of interglacial ages, and the length of time since the *last* maximum stage of glaciation in North America and Europe. Many of the factors are indeterminate; therefore, no accurate statement can be made. Based on analysis of all the conditions involved in the problem, it is *estimated* that the elapsed time from the beginning of the Nebraskan (Jerseyan) age to the end of the Wisconsin glaciation in North America is about 1,000,000 years.

Relative Weathering of Drift. — Comparison of the drift deposited by the four North American continental glaciers reveals some interesting facts. The Wisconsin drift is only slightly weathered; its boulders are fresh and only small amounts of residual soil have formed. The Illinoian drift is much more weathered than the Wisconsin and the thickness of residual soil, gumbotil and loess are comparable to that of the Nebraskan drift, where the latter is covered by the Kansan; thus indicating that the Sangamon and Aftonian interglacial ages were approximately the same length. Where the Kansan drift is covered, it is *much* more weathered than are the *covered* drift sheets of Nebraskan or Illinoian ages; therefore, it is believed that the length of the Yarmouth interglacial age was at least twice as great as either the Aftonian or Sangamon ages.

The Retreat of the Last Ice Sheet. — It is impossible, with our present knowledge, to say how long a time has elapsed since the continental glaciers *entirely* disappeared from Europe and North

America. However, it is possible to estimate with a considerable degree of accuracy the time that has elapsed since the last ice melted from northern Germany; Long Island, New York; Niagara Falls, New York; and central Minnesota. This time has been placed by many glaciologists *at about 25,000 years*. If this estimate is correct, central Quebec could hardly have been uncovered more than 2,000 or 3,000 years ago. Such estimates are important in that they help one to understand something of the time required to produce changes in land surfaces by erosion since the glacial drift was deposited.

Several methods have been used to determine the length of the postglacial epoch in both Europe and North America, but only two are reliable. These are: first, through the study of varved clays; and, second, through determination of the rate of recession of postglacial waterfalls.

Varved Clays. — Early in the present century Baron Gerard de Geer of Stockholm worked out a method for determining the rate of retreat of glaciers based on the annual layers of silt and clay deposited in lakes which bordered the melting ice. The method has been applied in eastern North America by several glaciologists, but particularly by Ernst Antevs.

Through studies of present lakes fed by glacial streams, it has been determined that the streams bring in considerable material in the spring and summer, but very little, if any, in the winter. The coarse silt is quickly deposited, but the finest sediment remains in suspension for some time, gradually settling to the bottom of the lake during the winter. An annual layer or *varve* consists of a coarse, light-colored, lower part, which grades into a finer grained, usually darker colored upper part. The lower part represents summer and the upper part winter deposition. The thickness of the varve indicates the amount of summer melting and the capacity of the streams to bring sediment to the lake. A series of varves will, therefore, through their varying thickness, show fluctuations in climate. By studying the varved clays of many ancient glacial lakes and by matching the varves in different deposits, thus carrying the chronology from one region to another, the elapsed time since the ice retreated from certain regions can be determined with great exactness. Antevs states that the error is not more than one per cent. He shows, for example, that the last ice sheet retreated from Hartford, Connecticut, to St. Johnsbury, Vermont, a distance of 170 miles, in approximately 4,400 years, or at an average rate of 200 feet a year. In the Timiskaming, Ontario, region the rate of recession was much more rapid, being 454 feet annually. The studies of varved clays have not yet been completed, either for North America or for Europe. It may not be possible ever to complete them, due to lack of abandoned clay-filled lake basins, but it may be expected that the work will be continued until eventually the time-table of the last ice retreat will be quite definitely known.

.*The Recession of Waterfalls.* — Niagara Falls and St. Anthony Falls, in Minnesota, have been extensively studied for many years, and the rates of the recent recession are well known. Both waterfalls are post glacial in origin and both began their activities immediately after the last retreats of the ice from their sites.

Ontario Department of Mines.

FIG. 227. — Varved clay, west side of Angekum Lake, Ontario.

The rate of recession of Niagara Falls for the last one hundred years, based on sketches and surveys (the first accurate survey was made in 1842), is 4.5 feet a year. If this rate had been maintained throughout its whole history, the 7-mile gorge would have been cut in 8,200 years. But the rate of recession depends upon several factors, such as the geological conditions (here quite uniform), the width of the gorge and the amount of water that passes over the falls. The latter is indeterminate over a long period of time, but is known to have varied greatly and is less now than before water was diverted for power purposes. When all the factors are considered, the estimates of time required for the falls to recede from the Ontario escarpment to their present position range from a minimum of 20,000 years to a maximum of 30,000 or possibly 35,000 years.

St. Anthony Falls at Minneapolis may be used as an even more definite record of the time that has elapsed since the Wisconsin ice sheet uncovered this region. The falls have receded about 7 miles at a rate (during the last 250 years) of 2.4 feet a year. At this rate, it required about 15,400 years to cut the present gorge. However, the ice was about 700 miles south of the Falls at the time the last retreat began. Estimating the rate of recession at 300 feet a year, it required 12,300 years for the glacier to melt back to the Falls. This, added to the time required for the Falls to recede to the present position, amounts to 27,700 years, a figure which agrees fairly well with others as the elapsed time required for the complete melting of the Wisconsin ice.

THE AGE OF GLACIAL TOPOGRAPHY

Recalling the discussion of topographic ages in Chapter VIII, it was noted that age is determined by the *extent of erosion* rather than by the *number of years* during which erosion has taken place. There is, however, a certain rough correlation in case of glaciation between time and amount of erosion.

The topography produced by Wisconsin glaciers, whether erosional or depositional, is *youthful*. This applies with equal force to both mountains and plains. The drainage is poor, waterfalls, lakes and marshes are numerous, many streams still wander aimlessly. The Illinoian drift areas, where not covered by more recent drift, are better drained, streams are now in permanent valleys. The age is late or early maturity. The Kansan and Nebraskan drift regions being *much* older are, in most places, distinctly *mature* in age.

With few exceptions all well-glaciated mountainous and plateau regions, regardless of the nature or age of glaciation, are *youthful*. Some valleys occupied by glaciers of an early age have lost most of their youthful characteristics and may be classified as *mature*. Interesting topographic unconformities occur where a glacial topography has been superimposed on a pre-glacial mature or old region.

The Cause of an Ice Age

While it is not pertinent to a discussion of land forms, one of the questions most commonly asked by students is, "What causes an ice age?" An equally pertinent question is, "Are we now in an interglacial age, and, if so, when will a new ice age overwhelm us?" If one answers these questions frankly, he will be obliged to say that he does not know. It is entirely possible that we are living in an interglacial age and that a few thousand years from now ice again will creep down from the north covering central North America. However, there is no certainty of this. Millions of years may elapse before the earth is again as extensively covered with glaciers as it is right now.

Many hypotheses have been advanced to explain great changes of climate that are known to have occurred on the earth. Any theory deserving of consideration must explain not only the ice ages that have occurred at widely separated times in earth history, but their opposites as well. Fossils in Pleistocene strata, to say nothing of older formations, show alternations of warm and cold climates. During a cold climate, as the glaciers spread southward, musk oxen migrated as far south as Oklahoma, Missouri and Pennsylvania; Arctic foxes reached southern France. During interglacial ages the warm climate mastodon wandered north to Alaska, and the hippopotamus reached England; while rhododendrons now growing only in warm humid regions lived near Innsbruck in the Alps.

In earlier geologic ages one finds evidence of climates warmer than the present in the coal beds of Antarctica, fossil palm leaves in Colorado, cycads, figs and magnolias in the Yukon territory. These are mere suggestions of the definitely proven fact that for every part of the earth there have been significant climatic changes, warm and cold, wet and dry, all through earth history.

It is impossible to present adequately, in small space, all the hypotheses that have been proposed to explain changes of climate through the ages. Good summaries have been made by Chamberlin,[1] Schuchert,[2] Humphreys,[3] and Brooks.[4]   Brief statements regarding some of the more widely accepted theories follow:

Hypothesis of Wandering Poles. — Many people have suggested that the north and south poles may have moved far from their present positions. If this were true, there would be corresponding changes in climatic zones which would help materially to explain changes in climate. However, the earth is as rigid as steel. Any great shift of the poles would leave its evidence in structure of the earth. No forces are known that would cause such a change, and astronomers tell us that the poles move only 21 minutes, about 23 miles, in any direction from a central position.

Continental Drift. — This hypothesis has been discussed in another connection in Chapter II. If the outer shell of the earth could move at will in any direction over the inner core, it would explain many difficult geologic problems, including *some but not all* climatic changes. The doctrine of permanency of continents and ocean basins is directly opposed to the hypothesis of continental drift, and no forces are known that are adequate to move the continents from one place to another as required by the hypothesis.

Carbon Dioxide Hypothesis. — Carbon dioxide in the atmosphere acts as a thermal blanket holding radiant heat from the land near the earth's surface. Chamberlin has shown that an increase in the carbon dioxide content of the atmosphere would cause the temperatures over the earth to rise, while a pronounced decrease in amount would cause a corresponding reduction in temperature. Due to unusually active weathering of rocks (Chapter VII), which might well accompany or follow great uplifts of the land, the atmosphere would be depleted of its carbon dioxide, thus bringing on a colder climate and eventually glaciation. The weathering processes would also use up water from the atmosphere, thus further reducing temperatures over the earth.

[1] T. C. Chamberlin and R. D. Salisbury: *Geology.*   Vol. III, Chap. XIX. Holt, 1906.
[2] Charles Schuchert: *Historical Geology.*   Chap. XLV.   Wiley, 1915.
[3] W. J. Humphreys: *Physics of the Air.*   Part IV.   Lippincott, 1920.
[4] C. E. P. Brooks: *Climate through the Ages.*   Part II.   Coleman, 1826.

The glacial stage at length would be terminated by a direct return of carbon dioxide to the air from the ocean; by the ice covering which would reduce weathering of the rocks; by the increase in secretion of lime by marine organisms which would release carbon dioxide; and by many other attending factors.

Humphreys (op. cit.) shows mathematically that an increase of 100 per cent or a decrease by 50 per cent of the present amount of carbon dioxide of the air would have very little effect on earth temperatures. However, a larger decrease might be effective in bringing about a glacial climate.

Volcanic Dust Hypothesis. — Dust in the air reflects or absorbs and radiates heat from the sun back into the outer atmosphere. It is an observed fact that for some time after great explosive volcanic eruptions less than a normal amount of solar heat is received by the earth. There is good evidence that preceding both the Permian and Pleistocene ice ages, there was unusually great volcanic activity. It is natural, therefore, to assume that vulcanism has played a part in bringing about glacial climates. The hypothesis fails specifically when attempts are made to correlate periods of vulcanism with the known advances and retreats of Pleistocene glaciers. There are quantitative objections also that have not been overcome, but it seems probable that volcanic dust may be a subordinate factor in bringing about a glacial climate.

Effects of Diastrophism. — Profound elevations of major portions of the continents accompanied by great mountain growth have occurred repeatedly during earth history. Particularly marked diastrophism preceded Proterozoic, Permian and Pleistocene glacial epochs. Elevation of a large land area by 1,000 feet would cause a reduction of temperature over that area of approximately 3 degrees Fahrenheit. Moreover, changes in the height and position of land masses would cause changes in both the position and strength of moisture-laden winds. In strategic places, such as the East or West Indies and between Asia and Alaska or between Greenland and North America, such disturbances would change the positions of ocean currents. It is evident that continental uplift and mountain growth may well be strong contributing factors in causing glacial climates.

Variations in Solar Radiation. — It has long been known that there are variations in the amount of radiation given off by the sun. At times of maximum sun spots, which occur at approximately 11-year intervals (a maximum stage was due in 1938 or 1939), more heat is given off by the sun than in normal times. On the earth at mid-latitudes temperatures are *reduced*, atmospheric circulation is increased, clouds are more abundant, and *precipitation is greater*.

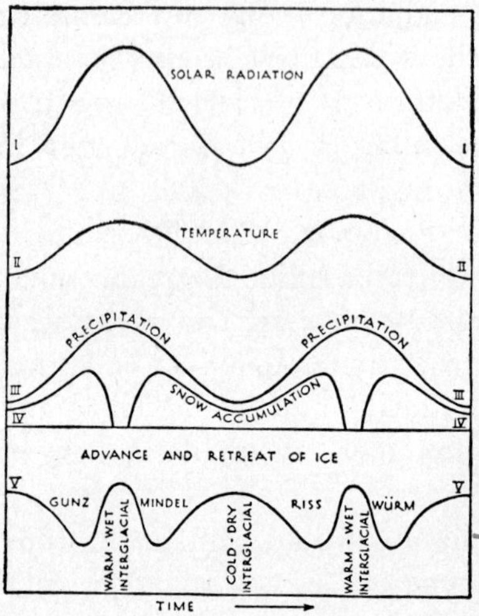

In view of the short periods of known variability in the sun's radiation, many scientists have proposed that there may be longer periods, possibly thousands of years in duration, when the sun radiates first much more, then less heat than normal. Huntington has suggested that in times of great but relatively short-lived activity the sun's atmosphere would be so dust-laden that the solar heat would be shut in, thus bringing about a glacial climate on the earth. Later, as the sun's atmosphere cleared, earth temperatures would rise and a warm interglacial age would follow the melting of the ice.

Simpson's Hypothesis. — Recently Sir George Simpson[1] has proposed a somewhat startling hypothesis based on large, long-continued cyclic variations in solar radiation. The whole paper is worthy of most careful consideration, for it seems to explain the known facts regarding Pleistocene

After Sir George Simpson, with permission of "Nature."

FIG. 228. — Curve I shows two complete cycles of solar radiation. Curve II represents the mean temperature of the world as a whole during those cycles. Curve III is the curve of precipitation which follows directly the curve of solar radiation. Curve IV is the curve of snow accumulation for high latitudes. Curve V shows four glaciations as worked out in the Alps with three interglacial epochs. The Gunz glaciation is the American Nebraskan, the Mindel is our Kansan, etc.

---

[1] Sir George Simpson: *Ice Ages.* Nature, Vol. 141, No. 3570, pp. 591–598, 1938.

glaciation to an astonishing degree.   Abstracts from his paper follow:

Increased solar radiation causes increased circulation of the earth's atmosphere, increased evaporation and increased cloudiness. Increasing cloudiness, however, would cut off some solar heat from the earth.   In the tropics increased radiation would merely cause increased precipitation, but toward the poles there would be more snowfall.   This would cause the formation of glaciers in high latitudes and at high altitudes.   As the solar radiation continues to increase, a time would come when more precipitation in high latitudes would fall as rain, melting and evaporation would increase, the annual accumulation of snow would decrease due to greater melting and evaporation.   Thus there would be a warm, wet interglacial age at the time of maximum solar radiation.   Then as radiation decreased toward normal, a second glacial age would come on. During a period of minimum radiation there would be a longer, cooler and drier interglacial age.

Two complete cycles of solar radiation would explain the four advances and retreats of the Pleistocene ice sheets, together with relatively short, wet, warm interglacial ages between the first and second and third and fourth glaciations.   It also would explain the longer Yarmouth interglacial age between the second and third advances of the ice.

Conclusions. — After discussing these various hypotheses regarding climatic changes, we find ourselves about where we started. No single hypothesis seems to explain all known conditions.   The Simpson hypothesis, while possibly adequate for Pleistocene glaciation, fails to account for the extremely long interval between Permian and Pleistocene times when there were no known continental glaciers.   It may well be that more or less accidental combinations of favorable conditions were responsible for the great ice ages.

REFERENCES

1. W. C. Alden: *Physiography and Glacial Geology of Eastern Montana.* U. S. Geol. Surv., Prof. P. 174, 1932.
2. Ernst Antevs: *The Recession of the Last Ice Sheet in New England.* Am. Geog. Soc. Research Ser. No. 11, 1922.

3. ———: *The Last Glaciation.* Am. Geog. Soc. Research Ser. No. 17, 1928.

4. W. A. Bentley and W. J. Humphreys: *Snow Crystals.* McGraw-Hill Book Co., 1931.

5. Louise Ann Boyd: *Fiord Region of East Greenland* with discussion of Physiography by J Harlen Bretz. Am. Geog. Soc. Sp. Pub. 18, 1925.

6. R. T. Chamberlin: *Glacier Movement as Typical Rock Deformation.* Jour. Geol., Vol. 44, pp. 93–104, 1936.

7. T. C. Chamberlin: *Recent Glacial Studies in Greenland.* Bull. Geol. Soc. Am., Vol. 6, pp. 199–220, 1895.

8. ——— and R. D. Salisbury: *The Intimate Structure and the Movement of Glaciers,* in Geology, Vol. 1, pp. 308–323. Henry Holt and Co., 1904.

9. A. P. Coleman: *Ice Ages, Recent and Ancient.* Macmillan and Co., 1926.

10. W. L. G. Joerg: *Editor, Problems of Polar Research.* Am. Geog. Soc., Sp. Pub. No. 7, 1928.

11. E. M. Kindle and F. B. Taylor: *Niagara Folio.* U. S. Geol. Surv., Geol. Atlas of the U. S. No. 190, 1913.

12. Frank Leverett and F. B. Taylor: *The Pleistocene of Indiana and Michigan and the History of the Great Lakes.* U. S. Geol. Surv. Mon. 53, 1915.

13. M. A. Peacock: *Fiord Land of British Columbia.* Bull. Geol. Soc. Am. No. 46, pp. 633–696, 1935.

14. Otto Nordenokjold and Ludwig Meeking: *The Geography of the Polar Regions.* Am. Geog. Soc. Sp. Pub. No. 8, 1928.

15. Sir George Simpson: *Ice Ages.* Nature, Vol. 141, No. 3570, pp. 591–598, 1938.

16. R. S. Tarr: *The Yakutat Bay Region, Alaska.* U. S. Geol. Surv. Prof. P. 64, 1909.

17. Warren Upham: *The Glacial Lake Agassiz.* U. S. Geol. Surv. Mon. 25, 1895.

CHAPTER XI

LAKES AND SWAMPS

Lakes are inland bodies of standing water. There is no sharp distinction between lakes and ponds or between lakes and the unusually wide portions of rivers. Some types of coastal lakes grade imperceptibly into lagoons or bays. The water of lakes may be

E. G. Fine.

FIG. 229. — Electra Lake, San Juan Mountains, Colorado. A beautiful glacial lake about 2 miles long.

fresh, brackish or salt, but fresh water lakes are far more abundant than the other types.

Nearly all lakes are definitely associated with other distinctive types of topography. Some are related to streams in early stages of development; others are characteristic of old stream-formed topography. Many lakes occur in recently glaciated regions, while others are found in regions where wind, waves, volcanoes or diastrophism have been dominant processes in changing the form of the land. Because of these varied relationships, the discriminating study of lakes in relation to their environment is of particular interest to the physiographer who is laying a foundation for investigations in the field of geomorphology. In many cases more than one process has contributed to the origin of a lake basin. For these reasons the discussion of lakes is grouped in a single chapter although it involves some repetition.

Lakes appeal to many sorts of people. From an esthetic point of view our clear blue glacial lakes at the foot of great mountains or surrounded by green meadows or primordial forests are unsurpassed by any other object of nature's handiwork. We go to them in order that we may enjoy their beauty and the majesty of their attending scenery. Lakes furnish food and cheap transportation; they serve as reservoirs which yield water for great cities, thirsty fields and hydro-electric power. Even lakes of moderate size are important factors in tempering the climates of adjacent regions. In these and a host of other ways lakes are of benefit to mankind.

DISTRIBUTION

Lakes are among the most widely distributed of all topographic features. They are found at all latitudes from the equator to the extreme limits of all the continents except Antarctica. They abound especially in the high latitudes of North America, South America and western Europe. Many coastal lakes are situated on the very borders of the continents, but there are thousands in the glaciated interior of North America and scores of very large lakes of different origin in the heart of Africa. They occur in great numbers in regions of mountains, plateaus and plains, particularly in humid, recently glaciated regions; yet hundreds are found on the floodplains of rivers. There are many lakes in deserts and semi-arid regions, although usually in such regions they are shallow and appear and disappear, or at least are greatly expanded and contracted seasonally. Other lakes are found on islands and in the craters of extinct volcanoes.

Some Remarkable Lakes of the World

Lakes vary so greatly in surface area, depth and position with · respect to sea level that it is impossible to describe them adequately in limited space. The five great lakes of the United States and Canada—Superior, Huron, Michigan, Erie and Ontario—constitute the greatest chain of lakes in the world. Other great groups are lakes Albert, Edward, Kiva, Tanganyika, Nyasa and Victoria in east central Africa; lakes Manitoba, Winnipegosis and Winnipeg in Manitoba; and Athabaska, Great Slave, Great Bear and associated lakes in western Canada. The highest large lake known is Titicaca in Peru and Bolivia; the largest in surface area is the Caspian Sea (really a salt lake) in Eurasia; the deepest is Baikal in Siberia. The lowest lake in the world is the Dead Sea (a salt lake) in Palestine. Lake Chad in the Sudan, central Africa, although only 8 to 20 feet deep, has the greatest range in surface area of any known lake. In dry seasons its area is only 10,000 square miles, while in rainy seasons it is nearly 50,000 square miles. Every continent except Antarctica has lakes of notable interest and importance. The following table indicates the great variation in size and position of some important lakes.

NOTABLE LAKES OF THE WORLD

Name	Square Miles	Altitude of Surface. Datum is sea level	Depth in feet
Caspian (Sea)	170,000	−85	3,200
Chad	10,000–50,000	840	8–20
Superior	31,200	602	1,000
Victoria	26,000	3,800	240
Aral	25,050	160	1,200
Michigan	22,500	581	870
Huron	22,320	581	700
Nyasa	14,200	1,500	2,300
Baikal	13,000	1,700	5,600
Tanganyika	12,000	2,700	4,706
Great Bear	11,200	390	270
Titicaca	3,260	12,500	700
Dead (Sea)	360	−1,268	1,300
Crater	25	6,239	2,000

THE ORIGIN OF LAKES

Two things are necessary for the existence of lakes: first, there must be a basin to hold the water; and, second, there must be a supply of water to fill or partially fill the basin. Most fresh-water lakes have streams flowing into them (*inlets*) and also streams flowing from them (*outlets*). The bottom of the basin must be *below* the outlet as long as the lake exists. Nearly all salt lakes have no natural outlets; evaporation usually prevents the water from filling the basin and running over the lowest place in the rim.

In the following discussion different types of lake basins are grouped under the earth processes dominant in their origin. However, it should be noted that in many cases more than one dynamic agent was involved in the formation of a particular basin. For example: the five Great Lake basins of the United States and Canada are the combined result of glacial gouging, glacial deposition and crustal warping. Some of the basins in western Nevada were formed by faulting followed by stream and wind erosion and deposition. Many coastal lake basins are due to subsidence of the land followed by the work of *littoral currents* which deposit *connecting bars* across the mouths of the drowned valleys.

Glacial Lake Basins

The close relationship between areas covered by Pleistocene glaciers and the distribution of lakes in North America has already been indicated in Chapter X. Similar associations are found in western Europe and, in fact, in all regions covered by Pleistocene or Recent glaciers. Glacial lakes are far more numerous than all other types put together; they occur by the hundred if not by the thousand in Wisconsin, Minnesota, Manitoba, the plateau of Quebec, New England, Finland, and in high, glaciated mountains all over the world.

Basins in Ground Moraines. — During the last retreat of continental glaciers from Europe and North America, the debris that they carried was dropped in irregular fashion as the ice melted. The depressions were filled with water from the melting ice or were filled later by direct rainfall or seepage water from the surround-

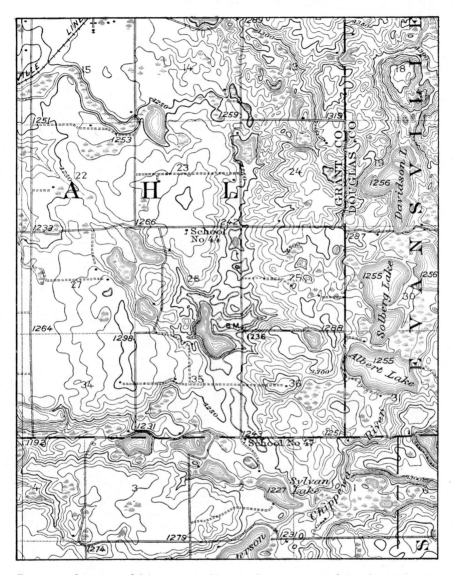

FIG. 230. — Swamps and lakes, many without outlets, on a ground moraine. Note the unfilled depressions. Barrett Topographic Map, Minnesota. Scale about 1 inch to the mile, contour interval 10 feet.

ing ground. Rapidly retreating valley glaciers also left ground
moraines in mountain and plateau valleys.

Many ground morainal lake basins had no outlet at the time
they were formed, and thousands still are without outlets; but in
most cases their waters are kept fresh through circulation by seepage out of the basins. Most of these lakes are relatively small,
having shallow depths and surface areas ranging from a few acres
to 10 or 20 square miles. However, some are very large, and

Fig. 231. — A chain of lakes, Arapaho Valley, Colorado. Some are behind moraines.
The lakes in the foreground are in gouged basins. In the distance a lateral
moraine dams the valley.

their basins, which may be in part rock basins, are due to glacial
gouging or crustal warping as well as to the deposition of drift.
More lake basins are found in ground moraines than in all other
situations combined.

Basins Behind Terminal or Marginal Moraines. — Many
chains of lakes in glaciated valleys owe their position to successive
terminal moraines made during the retreat of valley glaciers. Each
moraine marks a halt in the last retreat of the ice. Some of the
moraines are very high; therefore, the basins are very deep. The
depth of water in Grand Lake, Colorado (Fig. 232), a terminal

morainal lake, is 285 feet. Thousands of basins of similar origin can be found in the various glaciated regions of the world.

Basins Behind Lateral Moraines. — Lateral moraines give rise to lake basins of two distinct kinds.

Valleys Dammed by Lateral Moraines. — Many alpine glaciers extend far down their valleys. Their lateral moraines dam unglaciated tributary valleys or glaciated valleys in which the ice does not

F. Fortson.

FIG. 232. — Grand Lake, Colorado, from the air. A glacial lake hemmed in on the north by a lateral moraine and on the west (at the right) by a terminal moraine. The loop of this moraine is clearly shown by the heavy growth of trees. The lake is 1½ miles long.

reach the main valley. The lakes thus formed, like terminal morainal lakes, usually are short-lived, for the lakes soon overflow and outlets are cut through the moraines.

Lakes Between Lateral Moraines and Valley Walls. — In many valleys occupied by alpine glaciers, lateral moraines were deposited some distance inside the valley walls. Where landslides or alluvial deposits have connected the rock walls of the valley with the lateral moraine, long narrow lakes may be found.

Gouged Basins. — Both valley and continental glaciers are capable of gouging basins of considerable size out of solid rock. There are hundreds of such lake basins in New York and New England that were formed by the Labrador ice sheet. The Finger lakes of central New York State are in pre-glacial valleys that were deepened by a continental glacier. Some drift is found at the lower ends of the lakes, but the basins are chiefly in solid rocks.

R. D. Crawford.

FIG. 233. — Boss Lake in a gouged basin, Sawatch Range, Colorado.

Gouged basins (Fig. 199) are very abundant in alpine glaciated valleys, particularly at the heads of glacial benches, just below steep cliffs and in cirques. Some of these basins are surprisingly deep in proportion to their area, and many have been called, incorrectly, crater lakes. Because they are surrounded by solid rock they make exceptionally good locations for dams where there is need for storage reservoirs.

Ice Dammed Basins. — Valley glaciers may completely block tributary valleys, thus making lake basins. The Marjelen Sea in

Switzerland is an example of such a lake. Usually these basins are shallow, rarely deeper than the thickness of the glacial dam.

Due to fluctuation in the length of the glacier, to crevasses and to the fact that streams can cut outlets easily through the ice, such lakes usually are quite temporary in nature. Some, however, in the past seem to have endured for a long time. Waters has described great alluvial terraces in the Columbia River valley which he believes were formed by wave action in a great lake. The lake, in turn, was formed by the Okanogan lobe of a glacier of Wisconsin age that dammed the Columbia Valley and forced the river to find a new outlet (through the Grand Coulee).

Ice Jams. — Anyone who has seen the ice "go out" of large rivers in northern latitudes must be impressed by the efficacy with which large blocks of ice lodged against bridge piers, sand bars or sharp bends in the valleys block and pond the streams. In many places the water backs up for miles, overflows the river banks, and accumulates in low places on flood-plains, etc., forming temporary lakes.

Fluvial Basins

Streams have been aptly described as "the mortal enemies of lakes," yet under certain conditions they form lake basins. Usually such basins are shallow and the lakes are relatively short-lived.

Plunge Basins. — At the foot of a great waterfalls, pot-holes are of common occurrence. Where the falls recede more rapidly than streams below, the falls deepen their valleys, the potholes or plunge basins increase in size and eventually become large enough to be called lakes. The most notable examples of basins of this type that have been described are in the Grand Coulee in Washington.

Flood-Plain Basins. — Two types of basins are common to flood-plains — oxbows and irregular depressions.

Oxbow Lakes. — These shallow basins in abandoned meanders have already been described in Chapter VIII. They are characteristic of mature and old topography. Usually the basins soon fill with vegetation and become swamps or marshes.

Irregular Lakes. — On many flood-plains small, shallow depressions are left, due to <u>irregular deposition of alluvium</u>. After floods or in regions of heavy precipitation, these basins are filled with water, making lakes without natural outlets.

Raft-dammed Basins. — Occasionally rivers dam their own valleys, forming natural lakes. This action is particularly common where meandering streams in humid regions under-cut their banks

Photograph U. S. Army Air Corps.   Pub. by authority Miss. River Commission.
FIG. 234. — Wentworth cut-off on the Mississippi River Flood-plain. Similar natural cut-offs result in the formation of ox-bow lakes.

and dislodge trees and underbrush. This <u>tangle of vegetation may lodge on a sand bar or island</u>; gradually more trees, drift wood and sediment accumulate behind the original obstruction until a dam miles in length may be formed. The Red River of Louisiana accumulated a series of remarkable rafts of this sort in the early part and middle of the 19th century. Not only was the river ponded, but the lower ends of many tributaries were converted into lakes.

Delta Lakes. — Lake Ponchartrain in Louisiana is a good example of this sort of a lake. Alluvium was deposited on the Mississippi delta around a low subsiding region, thus producing a basin. It is probable that subsidence of the land due to loading of the Gulf coast by the delta contributed to the formation of the Basin. Another example is the Salton Sea, a salt lake without an outlet made by the delta of the Colorado River, which dams the Imperial Valley of southern California. At one time this great intermontane trough was continuous with the Gulf of California. The river coming in from the east gradually built its delta across the valley, finally making such a complete dam that the Salton Sea was formed. During most of the latter part of the last century, the river found its way across the delta, along the east margin, to the Gulf of California; but in 1890 and again in 1905 it broke out of its channels and swept to the north into the Salton Sea, doing great damage to the region.

Basins Behind Alluvial Fans. — In arid regions the concentrated drainage of canyons in highlands may cause alluvial fans to be deposited on the adjacent plains or valley floors. If it happens that two streams on opposite sides of a valley discharge their alluvium on the valley floor, the fans may completely dam the valley forming a lake basin. Free [1] has described numerous basins of this variety in the arid regions of western United States. For example, Owens Lake in eastern California is separated from Searles Basin by an alluvial divide, although both lie in the same great structural trough.

Wind-Formed Basins

Wind forms lake basins both through erosion and deposition; the eroded basins are generally much larger, but since they are chiefly confined to semi-arid and arid regions the lakes that they may contain are rarely permanent.

Wind-Excavated Basins. — Hundreds of small basins have been scoured out by the wind in Wyoming, eastern Colorado and western Nebraska. All have been carved out of poorly cemented sandstones, shales or unconsolidated alluvium. Many have been enlarged by man-made dams and are now used as reservoirs for

[1] E. E. Free: Bull. U. S. Dept. Agric. No. 54, pp. 6, 34, 35, 39, 50, 56, 1914.

storing water for irrigation purposes. These are characteristic of semi-arid regions all over the world.

Lakes Between Dunes. — The irregular distribution of dunes formed by the wind has already been noted. In Dune Park, Indiana, at the south end of Lake Michigan, depressions between the dunes are filled with rain water forming lakes. In the great dune area of San Luis Valley, Colorado, depressions are filled with water from streams that flow down the west slope of the Sangre de Cristo Mountains. Some of these lakes are permanent and are

FIG. 235. — A wind-eroded lake basin a mile long, half a mile wide and very shallow, eastern Colorado.

well-stocked with trout. In the "sand hills" region of northeastern Colorado and western Nebraska, a struggle between wind-drifted sand and the streams of the area has been going on for centuries. The streams are intermittent and feeble, while the winds are strong. As a result, hundreds of small valleys have been dammed by the wind-blown sand with consequent formation of small ephemeral lakes.

Basins Due to Diastrophism

Earth movements give rise to lake basins in many different ways. Some of the largest lakes known are in whole or in part the results of diastrophism. General uplift of a region or folds and faults of various kinds may be involved in the crustal disturbances; structural basins may be formed or rocks may be so shattered and weakened by faults that erosion, particularly chemical action, forms basins. Diastrophism also is an important agent in changing fresh water lakes to salt lakes.

Relic Lakes. — On the continental shelves there are many shallow depressions. If through crustal movements the shelves are lifted out of water, lakes will result. Yucatan and Florida are recently emerged land areas and many of their lakes are believed to have originated in this way.

Basins Between Mountain Ranges. — During the uplift of the Rocky Mountains in late Cretaceous or early Eocene times and also in the Miocene and Pliocene epochs, the land was elevated very unevenly. Large intermontane basins were left down while the mountains rose around them. Many of these basins were occupied by lakes that are now extinct, but the former presence of the lake water is plainly indicated by well-stratified shales and other sediments containing fresh water fossils that were deposited in the lakes. Good examples of such extinct lakes are found near Bozeman and Livingston, Montana, and in South Park and San Luis Valley, Colorado. A very large lake of this type once covered much of the Uinta Basin in western Colorado and eastern Utah. In this lake vast quantities of shale containing vegetable material were deposited. These shales, known as the Green River formation, constitute a very large potential source of petroleum, for the organic material can be heated and through proper methods of retorting and refining, converted into lubricating and fuel oils.

Synclinal Basins. — It might be expected that downwarped areas would produce lake basins, but usually it is difficult to determine whether the land has actually been downfolded or whether the ground around the relatively depressed region has been elevated. Many basins that *appear to be synclines* are known, but none, at least on the North American continent, can be cited with assurance as being of this origin. Some of the African Lakes, notably Edward and George, are believed to occupy downwarped basins, but they may prove to be left down when the surrounding land was upwarped.

Basins Behind Anticlinal Dams. — During the long period of a river's history, crustal movements may occur in such fashion that anticlines rise across a river valley, causing lakes to form behind the dam. Several such dams are described by Free in the great troughs of the Basin and Range Province of western United States.

Fault Basins. — Two types of fault lake basins are of very common occurrence. They are single faults which result in tilting of the land, and relatively depressed blocks bounded by at least two faults, but in many cases by more.

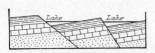

After U. S. Geol. Survey.

Fig. 236. — A diagram to show the occurrence of lakes on tilted fault blocks.

Single Fault Basins. — Basins of this type are found in many parts of the world; examples are San Andreas and Crystal Springs lakes located on the San Andreas fault a few miles south of San Francisco, California. The fault has been active for many years. Repeated movements in the fault zone have fractured and displaced the rocks so that erosion has been rapid. Due to the combined activities of earth movement and erosion, the two lake basins have been formed along portions of the great San Andreas rift. Other long narrow lake basins, such as lakes Abert and Warner in eastern Oregon, are found on tilted fault blocks.

Ramp or Rift Basins. — Basins in great troughs or depressions that lie between two more or less parallel faults are found in many parts of the world. Typical examples are the so-called "Rift Valleys" of Africa, the Dead Sea-Jordan trough (graben or ramp) in Palestine, and supposedly similar structural valleys in Germany, British Columbia and in the Basin and Range Province of western United States.

Originally such troughs were regarded as actual depressions of land or *graben*, following Suess, who defined a graben as *"a depression produced by the subsidence of a strip of land between two normal faults"* (Fig. 55). Later Gregory introduced the terms *rift* and *rift valleys*. According to his definitions, *"a rift (fault) is a displacement due to gravitative subsidence,"* and *"a rift valley is produced by the subsidence of a strip of land between two parallel rifts."* In other words, rift valleys and graben valleys are formed in the same way. Still more recently Willis[1] has introduced the terms *ramp* and *ramp valleys*. *"Ramp is an upthrust, a compressive fault, the opposite of rift."* *"Ramp valley is a valley produced by the ramping or upthrusting of two masses one on either side of the intervening strip"* (Fig. 56).

The Dead Sea basin and many of the basins of African lakes, including Albert, Tanganyika, Edward and Nyasa have long been regarded as rift or graben basins. Willis has shown that this interpretation is incorrect and that the Dead Sea lies in a ramp valley, as do lakes Albert and Tanganyika. Lake Edward is in a downwarped depression or in one left down when the surrounding land was upwarped. Both upfaulting of the sides and downwarping of the trough appear to have taken place in case of the Nyasa basin. In view of Willis'[2] remarkable analysis of the African (so-called) rift valleys, all other structural depressions with similar characteristics should be re-examined in order to determine whether or not they are rift or ramp valleys.

The Rocky Mountain Trench. — One of the most remarkable troughs in North America is the Rocky Mountain Trench which extends northward for 1,000 miles from the Flathead lakes of western Montana through British Columbia to the Yukon territory. The width of the trench varies from 3 to 14 miles and averages about 6 miles. On the sides, mountains rise to elevations of 10,000 feet above the floor of the valley. Numerous lakes occur in the trench, and several large rivers, notably the Columbia and Kootenai, head in it.

At one time the trench was supposed to be a rift valley or graben and near the International Boundary it has that apparent structure, although in the light of Willis' work in Palestine and Africa it must be re-examined to determine whether it is actually a rift or ramp structure. Further north near Golden, British Columbia, the structure is found to be that of an eroded *horst* rather than a graben.

[1] Bailey Willis: *Dead Sea Problem: Rift Valley or Ramp Valley?* Bull. Geol. Soc. Am., Vol. 39, pp. 490–542, 1928.
[2] Bailey Willis: *East African Plateaus and Rift Valleys.* Carnegie Institution of Washington, Publication No. 470, 1936.

Our present knowledge indicates that the trench was blocked out by complicated faulting and folding and later was subjected to great stream and glacial erosion.

Basins Due to Landslides, Mudflows or Slumps

On the walls of steep canyons in mountainous and plateau regions, slumps and landslides are of common occurrence. They also are found on gentle slopes where the underlying shales, clays or

U. S. Geol. Survey.

Fig. 237. — Slumgullion mudflow, Colorado. The great flow, 6 miles long, dammed Lake Creek, making a lake more than 2 miles in length.

decomposed igneous rocks are so saturated with water that gravity causes the land to move. In earthquake regions landslides are very numerous on both steep and relatively gentle slopes.

Landslide Basins. — Large landslides may very effectually block valleys, dam streams and form lakes. Most such lakes soon overflow; the outflowing stream cuts through the obstruction and drains the basin. However, very large slides create thick dams that may retain the water for a long time. Many such conditions are known in the Alps and in the mountains of western North

America.   The Gros Ventre slide of 1925 (see Fig. 291), which occurred on the western side of the mountain of that name, made a lake basin, part of which has endured to the present time.

Mudflow Basins. — There are all gradations between land-slides, mudflows and stream floods, but the mudflow contains more water than the landslide and more mud than the stream flood.   A large mudflow is capable of carrying large boulders and trees; its motion is that of a viscous substance.   Lake San Cristobal in south-western Colorado is a remarkable example of a large lake in a basin formed by the Slumgullion mudflow, which moved six miles down a comparatively gentle slope and filled the main valley with many thousands of cubic yards of debris.

Slump Basins. — Near the base of many canyon walls and on shale hills and ridges, small irregular slumps give rise to basins which may be filled with water that runs down the higher land surfaces.   Such basins usually are shallow and the lakes that they contain are short-lived.

Solution Basins. — These are particularly abundant in regions underlain by limestones.   They may be limestone sinks which are so numerous in Yucatan, Florida, Kentucky and southern Illinois; or they may be cavities made in limestones that outcrop at the sur-face of the ground (Fig. 298).   The former attain depths of many feet; the latter are invariably shallow.   Tiny lakelets occur in solu-tion depressions in many kinds of rock other than limestone.   Small solution basins in massive granite rocks are very abundant in many regions.

Basins made by Waves or Shore Currents

Connecting bars formed by *littoral currents* are able to block completely the mouths of many bays, converting them into lakes (Fig. 273).   Also waves may build offshore bars in such fashion that the water behind them becomes lagoons.   Under favorable conditions the lagoons may be shut off from the adjacent bodies of water (either oceans or large lakes) leaving small lakes back of the bars.

Volcanic Basins

Lake basins due to volcanic activity are of several different types. The basins may be made by lava dams; they may occur on the irregular surfaces of a lava flow; or they may be situated in the *craters or calderas* of extinct volcanoes.

Lava-Dammed Basins. — Where a valley already has been formed by stream, wind or glacial erosion, a lava flow from a central

U. S. Dept. of the Interior.

Fig. 238. — Crater Lake, Oregon.

type of volcano or from a fissure may dam the valley, giving rise to a lake basin. Beautiful Lake Tahoe in California is of this type. Very large lakes now drained were formed in comparatively recent times by lava dams in the Yukon River Valley and in the Rio Grande del Norte Valley in New Mexico. Other lava-dammed basins, both extinct and modern, are situated in western Oregon and Washington.

Crater Lakes. — Lakes occupying the craters of dormant or extinct volcanoes are known throughout the volcanic regions of the

world.   Typical occurrences are in Italy, France, Germany, the
Philippine Islands, the East Indies, New Zealand, Alaska, Mexico,
California, Arizona and Nevada.

Crater Lake, Oregon. — This lake, one of the most famous in
North America, partially fills a deep, circular depression in the old
volcano, Mount Mazama, which is situated in the Cascade Mountains of western Oregon.   The present basin is roughly circular in
form with a maximum diameter of 6½ miles.   Its depth from the
highest point on the rim to the lowest place on the lake floor is
3,975 feet.   The maximum depth of the lake water is 1,980 feet.
Because of the unusual beauty of the lake and its surroundings, and
because of the extraordinary geologic conditions involved in the
origin of the basin, the region was made a National Park in 1902.

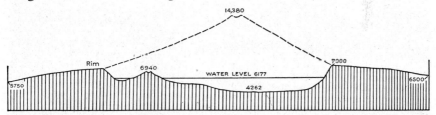

FIG. 239. — A profile through Crater Lake and Mount Mazama (reconstructed).   The
elevations are in feet above sea level.   The exact height of the original mountains
is not known.

Authorities differ as to the origin of Crater Lake Basin.   There
is general agreement that the original Mount Mazama was a volcanic mountain whose *composite cone* was built up to a height of
from 12,000 to 15,000 feet above sea level.   During a dormant
stage, great glaciers accumulated on the higher slopes.   The first
period of glaciation was followed by more volcanic activity; then
came a long period of more intense glaciation with the production
of deep glacial valleys.   From this stage in the history of the region,
opinions are divided regarding the subsequent events that account
for the present basin.

One group, led by Diller, believes that due to adjustments beneath the mountain, the whole top of the mountain subsided, completely engulfing some 15 to 17 cubic miles of rock material that
composed the mountain above the rim, together with the material
that occupied the present depression.   Another group represented

by Smith and Swartzlow [1] seriously questions the collapse hypothesis and presents much convincing evidence to the effect that the top of the mountain was blown off by a violent explosion. They find pumice and other fragmental materials believed to represent the shattered rocks of the mountain scattered over an area 80 miles east and about 40 miles north and south of the present lake. The volume of this material is estimated at more than 11 cubic miles and, of course,

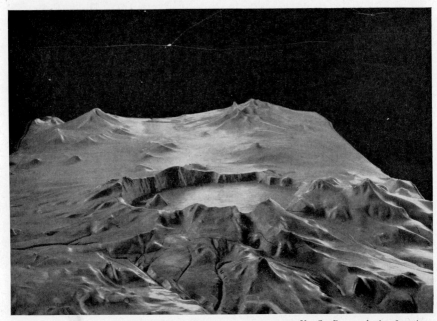

U. S. Dept. of the Interior.

FIG. 240. — A relief model of Crater Lake, Oregon, and adjacent regions. Note the wide glaciated valley in the right foreground channeled by a postglacial stream.

much fine material could have been washed away since the explosion.

Following the collapse or explosion, there was more volcanic activity when three subsidiary volcanic cones were built up on the floor of the basin. Two of these are covered by the present lake water, but one, Wizard Island, projects above the surface of the lake.

The last events in the history of this region were another period

[1] Warren D. Smith and Carl R. Swartzlow: *Mount Mazama: Explosion versus Collapse.* Bull. Geol. Soc. Am., Vol. 47, pp. 1809–1830, 1936.

of glaciation as shown by glacial grooves on the rocks of Wizard Island and stream erosion.

The basin in which Crater Lake rests has been called a *caldera*, which is defined as *an enlarged volcanic crater*. If the explosion hypothesis is correct, as now seems probable, the basin should be called a crater, since it was actually formed by volcanic action without notable enlargement through other processes. The lake is fed by direct rainfall and snowfall, run off from the rim, and by underground springs.

Basins Due to Organic Agencies

In general, lake basins made by organic agencies, including man, are relatively small and of recent origin.

Basins Due to Vegetation. — According to Russell, many shallow lakes hemmed in by moss and other vegetation are found in the tundras of North America and Eurasia, bordering the Arctic Ocean. He suggests that they are formed by accumulations of vegetable material around slowly melting snow banks that last well into the summer. Several years' accumulation would result in a distinct basin.

Beaver Ponds. — The industrious beaver must not be overlooked when considering the origin of lake basins. Beavers have proven their ability to make dams, and the products of their efforts, widely scattered over North America, are numbered by the thousand.

Buffalo Wallows. — Hundreds of shallow basins on the plains of North America are believed to have been made by buffalo. These animals found water holes near springs and seepages, and apparently many wallowed or rolled in the water and mud in order to cool themselves. Quantities of mud were carried away in their hairy coats, leaving the present depression.

Man-Made Basins. — Man, a recent actor on the stage of the earth's surface, has made artificial lakes and reservoirs for many years, but with the development of engineering sciences his *recent* achievements far surpass all former efforts. Building dams out of earth, rocks, logs, sheet iron and, especially, reinforced concrete, he now rivals nature in the construction of lake basins. He not only makes lakes where there were none before, but he enlarges and strengthens basins already made. As human beings demand more and more water for hydro-electric power, irrigation, or domestic and municipal supply, man meets the challenge and builds larger and larger storage space.

Sutherland [1] lists more than 600 dams in the world that are 100

Courtesy U. S. Reclamation Service.

Fig. 241.—Boulder dam and part of Lake Mead, the largest man-made lake in the world. When full the lake will be more than 115 miles long and will contain 30,500,000 acre feet of water.

feet or more in height. There are unrecorded thousands less than 100 feet high. In one section of India alone it is estimated that there are 43,000 earth dams less than 50 feet high in use.

Some of the world's great dams and reservoirs are listed below. Each dam is more than 100 feet high, and each reservoir stores more than 900,000 acre feet of water when it is full. One acre foot

[1] Robert A. Sutherland: *Dam Building Reaches a Climax.* Engineering News-Record, Dec. 10, 1936, pp. 807–815.

of water is sufficient water to cover an acre of land to a depth of one foot. An acre foot equals 315,829 gallons. Multiplying this number by 30,500,000, the storage capacity (in acre feet) of Lake Mead, we find that the Boulder dam is capable of storing in Lake Mead 9,632,784,500,000 gallons of water!

SOME GREAT DAMS AND RESERVOIRS OF THE WORLD

Name	Location	Height in feet	Capacity of reservoir behind the dam in acre feet
Almanor	United States	135	1,308,000
Aswan	Egypt	174	4,040,000
Big Meadows	United States	130	1,300,000
Boulder (Lake Mead)	United States	726	30,500,000
Bridge River	Canada	157	1,250,000
Chelsea (Bitobee)	Canada	100	1,980,000
Coolidge	United States	249	1,300,000
Dnieprostroy	Russia	168	900,000
Don Martin	Mexico	105	1,124,000
Elephant Butte	United States	306	2,637,000
Fort Peck	United States	270	19,500,000
Gatun	Panama	115	4,413,000
Grand Coulee	United States	540	9,610,000
Hamilton	United States	154	1,000,000
Hume	Australia	142	1,250,000
Krishnarajah Sagara	India	146	1,110,000
Martin (Cherokee Bluffs)	United States	145	1,620,000
Mettur (Cauvery)	India	214	2,150,000
Norris (Cave Creek)	United States	240	2,710,000
Pathfinder	United States	210	1,070,000
Quabbin Reservoir	United States	170	1,270,000
Ricobaya	Spain	326	960,000
Roosevelt	United States	280	1,637,000
Saluda	United States	208	2,300,000
Seminoe	United States	260	910,000

THE SOURCES OF LAKE WATER

Lake water is derived chiefly from streams that flow into lake basins. However, some lakes are fed directly by meltwater from glaciers or snow banks; others receive their supply from direct precipitation or immediate run off from the surrounding land. Still others, and this includes many glacial and solution lakes, get their water from underground sources. Many of them are fed by springs, but in some cases seepage water that moves through the ground from higher elevations is the chief source of water.

Salt Lakes

In western North America and in other arid and semi-arid regions of the earth there are many salt lakes. A large majority of them are relics of older fresh or salt lakes. Great Salt Lake in Utah with a present average area of about 2,000 square miles (the area fluctuates periodically from 1,750 to 2,170 square miles) is the remnant of fresh water Lake Bonneville, whose maximum area was 19,750 square miles. Carson, Pyramid, Winnemuca, Walker and Honey lakes in western Nevada — all salt lakes with a present combined area of less than 800 square miles — are remnants of the salt lake Lahontan that attained a surface area of 8,922 square miles during Pleistocene times. The Caspian, Dead and Aral seas are examples of unusual salt lakes.

Scores of small playa lakes, many of them intermittent, are found in the arid and semi-arid regions of western North America, as well as in Chili, Peru and other arid countries.

Fresh water lakes may become salt or salt lakes may become fresh as a result of changes in climate. Also, due to diastrophism which may change the outlet or cut off an inlet, a fresh lake may become salt. In any case where evaporation is greater than the inflow of water, the lake tends to become salt. A salt lake partially filling a basin becomes fresh when excessive inflow causes the basin to overflow, thus creating an outlet and establishing currents through the lake which gradually wash out the salt water. The salt of salt lakes usually is not derived directly either from salt beds or sea water, but rather from the chemical weathering of rocks and the drainage of the mineralized solutions into the basin.

The beds of many extinct salt lakes may be recognized by deposits of various salts, such as sodium chloride, potash and borax that were precipitated as the lakes dried up. Some of these deposits were formed long ago and have been deeply buried by sand, clays or other sediments washed or blown into the old lake basins. Present salt lakes yield commercial salts of various kinds. In 1936 the value of the salt produced from Great Salt Lake amounted to $168,700.00. From Searles Lake in California, potash, borax and sodium salts are being produced in large amounts. During the World War, when importations of potash minerals were shut off from the United States, potash was recovered in commercial quantities from the brines and muds of salt lakes in western Nebraska and other regions.

LIFE HISTORY OF LAKES

With the exception of fluvial lakes that occur on flood-plains, deltas and valley flats, nearly all lakes are themselves youthful and are representative of topography of youthful age. There are several reasons for this. As we have already learned, the great majority of all lakes on the earth today are of glacial origin. The glaciers that formed their basins were of Pleistocene or Recent age. Since the lakes were formed there has not been time for streams to drain them or for vegetation or sediment to fill their basins. Alpine glacial lakes are usually in youthful topographic regions of high relief. Lakes of arid regions may be situated in a topographic environment of any age, yet youthful types are more common.

The Fate of Lakes

Even the largest and deepest existing lakes must ultimately disappear. However, the time required for their extinction will vary tremendously, depending on their own characteristics and on extraneous attending conditions.

Lowering of Outlets. — Streams flowing from lakes deepen their outlets, thus draining lake basins whose bottoms are above the level of the stream-cut valley.

Filling of Basins. — Lake basins are filled in various ways. Assuming a uniform amount of water, it is evident that as a basin is filled the water level rises. This permits a greater outflow and aids in deepening the outlet. Thus filling is complementary to lowering the outlet in draining the lake.

Filling by Sediment. — All streams that flow into lakes bring in more or less sediment which is deposited in the basin. The amount varies greatly. Some of the New England streams which flow from one lake to another carry very little sediment into the lower lakes, while streams in semi-arid regions like the Colorado River carry enormous amounts. It is estimated that this river will deposit annually 137,000 acre feet in Lake Mead. The filling of lakes in this way is well illustrated by the deltas that are being built by many streams at the present time. Slopewash from their borders also contributes sediment to many lakes.

Filling by Wave-Action. — Waves are cutting into the shores of large lakes and most small lakes much of the time. The debris thus loosened is washed into the basin, gradually filling it.

FIG. 242. — Sketch to show the draining of a lake and the development of a topographic unconformity. In (B) the streams that are dissecting the lake floor are making youthful valleys in contrast with the more mature topography of the surrounding highlands.

Wind Filling. — Large amounts of dust and sand are blown into arid lakes by the wind. Also in some lakes both ancient and modern volcanic dust has been blown into basins, in some cases in incredibly great quantities. The extinct lake Florissant in central Colorado which was largely filled by volcanic dust in Oligocene or early Miocene times is one of the most remarkable localities for certain types of fossils known.

Filling by Vegetation. — On the shallow borders of many lakes vegetation accumulates, gradually growing farther and farther into the lake. In glaciated regions thousands of lakes have been converted into peat bogs, marshes and muskegs. In many places the filling has been complete and new land results. Also some plants, especially algae, help to precipitate calcium carbonate from solution. In Pyramid and other lakes in Nevada enormous amounts of material have been accumulated from the lake water.

Filling by Animals. — Numerous lime-secreting shell animals live in lake waters. When they die the shells accumulate on the lake floor, thus helping to fill the basin.

Filling by Landslides, Avalanches, etc. — Lakes in mountains and plateaus at the foot of steep cliffs receive much material brought in by landslides, mudflows, avalanches,

D. F. Higgins.

FIG. 243. — A lake basin nearly filled by vegetation, Colorado.

etc. Huge heaps of boulders, split off by frost action from adjacent cliffs, are found in mountain lakes all over the world.

FIG. 244. — A typical cirque lake in Colorado that is being rapidly filled by boulders that fall from adjacent cliffs. The snowbanks aid greatly in this process.

Obliteration of Basins by Glaciers. — Advancing glaciers may remove morainal dams and destroy lake basins. This evidently has happened in many cases in the past and is of common occurrence in regions of modern glaciers.

Warping of Basins. — The shorelines and terraces of many ancient lakes show unmistakable evidence of earth movements. Warping is the most common type. If, as is conceivable, a basin is sufficiently upwarped, the whole lake would disappear.

The History of the Great Lakes

The history of the Great Lakes, as worked out by Leverett and Taylor,[1] shows in dramatic fashion the processes involved and the changes that have taken place in the physiography of the region to develop the lakes as we know them now. Only a brief outline can be presented here, but the whole history should be read by all who wish to know the details of the subject.

Pre-glacial Topography. — Before the Pleistocene glaciers moved south from the Keewatin, Patrician and Labrador centers, the basins where the Great Lakes are now were broad river valleys with free drainage to the sea. The whole region seems to have been considerably higher than now, and the valleys were bordered by higher land.

Early Glacial Stages. — During at least one of the three glacial stages preceding the Wisconsin, the lake basins existed essentially as they are today, except that in case of some of the lakes the land on which they stood was higher above the sea. The exact age of these first basins is in doubt, for the Wisconsin glaciation obscured the details of previous glacial action.

The Wisconsin Glacial Stage. — With the retreat of the ice of the Wisconsin stage, the record of the history of the lakes becomes relatively clear. It is indicated by both the glacial and lake deposits, which show the extent of the lakes and the changes that have taken place in their area, their outlets and the surrounding topography. However, the lake history is complicated by minor advances and retreats of the ice, by irregularities of topography of the region, by variations in direction of retreat of the ice, and

[1] Frank Leverett and F. B. Taylor: *The Pleistocene of Indiana and Michigan and the History of the Great Lakes.* U. S. Geol. Survey, Mon. 53, 1915.

by differential elevation of the land during and following the last occupation of and retreat from the region by the ice. Some of the details of these conditions are shown by different marginal moraines, by warped shorelines, raised beaches and by the former outlets of the lakes that do not now drain them.

Lake Maumee Stage. — This represents an early stage in the history of the lakes (Fig. 245). Great lobes of ice covered most

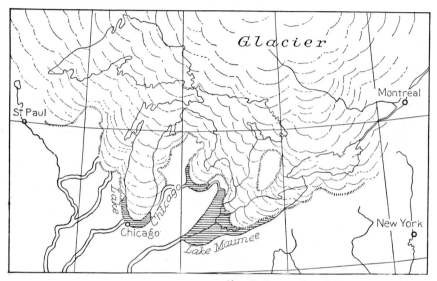

After Taylor and Leverett, U. S. Geol. Survey.

Fig. 245. — The Lake Maumee stage in the history of the Great Lakes. In this series, figures 245-249, each succeeding stage marks a further retreat of the ice. Note the many changes in the outlets of the lakes as well as the differences in size and positions of the lakes.

of the present sites. Meltwater from the retreating ice impounded by the ice on the north and moraines and high land on the south formed the small crescent lakes Chicago and Saginaw, as well as the larger triangular-shaped Lake Maumee. The water level of these lakes was so high that outlets were formed through the Wabash and Illinois rivers to the Mississippi. Further north, drainage from the melting ice also reached the Mississippi. Figure 245 and the following figures in this series show only generalized conditions. Due to fluctuations in melting and to advances and retreats of the ice front, there were oscillations in the depths and areas of the lakes which are clearly shown by their beaches.

Lake Whittlesey Stage (Fig. 246). — Between the Maumee and Whittlesey stages, Lake Maumee, due to recession of the ice, grew into Lake Arkona which covered the site of and was about three times the size of present Lake Erie.

Lake Whittlesey stood at a higher level than Arkona due to a *readvance* of the ice, particularly the Huron lobe. On the south-

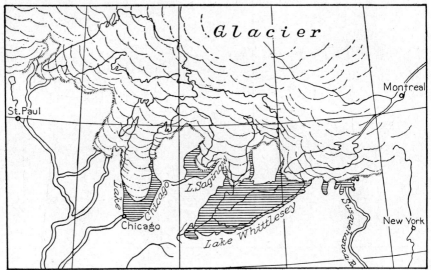

After Taylor and Leverett, U. S. Geol. Survey.

FIG. 246. — The history of the Great Lakes, Lake Whittlesey stage.

west the lake level was slightly below the Wabash River outlet; therefore, the lake drained northward around the thumb of Michigan into Lake Saginaw, thence across Michigan through Grand River to growing Lake Chicago and down the Illinois to the Mississippi. By this time the ice had melted from the Finger Lakes region in New York, and drainage reached the Atlantic Ocean through the Susquehanna.

Lake Duluth Stage. — Continued retreat of the ice, particularly the Superior and Huron lobes, permitted the formation of glacial Lake Duluth, and the growth of Lake Chicago almost to the size of present Lake Michigan. There were also significant changes further east. The Illinois River outlet from Lake Chicago to the Mississippi persisted, but the Susquehanna outlet was cut off due to the lowering of the water in western New York. A new outlet from the east tongue of Lake Lundy was formed along the present Mohawk and Hudson valleys to the Atlantic.

Lake Algonquin Stage. — This stage represents the greatest expansion of water in the history of the Great Lakes. The generalized

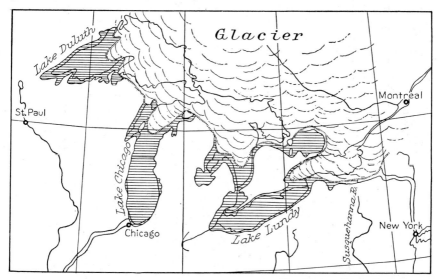

FIG. 247. — The history of the Great Lakes. Lakes Duluth, Chicago and Lundy stage.

map (Fig. 248), however, does not show the details of the long, complex history of the region.

At first Lake Algonquin occupied only the south part of the Huron basin, including Saginaw Bay. The outlet was through the St. Clair and Detroit rivers to Lake Erie.

When the ice withdrew sufficiently, it permitted Early Lake Algonquin to combine with Lake Chicago, and the outlets were divided between the St. Clair and Illinois rivers. It is probable that the outlet across Ontario from Georgian Bay region to Lake Iroquois was not yet open.

Later, the basins of Superior, Michigan and Huron were covered by Greater Lake Algonquin, which also was expanded far over the Georgian Bay basin. At this stage there apparently was only one outlet, which was across Ontario from the expanded Georgian Bay to Lake Iroquois. The former outlets through the Illinois and St. Clair rivers were above the lake-level.

Then came the first notable uplift on the north, due to the unloading of the land by the waning ice sheet. This cut off the direct outlet to Lake Iroquois, and forced the water of Lake Algonquin

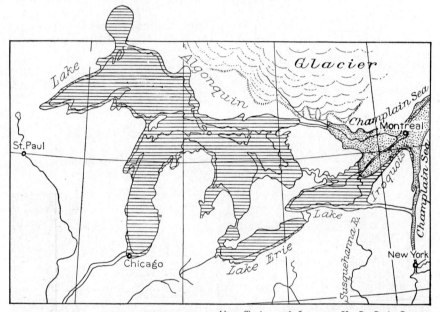

After Taylor and Leverett, U. S. Geol. Survey.

Fig. 248. — The history of the Great Lakes, Lake Algonquin stage. Note the marine invasion from the east. Recent observations indicate that the sea did not extend all the way down the Hudson Valley to New York as indicated on this map and the next one.

to discharge again through the St. Clair and Illinois rivers. At this time the regions north of Georgian Bay, Lake Huron and Lake Superior were raised at least 600 feet. Continued withdrawal of the ice allowed the formation of a later outlet through Ottawa River to the Champlain Sea that had flooded the St. Lawrence and the Lake Champlain regions. This encroachment of marine water, apparently, was the result of previous depression of the area due to loading the land by the great ice sheet.

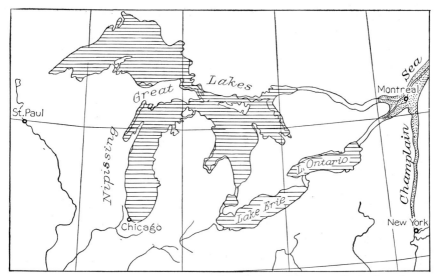

After Taylor and Leverett, U. S. Geol. Survey.

FIG. 249. — The history of the Great Lakes, Lake Nipissing stage.

Milwaukee Public Museum Photo.

FIG. 250. — Shore cliff of Lake Chicago, near Beach, Illinois.

Lake Nipissing Stage (Fig. 249). — This stage represents the condition of the upper three Great Lakes immediately following the final withdrawal of the ice from the region. As shown on the map, they were only slightly different from the present lakes except for their outlet, which was, *at first*, through North Bay and Ottawa River to the much diminished Champlain Sea. *Later, renewed uplift of the land on the north* shut off the Ottawa outlet and caused the upper lakes to discharge through St. Clair and Detroit rivers to the lower lakes, thence through the St. Lawrence to Champlain Sea. It is thought that, for a short time after the Ottawa outlet was closed, there was again drainage to the Illinois River, but a slight lowering of the St. Clair River channel soon reduced the lake level sufficiently to cause the abandonment of this outlet.

Summary. — Pre-glacial stream erosion, glacial erosion which widened and deepened the valleys, deposition of moraines and beaches, warping and tilting of the land due to loading and unloading by the ice, flooding the region by meltwater from the glacier, invasion of the downwarped regions by seawater from the Atlantic Ocean, and uplift during and following the last melting of the ice were the outstanding geomorphic events in the long and complicated history of the Great Lakes region.

SWAMPS

Swamps are basins filled or partially filled with a mixture of water, fresh or decayed vegetation, and soil. The proportions vary greatly in different cases. The term swamp will be used here to include such similar forms as *swale, marsh* (except tidal marsh), *bog, morass,* and *muskeg;* although the vegetation of swamps and muskegs may include many trees and even forests; while in marshes, swales and bogs the vegetation consists of grasses, mosses, lichens, etc. The water of swamps may be fresh, brackish or salt. The distribution of swamps is essentially the same as that of lakes. They are most numerous in recently glaciated regions, but are very abundant in humid regions on coastal plains and on flood-plains and deltas. Although much less common in arid regions, they are by no means unknown even in deserts.

Peat Bogs. — Many shallow lake basins in humid regions and in high latitudes become filled with various species of vegetation, particularly *sphagnum* moss. The growth begins on the borders of the lake and gradually extends farther and farther out until the lake is completely filled. The lower layers of vegetation decompose under water which, because of its antiseptic properties, prevents complete decay. The partially decomposed vegetable material, which may be many feet thick, turns brown in color and becomes *peat*, the first stage in the formation of coal.

Muskegs. — Over vast areas in northern Canada and similar regions ancient glacial lake basins have become largely filled with black decayed vegetation, *muck*, which in some places is so mixed with water as to be practically a liquid but in others is firm enough to support the growth of tufts of grass, mosses, and even trees. In many cases the grass and moss have formed a crust-like covering over the muck, which trembles when one steps on it, giving rise to the name *quaking bogs*. The underlying muck is so deep and often in such a liquid condition that if persons break through the crust they may have difficulty in getting out; while without human aid cattle, horses and other large animals that break through usually become hopelessly bogged down.

Tidal Marshes

Along many coasts there are lagoons and shallow bays fringed and more or less filled with grasses and other vegetable materials that grow in salt water. The flow and ebb of tides alternately covers and uncovers this material which is quite different in composition from ordinary freshwater swamp growth. These marshes, usually, are almost flat, but some slope gently seaward and others are slightly channeled by tidal currents.

The Origin of Swamps

Swamps form in many different ways, but the great majority occupy glacial basins that have been filled or covered by vegetation. Another large group of swamps is found on the seaward margins of coastal plains. These are the result of a slight uplift of the sea-floor or of the filling of lagoons by silt and vegetation. A third major group of swamps are those on flood-plains and deltas where abandoned river channels have been filled with vegetation. In arid and semi-arid regions, many swamps, which support vegetation that grows in salt and brackish water, fringe playa lakes or other types of salt lakes. When the lakes have a maximum volume of water, the swamps may be entirely covered. When the water level drops, the swamp appears. Other minor types of swamps are correlated with types of lake basins discussed in preceding pages.

Topography of Swamps

Most swamps are relatively small, and like lakes suggest youthful topography. However, swamps on flood-plains, deltas and some coastal plains are indicative of old topography.

In the great glaciated areas of North America and Eurasia, there are thousands of swamps that vary from less than an acre to many square miles in surface area. The surfaces of the swamps themselves are quite flat, although many small elevations and depressions are likely to occur, but associated with them are numerous larger hills and depressions, the hummocks and kettles of ground moraines (Fig. 230). Naturally where large shallow basins have been filled with vegetation, the flattish surfaces of the swamps are less broken and interrupted by knobs and hills.

The Everglades of Florida and the Dismal Swamp of Virginia are good examples of the marginal swamps of coastal plains. Both lie practically at sea level, and are essentially flat.

The Everglades. — This great region, half lake, half swamp, occupies a shallow rock-walled basin some 100 miles long and 40 miles wide between Lake Okeechobee and the southern tip of Florida. The Everglades are fed by water from heavy rains and from the overflow of Lake Okeechobee, which is the second largest body of fresh water wholly within the United States. The water in the 4,000 square mile swamp is fresh. When high, it stands barely above sea-level, and moves with a distinct current into rivers and canals which partially drain it.

Small rock islands, clothed with many varieties of tropical vegetation including cypress, palms, bay, live oak, papayas, wild rubber, giant ferns and wild orchids, abound in the Everglades. Saw grass grows under water and above water to a height of 8 or 9 feet. Decayed vegetation, *muck*, underlies the whole area, which is a flat, nearly impenetrable wilderness. Where properly drained, the fertile soil yields fabulous crops of sugar cane and vegetables. Similar, but less extensive swamps border many of our coast lines and offer interesting possibilities for reclamation of the extremely fertile swamp land.

REFERENCES

1. J. S. Diller and H. B. Patton: *The Geology and Petrology of Crater Lake National Park.* U. S. Geol. Surv., Prof. P. 3, 1902.
2. Florida Everglades Commission: *Florida Everglades.* 63d Congress, 2nd Session, Doc. 379, 1914.
3. E. E. Free: *The Topographic Features of the Desert Basins of the United States.* U. S. Dept. of Agr. Bull. No. 54, 1914.
4. Ernest Howe: *Landslides of the San Juan Mountains, Colo.* U. S. Geol. Surv., Prof. P. 67, 1909.
5. Frank Leverett and F. B. Taylor: *The Pleistocene of Indiana and Michigan and the History of the Great Lakes.* U. S. Geol. Surv., Mon. 53, 1915.
6. I. C. Russell: *Lakes of North America.* Ginn and Co., 1900.
7. Warren D. Smith and Carl R. Swartzlow: *Mount Mazama: Explosion vs. Collapse.* Bull. Geol. Soc. Am., Vol. 47, pp. 1809–1830, 1936.
8. Robert A. Sutherland: *Dam Building Reaches a Climax.* Engineering News-Record, Vol. 117, pp. 807–815, 1936.
9. Godfrey Sykes: *The Colorado Delta.* Carnegie Institution of Washington, Pub. 460, 1937.
10. A. C. Waters: *Terraces and Coulees along the Columbia River near Lake Chelan, Wash.* Bull. Geol. Soc. Am., Vol. 44, pp. 783–820, 1933.
11. Bailey Willis: *Dead Sea Problem: Rift Valley or Ramp Valley?* Bull. Geol. Soc. Am., Vol. 39, pp. 490–542, 1928.
12. ———: *East African Rift Valleys and Ramp Valleys.* Carnegie Institution of Washington, Pub. 470, 1936.
13. Warren Upham: *The Glacial Lake Agassiz.* U. S. Geol. Surv., Mon. 25, 1895.

CHAPTER XII

SHORE FORMS AND SHORE PROCESSES OF SEAS AND LAKES

In general, the shore forms of seas and lakes are similar. Also, with three notable exceptions, tides, the work of corals which is unimportant in lakes, and the work of algae which produces minor topographic forms in lakes but is probably less important in seas, the processes that produce the topography of shores are essentially the same for both seas and lakes; therefore, it is appropriate to discuss them together.

Many conditions must be considered in explaining the physiographic development of shores. First, one must know the composition and structure of the rocks. It is safe to say that every important type of both can be found on some shoreline. Then the relief of the coast is important, and, again, almost all types occur near some shore. Third, land processes, such as wind, streams and glaciers, have much to do with the topography of shores. Fourth, the internal earth processes, vulcanism and, *particularly, diastrophism,* are of outstanding importance. Finally, the activities of waves, shore currents, tides and organisms combine with the factors already mentioned to develop our present shore forms.

Disregarding small bays, promontories and other minor irregularities, the length of the shoreline of North America is 15,000 miles; that of Eurasia is 25,000 miles. When the combined length of all the shores of all lakes and oceans are considered, it is evident that the variety of topographic features is too great to be included in any simple classification. The following discussion describes typical shore forms and explains their origin. Special types will yield to analysis after the fundamental principles governing shore processes are established.

Definitions. — Most of the terms applied to shoreline phenomena have been in common use for a long time and are well established in the literature; but certain terminology, especially as applied
to shores, beaches and coastlines by various writers, lacks uniformity.
The definitions that immediately follow are, with minor variations,
those used by Johnson.[1]   They are precise and characteristic of
distinct phases of shoreline development.

Royal Canadian Air Force Photo.

FIG. 251. — Cape D'Or, Nova Scotia. A youthful shoreline. Note the backshore beach,
and the fine sea cliffs and caves.

Shore. — The zone between low and high water marks over
which sea or lake water migrates is the shore.   The *foreshore,* in
the case of seas, is a somewhat narrower zone that lies between
low and high tide shorelines.   *Shoreface* is the rather steeply sloping
zone that extends seaward from the low tide shoreline to the (generally) rather flat surface of the continental shelf.   *Shoreline* is the
line that separates land and water.   It is a migrating line, particularly noticeable on sea shores.   At high tide it is the *high tide*

[1] D. W. Johnson: *Shore Processes and Shoreline Development.*   Chapter
IV.   John Wiley and Sons, 1919.

shoreline; at low tide is the *low tide shoreline.* Often the low tide shoreline is meant when the term shoreline is used. Since even the largest lakes are but slightly affected by tides, the terms high and low tide shorelines are inapplicable to lake shores. However, due to seasonal or cyclic changes in climate and water supply, the level of many lakes changes. Therefore, *high shoreline* and *low shoreline* are useful terms in such cases. The *offshore zone* extends from the outer margin of the shoreface to the outer edge of the

D. F. Higgins.

FIG. 252. — A high coast, Egypt. The debris in the foreground has been washed down by streams.

continental shelf. In lakes there is no exact counterpart of the *marine* offshore zone. *Backshore* is the part of a shore that lies between the foreshore and the coast line. It is covered by water only during great storms (Fig. 251).

Coast. — The coast is an indeterminate zone that extends landward from the shore. A *coast line* marks the seaward limit of the permanently exposed coast. Coasts may terminate abruptly in steep cliffs at the coast line (Fig. 252); they may be gently sloping plains, or they may be characterized by other types of topography.

Beaches. — A beach is the deposit made by seas or lakes that rests on the shore. Three positions of beaches are recognized. A *lower foreshore beach*, resting on the lower foreshore, is formed by the action of waves and littoral currents. The *upper foreshore beach* lies high on the foreshore, and is formed primarily by waves. A *backshore beach* lies on the (usually) narrow backshore, and is formed through the combined action of storm waves, sheet flood from waves at high tide, and wind. Also, in many places streams

U. S. Dept. of the Interior.

FIG. 253. — A low coast, Acadia National Park, Maine.

contribute material to the backshore beach. *Other forms,* less subject to the confusion in terminology, are defined in later sections of this chapter where their origin is first discussed.

SHORE PROCESSES OF SEAS AND LAKES

The dynamic agents that have their origin directly or indirectly in seas or lakes are waves, littoral currents, tides, ice push, and organisms, particularly corals and algae. It should be noted that although tides are perceptible in large lakes, they are unimportant physiographic agents except on *sea* shores. Organisms that affect shores are largely marine, although fresh water algae are important in some lakes. Ice push is effective on many lake shores, but rarely on sea shores.

Water Waves

Waves are formed in various ways; landslides entering lakes or seas, blocks of rock broken from cliffs, boats moving through the water, submarine earthquakes — all produce waves. The waves that are most important in developing shore forms are caused by the pressure and friction of wind on the mobile water. The wind blows in gusts rather than with uniform force. Because of the unequal pressure an undulatory form is developed on the surface of the water. As soon as undulations appear, there is selective action

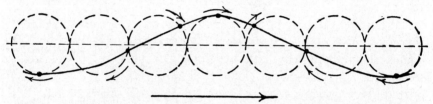

FIG. 254. — Wave of oscillation showing the movement of water particles in the wave.

of wind. The upper part of the growing wave is pushed forward more than the bottom; thus, the wave *form* advances in the direction that the wind is blowing, and the individual particles of water in the wave tend to move in circular orbits, coming to rest after they have completed their orbital motion.

Waves of Oscillation. — These waves are formed in water deep enough to permit each drop of water to move in a circular orbit. *Theoretically*, there should be no forward movement of the water, although the wave *form* moves in the direction of the wind. *Actually* the water does move forward to a slight extent, especially where it is shallow.

Form and Motion. — Figure 254 shows the forward movement of an oscillatory wave and the direction of movement of particles of water with respect to the wave form. It should be noted that the motion of the water particles is forward on the crest, backward at the bottom of the trough, upward on the front and downward on the back of the wave. This simple wave form, which in profile is a *trochoidal* curve, is subject to many modifications. Where strong winds are blowing in the direction of movement of the wave, the forward motion of the water is accelerated on the crest but retarded in the trough. The result is to make the wave higher and to give it an unsymmetrical form with over-steepened front. Water from the crest may be blown over into the trough giving rise to spray or foam.

It frequently happens that two waves coming in from different directions combine to form a *compound* wave whose motion is a complex resultant of the other two. The form under such conditions also becomes complex, and unusually high waves or correspondingly low ones due to interference are momentarily formed.

Where oscillatory waves enter shallow water, there is a marked change in form. The wave becomes shorter, higher, and develops an over-steepened, crescent-shaped front. The unsupported crest crashes forward and downward forming *surf*. The zone in which surf forms is called the *breaker* zone.

FIG. 255 — The wave front of a "breaking" wave.

Height.—Much has been written about the height of waves of oscillation in open water. By height is meant the vertical distance from crest to trough. Height is difficult to measure, but close approximations can be made. In general, the height increases with the velocity and duration of the wind, and with the *fetch* or distance that the wave has been propagated. The heights vary from those too small to measure up to great storm waves. Cornish reports waves 23 feet high on Lake Superior. Several authorities have recorded heights of 43 feet in the North Atlantic with peaks of more than 50 feet where two waves intersected.

Waves which ride in on high tides may break and cast their spray 300 feet or more above mean sea level, but this must not be confused with the height in open water.

Cornish has given the following formula for determining the relationship between wave height and wind velocity. The wind velocity, in statute miles per hour, divided by 2.05 equals the height of the wave in feet. This factor, however, is modified by the others mentioned above.

Length. — The wave length is the distance from crest to crest or trough to trough. There is some relationship between height and length. In waves less than 100 feet long, the ratio of height to length is about 1 to 17; with lengths of 300-400 feet, the ratio is 1 to 27. In open oceans, lengths of as much as 700 feet are rare. In the English Channel wave lengths of 2,594 feet have been observed.

Depth of Wave Action. — Wave motion decreases rapidly with depth. Moderately strong waves barely move fine, loose sediment at a depth of 200 feet. The maximum depth of water affected by great storm waves is about 600 feet.

FIG. 256. — Motion of water in waves of translation.

Waves of Translation. — These differ from oscillatory waves in several important respects. The water particles instead of describing circular orbits are actually carried forward in the direction of wave propagation, all the water from surface to bottom being moved the same distance. Each particle starts from rest as the wave approaches, is lifted and carried forward in a semi-ellipse as the wave advances and comes to rest in its new position when the wave has passed.

Waves of translation may be observed in many places between the breaker line and the shore. As the oscillatory waves come into this zone, they break, and their plunging crests furnish the water for the new waves of translation. The latter ride on shore with narrow crests and broad, nearly flat interspaces between the crests. Such waves break on shore just as do waves of oscillation.

Undertow. — Wherever waves come in to a shore, there must of necessity be an outward movement of the water back to the sea or lake; this is the *undertow.* If the waves come in obliquely to a shoreline, much of the water may be converted into a *littoral current* and the undertow will be reduced. Under normal conditions where the offshore and shoreface zones are beneath shallow water, the undertow is stronger some distance out from the shoreline, for in those zones strong waves break, and some of the water is turned back without ever reaching the backshore. The strength of undertow diminishes rapidly with increasing depth of water, the current being broken up much as is that of a stream which enters the deep water of a lake. The work of undertow is to move sediment from the shore out into deep water; this work is favored where its current is concentrated and its volume and velocity are great.

Littoral Currents

Next to waves, *littoral currents* are the most important of the moving water agents that modify shorelines. Many types of currents are observable on shores, and the total results of their work is difficult to analyze. There are *wave currents, tidal currents, salinity currents, planetary currents* and many others. Without attempting to discriminate here, we may consider the more important types of these currents under the term *littoral or shore* currents. The velocity of these currents depends upon the force of the wind, strength of the waves, depth of water and configuration of the shore. Where the shorelines are relatively smooth and large amounts of sediment are available, the littoral current is an important agent of transportation. On weak or unconsolidated rocks at the shoreline, it may be a powerful erosive agent. If sediment is carried from shallow to deep water, the shore current becomes an agent of deposition.

Origin of Littoral Currents. — Where prevailing winds drift water against a shoreline or cause waves to break obliquely to a shore, there is a tendency for much of the water to move parallel with that shore. Part of the water, in the form of under-tow, moves back directly to the sea or lake under the influence of gravity. Part moves back into deep water in an ir-

FIG. 257. — The development of littoral currents.

regular course whose direction is a resultant of the undertow, the shore current and the position of the incoming wave, and the larger part of the water moves along shore with a distinct current. This is the littoral current.

Rip Tides and Rip Currents. — Due to a peculiar and not well understood combination of conditions, so-called *rip tides,* or whirlpools, are developed where littoral currents meet ebb tides coming out from the shore through narrow inlets. Bathers and even boats are dragged down by the whirling water, which sometimes is very violent.

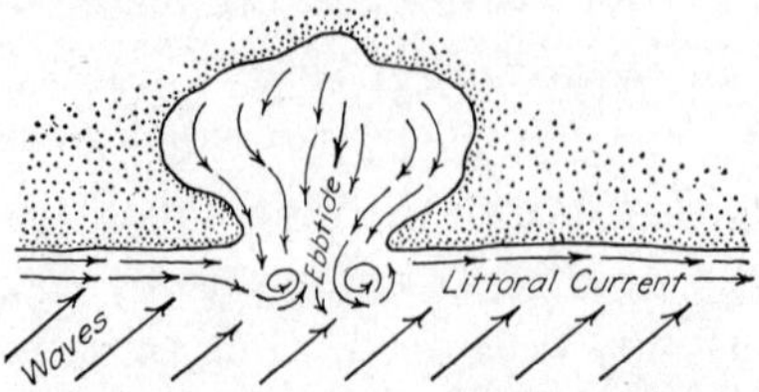

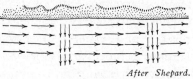

After Thompson.

Fig. 258. — A diagram to show the development of rip tides, the whirlpools, where the ebb tide, littoral currents and waves meet.

There has been some confusion between rip tides and *rip currents.* The condition just described apparently may correctly be called a *rip tide.* In addition there are equally little understood *rip currents,* which usually have been called *rip tides.*

Rip currents, according to Shepard,[1] "are masses of water that move straight out from the beach carrying water at both the surface and near bottom, but probably chiefly at the surface at a distance of a thousand feet from the shore. They exist under all sorts of conditions of currents, waves and wind, but are not continuous. Some of the strongest are developed during periods of very large surf. However, there are at times very distinct outward movements when

After Shepard.

Fig. 259. — A diagram to show rip currents.

the sea is very flat and when there is no wind. These currents have nothing to do with tides."

THE TIDE

The tide is a great wave produced by the attraction of the sun and moon on the waters of the earth. Two high tides are formed on opposite sides of the earth at the same time. If the whole lithosphere were covered by a single universal ocean, each high tide would pass completely around the earth from east to west in 24 h. 52 m. Since there are two high and two low tides every day, all seashores experience high tides every 12 h. 26 m. and low tides at a time halfway between the high tide intervals. During a rising

[1] Personal communication.

tide (*flood tide*) the water comes in over the shore in a form inter-mediate between that of waves of oscillation and translation. The orbit of the wave particles is a much elongated ellipse, whose long axis rises toward the land. There is a direct shoreward movement of the water which continues to the instant of high tide. Unlike waves coming in to shore, the rise of a flood tide is so gradual that it is hardly noticeable. It creeps up the shoreline, then seems to retreat a little, then creeps up a little farther covering tidal flats and rocks, filling lagoons, until, finally, it reaches its maximum height.

The importance of tides in modifying shores frequently is very much underestimated. Probably its most important function is to raise the water level and thus make wave action more effective. When storm waves ride in on high tides, they dash against the shores with tremendous force and reach unusually great heights.

The currents of a rising tide, especially where they move through narrow openings and over unconsolidated sediments, scour their channels and carry sediment inland. The sediment may be de-posited at the heads of bays, in the mouths of harbors, and in lagoons behind barrier bars. In many places the current attains a velocity of from 2 to 6 miles an hour. In exceptional cases it may reach more than 12 miles an hour. These velocities permit both erosion and transportation of sediment on a large scale. Also strong littoral currents may develop from rising tides.

The depth to which tidal currents may scour the ocean floor is much greater than in the case of wave erosion. Extensive tidal erosion occurs at depths of from 300 to 600 feet, and cases have been cited of some scour at a depth as great as 6,500 feet.

While landward and *longshore* tidal currents seem to be more effective erosive and transporting agents than are *seaward* currents, the latter are by no means unimportant. During the falling (*ebb*) tide, strong outward currents are developed. These may be aug-mented by river currents; with such combinations, the transportation of sediment is much greater than where the ebb tidal current acts alone.

Height. — In the open ocean the crest of the tide averages about 1½ feet in height. In bodies of sea water connected by narrow inlets with the open ocean, it is not much higher. In Lake Michigan the tide is only 2 inches high. On open seashores the height varies so greatly, depending upon the shape of the shoreline, the position of the sun and moon, and other factors, that no significant figures can be given. In the Bay of Fundy (an exceptional case) the average height of the flood tides is 37 feet. An ingeniously built calculating machine at Washington permits the operator

N. M. Fenneman, courtesy Wisconsin Geol. Survey.

FIG. 260. — The result of ice push, Lake Mendota, Wisconsin.

to predict the time and height of flood tides and of low tides for the principal ports of the world 100 years in advance.

Tidal Bore. — In funnel-shaped estuaries, such as the Bay of Fundy, and in large rivers such as the Amazon, the concentration of water results in waves called *bores,* which rush up bays or rivers with great speed and may raise the water level as much as 60 feet; in such cases the erosive power is particularly great. The tidal bores in the Yellow River are spectacular and often disastrous to the light Chinese river craft.

Ice Push

Although unimportant on most sea shores, the shores of many lakes that freeze over in winter are profoundly affected by *ice push*. After the covering of ice has formed on the lake, if the temperature drops, the ice *contracts* and cracks open, often with a noise like the report of a gun. Water from below fills the crack. Upon the return of warmer weather, the ice expands, making the body of ice larger than necessary to cover the lake. The consequent push on shores composed of poorly consolidated rock debris forms ramparts or irregular ridges. In many places loose blocks of rock are imbedded in the banks of the lake, forming a stone mosaic which effectively resists erosion by waves and shore currents. Where ice pushes against high shorelines and cliffs composed of resistant rock, the ice may be folded into long ridges, faulted, or greatly shattered.

Organisms

Reef-building corals (*polyps*) are the most important of all marine organisms that have to do with our changing shorelines. Their activities will be more fully considered in Chapter XV, but for the sake of continuity a brief statement is included here.

The polyp is a tiny animal that *thrives* in sea water up to 120 feet in depth and *lives* in water as much as 150 feet deep. The water must contain little or no sediment, but must have abundant calcium carbonate in solution. The temperature of the water must not fall below 68°, and warmer water stimulates the growth of the organisms. A mild circulation of water is essential to reef-building, but frequent violent storm waves are disastrous.

Under favorable conditions the polyps secrete calcium carbonate from the sea water and build *fringing reefs, barrier reefs, atolls* (Chapter XV), and other more irregular topographic forms. At the present time the western part of the tropical portion of the Pacific is the great coral sea of the earth. Other large regions of present coral growth are the east side of the Indian Ocean, the Caribbean Sea, and parts of the Gulf of Mexico.

Algae. — Algae are minute plants that live in both fresh and salt water. Where calcium carbonate is highly concentrated in water, algae aid in its precipitation from solution. Russell [1] has described immense deposits of *tufa* (calcium carbonate) in Pyramid Lake, Nevada, which is a remnant of ancient Lake Lahontan. "Every island and rocky crag that rose in Lake Lahontan became a center of accumulation for tufa deposits and was transformed into strange and frequently fantastic shapes by the material precipitated upon it. Now that the waters of the ancient sea have disappeared, these structures stand in the desert valleys like the crumbling ruins of towers, castles, domes and various other shapes in keeping with the desolation surrounding them." Some of the towers are 500 feet high. The total amount of calcium carbonate deposited is "millions if not billions of tons." This is perhaps the most remarkable deposit on record, but smaller deposits are widespread in both fresh and salt-water lakes. Since the material is more likely to be precipitated on rocky shores than elsewhere, it follows that in lakes, where they are active, algae aid materially in changing such shorelines.

CLASSIFICATION OF SHORELINES

Before proceeding with a detailed discussion of topography developed by shore processes, it is well to examine and classify existing shorelines, for the results of the work of waves and currents are very different on different types of shores. If a thoroughly dissected land area of high relief has been submerged recently, the shoreline will be extremely irregular, and youthful shorelines will prevail. If the land has stood still for a very long time, a mature shoreline may have developed. Where a shoreline represents the edge of a recently uplifted coastal plain, the relief of the coast will be low and the shore regular.

These simple types may be used as starting points in considering the development of shorelines. Actually, variations from type may be very great. Moreover, within short distances along a coast, shore conditions may differ greatly.

Following Johnson [2] shorelines are divided into four principal

[1] I. C. Russell: *Lakes of North America.* Ginn and Co., p. 111, 1900.
[2] D. W. Johnson: *Shore Process and Shoreline Development.* Chap. IV. John Wiley and Sons, 1919.

types: *shorelines of submergence, shorelines of emergence, neutral shorelines, and compound shorelines.* It is not always easy to recognize all shores under this or any other simple classification, but typical representatives exhibit characteristic topographic features.

When considering either submergence or emergence of shorelines, one constantly is faced with the problem of whether it is the land or sea that has changed position. This question already has been discussed and need not be reconsidered here. However, it should be noted that the borders of continents and islands give very sensitive and accurate records of movements of the land relative to sea level.

We speak rather freely about mean sea level as if it were something easy to determine. As a matter of fact, it is not. Recent work has indicated that it is necessary to record the height of water *every hour for a 20-year period* in order to determine the exact mean elevation of sea water on any shore. Even after this has been done, the determination may be inaccurate, for, during this time, the land along shore may have moved up or down enough to vitiate the results of the long series of measurements; but, considering the matter from a broader point of view, there is usually good evidence for recognition of the relative permanence, emergence or submergence of most shorelines.

Shorelines of Submergence

If we examine our coast and shorelines, we can find unmistakable evidence of submergence of many sorts of topographic forms; mountains, plateaus, plains, volcanoes, dune areas and glaciated regions are typical examples. Naturally, the results of such submergence give rise to a great variety of shorelines against which the attack of waves and currents will take place. There may be bold, nearly vertical cliffs that stand hundreds of feet above and project other hundreds of feet below sea level; or there may be a low plain which projects with gentle slope far out under the water. In either case, if the land stands still long enough and there is sufficient activity of waves and currents, the topography of the shorelines will be changed progressively in cyclic development from youthful to mature forms. Theoretically old shorelines should exist, but none have ever been described.

Outlines of Submerged Shorelines. — The outlines of *recently submerged shorelines* are usually extremely irregular. This is, of course, due to the fact that glaciers, streams or wind thoroughly dissected the land before it was submerged. As noted in Chapter X, glaciated coasts in high northern and southern latitudes,

Royal Canadian Air Force Photo.

FIG. 261.— Graham Beach, a typical British Columbia fiord showing youthful shorelines.

such as those of southern Chili, southern Norway, Labrador and British Columbia are good examples of fiord shorelines. Many of the great glacial troughs which were cut well below sea level by alpine glaciers have been submerged since the glaciers melted, thus allowing the sea water to back in far over the land. In some cases islands have been left which were formerly hills and ridges on the land surface. (Fig. 327.) All such shorelines are exceedingly irregular.

Estuaries, or *drowned river valleys* usually are bordered by small bays. Each bay or cove is a submerged valley, made originally by a stream tributary to the main trunk stream (Fig. 92). Where the submergence has been slight and the original relief low, the sea or lake water usually forms only small indentations; but where the submergence or the original relief was great, large, deep indentations may be found.

On irregular coasts, promontories and the shores of open bays are particularly susceptible to the attack of waves and currents. In

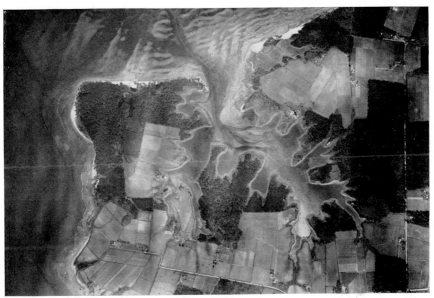

Photo by U. S. Army Air Corps. From "The Face of the Earth as Seen from the Air." Published by Am. Geographical Society, N. Y.

FIG. 262. — Channels, shoals and terraces in a drowned river valley, York Creek, 9 miles southeast of Yorktown, Virginia.

partially enclosed bays, fiords and winding estuaries, wave erosion is greatly reduced, although bottom erosion and deposition by currents may be great.

Shorelines of Emergence

In regions where part of a sea or lake floor has been raised above the water level or where the water surface has been lowered, the shoreline is one of *emergence*. If the land was under water for a *long time* before the uplift, waves and currents would have produced a relatively smooth plain in the offshore zone and on the continental shelf. The result of uniform emergence of this plain would be a rather straight shoreline in sharp contrast to the typical irregular shoreline of submergence.

However, not all shorelines of emergence are smooth and straight. In many places hilly or mountainous regions have been partially submerged and soon re-elevated. In such cases there has

Geological Survey of Canada.

FIG. 263. — Upraised coast near Ottawa, James Bay. Compare the upraised coast with the shore that is under water.

not been time for much work by waves and currents, and the new shoreline has more of the characteristics of submergence than of emergence. The coast of Maine is of this type.

Where marine or lake plains have been raised through broad continental movements, the lower portions may extend out under shallow water for long distances. Under such conditions the results of wave erosion and deposition are distinctly different from those on submerged shorelines.

Neutral and Compound Shorelines

To "important groups of shorelines whose essential characteristics depend on causes independent of either submergence or emergence," [1] Johnson (op. cit. p. 187) gives the name *neutral shorelines*. Typical examples are the shorelines of deltas, outwash plains,
coral reefs, volcanoes, dunes, and those produced by faults. The

E. E. Wahlstrom.

FIG. 264. — A drumlin eroded by waves near Winthrop, Mass.

origin or formation of each type is discussed in the appropriate
place in this volume.

Compound shorelines are those that exhibit characteristics of at
least two of the other three main classes. Due to oscillation of
level, some shorelines exhibit features of emergence and submergence to about an equal degree; they may well be called compound
shorelines. Another example is an outwash-plain shoreline and an
emergent shoreline. These might easily include features of both
types. The details of the topographic features produced by waves
and other shore processes acting on these particular shorelines may

[1] Quotation reprinted by permission of author and publisher.

be inferred after the discussion of the attack on shorelines of submergence and emergence has been concluded.

Wave Erosion on Shorelines of Submergence

Regardless of the profile of the original shoreline, wave erosion will eventually modify it. Among the more important factors that govern the nature and amount of wave erosion are the size and strength of the waves, the seaward slope and height of the shoreline, the composition of the rocks, the depth of water and the length of time that the land stands still.

Where waves in deep water come against vertical cliffs, much of the water is reflected back and the attack is much less effective than it is on sloping cliffs that rise from more shallow water. Where the under-water slope is such that the wave breaks, the mass of water delivers a powerful blow on the shoreline. Also, the *push* of the advancing mass of water may be very great. Air in the joints of rocks on cliffs is compressed by breaking waves; when the water subsides the air tends to expand, forcing out loose boulders from the face of cliffs.

The Force of Waves. — Dynamometer records show that waves 5.5 feet high exert a pressure of over 600 pounds per square foot. Such waves in St. Augustine Harbour moved a block of concrete that weighed 21,000 pounds. According to Stevenson, in the winter, storm waves on the east side of the Atlantic strike the shoreline with an average force of more than 21,000 pounds per square foot. Exceptionally great storm waves strike with a force of more than 60,000 pounds per square foot and have moved blocks of rock weighing more than 100 tons.

The Height of Wave-Cutting. — The height of the waves that break on a shore at high tide marks the upward limit of direct wave erosion; however, through undercutting and caving, the total effect of wave work is much greater. Storm waves dashing small stones up the face of cliffs have broken the glass in lighthouse windows 300 feet above sea level, but this is a most unusual case.

The Cutting Tools of Waves. — In previous discussions of stream, wind and glacial erosion, the importance of cutting tools

shoreline recedes and the wave-cut plain widens.   As the shoreline is cut landward, *stacks, caves, islands,* and other typical erosion remnants may be left standing on the wave-cut platform as a result of inequalities in the rocks or of the unequal force of the waves.

The rate of wave-cutting depends upon the nature of the materials, the force of the waves and the capacity of undertow and currents to remove the debris.   Undercutting of a cliff permits large

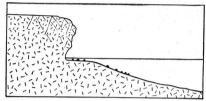

FIG. 267. — A wave-cut cliff and terrace.

amounts of rock to fall.   At first this material increases the rate of wave erosion, but as the wave-cut terrace widens, the waves may break at some distance from the shoreline, thus retarding and

Geological Survey of Canada.

FIG. 268. — Sea arch off Cape Split, Nova Scotia, at high tide.

eventually stopping erosion.   After undercutting ceases, weathering tends to make the slope of the cliff less steep.

The width of the wave-cut terrace depends upon a delicate balance of all the factors that govern wave erosion.   Under favorable conditions the attack may continue indefinitely with a consequent increase in width of terrace cutting; for example, where there is a slow subsidence of the land, it allows the water over the terrace to remain deeper and counteracts the clogging effect of debris. Uplifted, wave-cut terraces more than a mile wide now may be seen on parts of the coasts of California and Peru. An uplift of the land

W. O. Thompson.

FIG. 269. — An elevated wave-cut plain and newly formed wave-cut cliff and stack, south of Santa Cruz, California.

reduces and eventually entirely stops wave-cutting on the *old* shore-line. Then a new cycle of erosion begins.

Topography Produced by Wave Deposition. — On shorelines of submergence where the water, offshore, is deep, the first topographic forms produced by wave deposition are entirely under water. Later, as the wave-cut terrace advances landward, a narrow ephemeral beach may be deposited by strong waves on the backshore. Still later, after depressions of the sea or lake floor are filled and the wave-cut plain is well developed, beaches may form on the foreshore. Finally, *barrier, or offshore bars*, may be formed by wave deposition.

Beaches. — Beaches are the deposits of sediment made on a lake or seashore. The processes of beach formation are complex and only a simple statement will be made here.

Conflicting forces are constantly at work on shores. Where the wave-cut terraces are narrow, usually the undertow and littoral currents are strong enough to carry the debris eroded from the land out into deep water, where it is deposited. As the terraces widen, waves may break farther out in the water and waves of translation carry sediment shoreward. Strong waves erode the surfaces of the terrace and tend to steepen the seaward slope of a beach that may have formed well back on the shore. This steepening, however, strengthens the undertow and seaward currents and allows more material to be carried away from the land. Where conditions are favorable, the beaches may be built farther and farther out from the coastline, thus extending the land lakeward or seaward. Nearly all beaches are ephemeral. Violent storm waves may remove a whole beach in a few hours, cutting the shore clear down to solid rock, or moderately strong waves may erode the seaward slope of a low beach and carry much of the material over the crest where it is deposited on the landward side.

Beaches may lie high on the backshore or in any position on the foreshore. Some are much like ridges with a definite crest and a steeper landward than seaward slope. Others are merely broad sheets of sediment spread by waves and currents over the shore. They may be composed of rounded pebbles, gravel or sand, or mixtures of these materials, depending on the source of the material and the thoroughness with which waves have worked over the deposits. The sand of beaches may be composed of many different materials. On some beaches it consists of well-washed quartz grains, or, in regions of coral reefs and islands, it may be broken particles of the coral limestone. Many sandy beaches are robbed of much of their material by winds which blow the sand back from the shore to form dunes or loess.

The Beach Profile of Equilibrium. — Where shorelines of submergence have reached a stage in their development that permits the formation of wide beaches which spread well out on the foreshore, there is a tendency to bring about an equilibrium between the forces of erosion and transportation of the incoming waves and the depositional processes of undertow and other shore currents. When this delicate balance is reached, the slope is just steep enough so that the seaward currents, aided by gravity, can barely return the material that is driven toward the shore by the incoming waves. This is the profile of equilibrium. The profile is gently concave upward, steepening toward the land.

Cusped Beaches. — Peculiar but by no means unusual shore forms are the cusped beaches that are made in some way by wave action. On the seaward side of many beaches one finds deposits

W. O. Thompson.

FIG. 270. — Beach cusps, Balboa Beach, California.

of sand, gravel or boulders in rather uniform, low, regularly spaced ridges (*cusps*) which are separated by smoothly curved, shallow embayments. The cusps may be erased by strong waves only to be followed by new ones, although cuspate forms tend to form on certain shores and not on others.

Many observers have formulated theories to explain the origin of beach cusps. According to Johnson,[1] minor irregularities on the seaward slope of a beach are enlarged by the continual *swashing* of the waves. The original irregularities eventually develop into shallow troughs or embayments which in size are directly proportional to the size of the waves that wash the beach. Through selec-

[1] D. W. Johnson: *Op. cit.*, pp. 481–486.

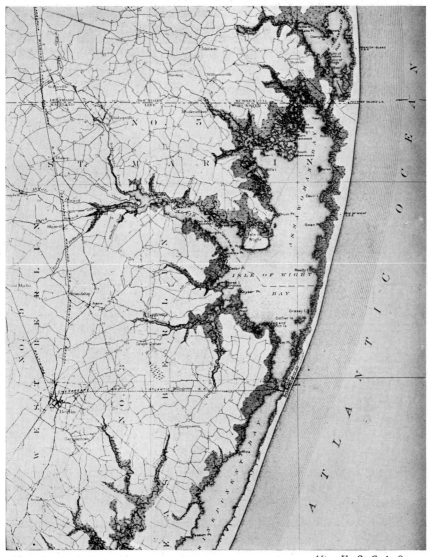

After U. S. Geol. Survey.

FIG. 271. — An offshore bar separating the ocean from narrow bays and lagoons, on the low Maryland and Delaware coast.

tive erosion the cusps are left rather uniformly spaced between the troughs.

Barrier, or Offshore, Bars. — After broad wave-cut plains have been formed and a large amount of sediment has been deposited on them, large storm waves breaking some distance from the land may form ridges roughly parallel to the shoreline. Such ridges have been called *barriers, bars* and *offshore bars.* The word *barrier* easily may be confused with *barrier reefs*, which are formed largely

W. O. Thompson.

FIG. 272. — A small spit at the entrance to Newport Harbor, California.

by the work of corals. *Bar* used alone is not distinctive for there are other kinds of bars. Both the terms *barrier bars* and *offshore bars* characterize the position of these bars, but the latter is preferable. Since offshore bars are probably more typical of shorelines of emergence, they will be described more fully under that subject.

Topography Produced by Littoral Currents. — In the early stages of shoreline development, littoral currents that are directed against headlands composed of soft or unconsolidated rocks are

strong eroding agents. The waste resulting from such erosion is
soon deposited in deep water. A little later in the cycle, these currents sweeping over the wave-cut terraces and beaches are able to

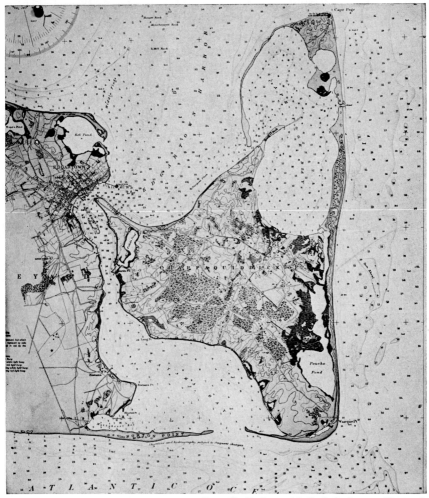

From U. S. Coast and Geodetic Survey, Chart 346.

FIG. 273. — Spits, offshore bars, connecting bars, lagoons and ponds, Massachusetts.

transport sediment stirred up by the waves into deep water where
it is deposited. These deposits may eventually reach the surface
of the water to make *spits, connecting bars* or *tombolos, hooks* and

loops. The sediment agitated by waves and carried along by these currents is called *shore drift.* In many places it is augmented by sediment brought in by streams. In some cases the littoral currents do not follow a definite course as they enter deep water. Then the shore drift is spread over the sea or lake floor, making *shoals* instead of bars or spits.

Spits. — On an irregular coastline the littoral current rarely follows all the indentations; instead, it tends to hold its course out into

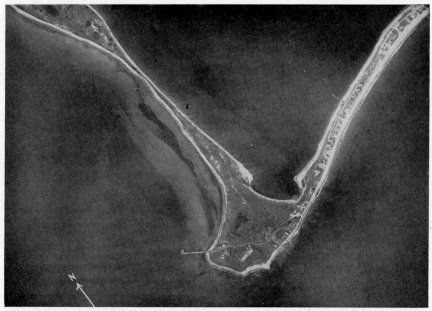

Photo by U. S. Army Air Corps. From "The Face of the Earth as Seen from the Air." Pub. by Am. Geographical Society, N. Y.

FIG. 274. — Two connecting bars, Long Island Sound.

the mouths of bays or into any deep water between land areas. As it enters the deeper water, it loses some of its velocity and the sediment it has been carrying is dropped. As more material is brought in by the current, the *embankment* grows longer, wider and higher. Eventually it is built up nearly to the water surface, and one end is attached to the headland. Incoming waves erode the outer edge of the embankment and wash the material up the slope, finally, aided by wind, building the deposit *above* the surface of the

water. The growing embankment directs the littoral current farther out into the deep water where more material is deposited.
This deposit of sediment which projects out into deep water from
an island or a headland is called a *spit*. The normal form of a spit
is slightly concave seaward.

    Connecting Bars. — Where a spit is built clear across any stretch
of water, so that it joins islands, headlands or islands and headlands, it is a *connecting bar*. Some authorities prefer to use the
term *bay bars* for bars that connect headlands across the mouths
of bays, and reserve the word *tombolo* to designate a bar that ties
islands together. This leaves no significant term for the bars that
connect islands with the mainland. Since all these are elongated
spits formed in essentially the same way, the Italian word tombolo
is unnecessary, as is the term bay bar. The
term connecting bar seems to fulfill all the
requirements. If tidal currents are strong,
or if the bay behind the growing spit receives much drainage from the land, the
sediment may be swept away so that connecting bars are not entirely completed.
Tidal scour, in many places, forms deep
inlets which connect the open sea with the
bays behind the bars.

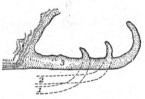

Fig. 275. — The development
of a hook, or recurved
spit.

    Hooks, or Recurved, Spits. — The littoral currents that form
spits are not always continuous. Also, they may encounter strong
conflicting currents. As a result, the shore drift at the end of a
spit may be deflected from its normal position and be deposited at
some angle to the main spit. The new deposit may be made either
seaward or landward. If it is seaward, it will soon be demolished
by storm waves, but if it grows toward the land, it is likely to become more or less permanent, forming a *hook, or recurved, spit*.
After one hook has formed, the spit may continue to grow longer,
and a second hook be formed beyond the first one. In fact, it is
not uncommon to find a whole series of hooks on the landward side
of a spit. These are called *compound hooks*, or *compound recurved
spits*. Hooks and spits become relatively permanent in position
when a balance has been reached between the work of littoral cur-

rents that tend to lengthen the embankments and conflicting currents that wash the deposits away. Sandy Hook (really a slightly hooked spit) at the mouth of New York Bay has advanced and retreated only 2,700 feet in 175 years.

Loops. — Under exceptional conditions opposing currents may encounter littoral currents in such a way that hooks grow landward until they connect with the coastline, thus forming *loops*.

Cycle of Development of Shorelines of Submergence. — We may now summarize the conditions that attend the various stages of shoreline development and note the topography characteristic of each stage. The cycle is comparable to that of stream erosion. It may be interrupted by crustal movements, and the topography of nearby shorelines may vary greatly in development, depending on the nature of the rocks, the configuration of the coastline and the strength of waves and currents; thus, youthful and mature topographic features may occur near one another on the same shoreline.

Initial Stage. — Assuming considerable submergence of a coast of moderate relief, the initial shoreline will be very irregular. Drowned stream-cut or glacial valleys give deep bays separated by high ridges and prominent headlands. Islands which were formerly part of the mainland may abound.

Youthful Stage. — In the early periods of wave-attack, shorelines become even more irregular in detail than in the initial stage. The waves proceed at once to etch the coastline, taking advantage of structural or lithologic conditions that favor rapid erosion and producing a *crenulate shoreline*. In early youth a notched sea-cliff and a narrow wave-cut terrace at the foot of the cliff with occasional temporary beaches on the backshore and isolated *stacks, chimneys, arches* and other irregular erosion remnants standing on the wave-cut platform are prominent topographic forms. Where irregular narrow peninsulas extend well out into the sea, waves may cut through the narrow necks, leaving arches or islands. In early youth, a few large islands will be formed in this way; later the number may be greater but the islands will be smaller. In late youth, after the wave-cut plain is well developed, the headlands are considerably removed by waves and shore currents. Beaches litter the shore; spits, hooks and connecting bars extend out into the deep water from headlands and islands. Another rather picturesque but uncommon topographic form characteristic of this stage is a sea-cliff on a headland or island from which two spits extend out into the water, one on either side. Offshore bars may occur at variable distances from the coastline. *Lagoons* may be formed behind either connecting bars or offshore bars.

Mature Stage. — In the mature stage of development of shore-lines of submergence, the topography characteristic of youth has largely disappeared. The marine or lake forces have become well adjusted to the shorelines on which they are working. Small islands, spits, connecting bars, etc., have been removed by wave erosion. The headlands have been cut back even with or beyond the heads of the original bays. The sea-cliffs are strongly weathered by atmospheric agencies and their slopes are reduced. Also, the general height of the coast near the shore has been lowered by wind and streams. Offshore the shore currents and waves are adjusted to the wave-cut terrace. Littoral currents may sweep sediment for long distances. The beach profile of equilibrium is well established, and the only beaches of consequence are on the backshore at the foot of the sea-cliffs. Few regions have reached full maturity, but the west coast of extreme southern Italy and the shores of southeastern England are cited as examples.

Old Stage. — By the time that an old stage of shoreline development is reached, the land agents of erosion should have worn the coast nearly or quite to sea level, while waves and currents were reducing the shore to a gently sloping plain. Therefore, the relief should be low both on coast and shore. No good examples of old shorelines of submergence are known, probably because the land does not stand still long enough to allow this stage to be reached

Cycle of Development of Shorelines of Emergence

The treatment of this phase of the subject departs from that in the preceding pages. The work of waves, littoral and tidal currents has already been outlined and need not be repeated. In this section topographic features produced by the various processes are discussed under the stage of which they are most typical.

The preceding discussion has shown that waves and currents tend to make the floors of lakes and seas near shore smooth and uniform through long-continued erosion and deposition; therefore, a typical shore of emergence would be an uplifted marine or lake floor of low relief. In the case of lakes the same results would be obtained through a permanent lowering of the water. Back of the shoreline there might be a coastal plain which slopes gently seaward, extending out an indefinite distance under water. On the landward side of such a plain, sea-cliffs, caves and other topographic forms characteristic of the former shore may be present. Off the west coast of Florida the slope of the submarine plain is so gentle that at an average distance of 8 miles from the shoreline the water is only 18 feet deep. Suppose such a region emerged above the sea; waves, tides and littoral currents would at once begin their attack, but the resulting topography in initial and youthful stages would be very different from that in the same stages of a shoreline of submergence. On the coast back of a new shoreline of emergence *topographic unconformities* are common. Before the emergence, streams may have dissected the land deeply and have formed youthful or mature valleys. During and following emergence, the streams are lengthened and start to cut new valleys across the uplifted plain. Therefore, the older valleys are upstream and the younger ones are nearest the sea (Fig. 265).

The Initial Stage. — The initial shoreline of a slightly uplifted marine or lake plain would be nearly straight and regular. The shore of Argentina southeast of Buenos Aires is of this type. At low tide great *tidal flats* occupy the shore. Back of the shore is a nearly flat coastal plain.

Nip. — The first work of waves on a shoreline of emergence is to cut a notch and low cliff in the edge of the plain, at the coastline. This cliff, slightly notched at the base, is called a *nip*.

Offshore Bars. — If a marine or lake plain slopes gently out under the water, the larger waves will break some distance from the shoreline. The distance will depend on the depth of water and height of the waves. Great sea waves may break several miles from the coast. The undertow from the breaking waves carries some loose material that lies on the submerged plain out into deeper water, but some is thrown shoreward by advancing waves. The two processes combine to form an offshore bar roughly parallel with the shoreline.

Youthful Stage. — The offshore bar and the original *nipped* coastline now furnish an outer and an inner shoreline, both of which are subject to water attack. The inner shoreline, being well protected by the offshore bar, is subjected to slight wave attack; but before the bar has grown above water through the combined action

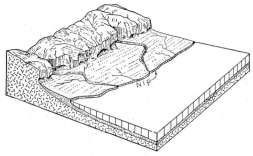

Fig. 276. — Nip on a shoreline of emergence, with elevated wave-cut cliffs and caves in the background.

of waves and wind, tidal currents may erode or deposit material behind the bar.

Lagoons. — The water between the coastline and an offshore bar is called a *lagoon*. If streams bring in much sediment from the land, the lagoon may become filled, extending the coastline out to the bar. In many places tidal currents help in this process. Where the scour of currents is not too great, *marshes* or *swales* *may* form due to the growth of vegetation in the lagoon. However, tidal currents are likely to keep *runways* open until the lagoon is nearly filled.

Tidal Inlets. — As the offshore bar grows, at first its height is variable, and tides ebb and flow over the low places. If the scour of the tides equals or exceeds the work of the waves, the low places will remain open as *tidal inlets* after the rest of the bar has grown well above sea level. However, as the bar increases in size, littoral currents sweep sediment along the outer face of the bar, thus combining with wave work in attempting to close the inlets.

In many cases the inlets are finally closed and offshore bars many miles in length occur without inlets crossing them. However, as the inlets become narrower the velocity of tidal currents is increased and, in some places, the tidal scour is great enough to keep the inlets open in spite of the conflicting waves and littoral currents. In

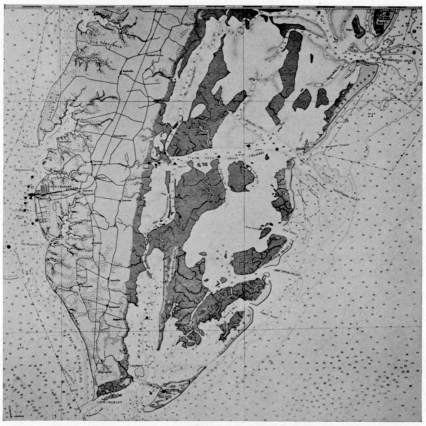

From U. S. Coast and Geodetic Survey, Chart 1222.

FIG. 277. — Offshore bars, tidal inlets and lagoon near the mouth of Chesapeake Bay.

this process the tides may be augmented by currents from streams which empty into the lagoons.

The work of waves is not always in conflict with tidal currents. Storm waves may widen existing inlets or they may reopen those that have been filled. Therefore, the occurrence and position of

tidal inlets as related to offshore bars represent an equilibrium in
conditions that involve erosion by waves, tidal and stream currents,
and deposition by waves and shore currents.   As lagoons become
increasingly filled with
sediment, tidal scour is, of
course, retarded.

*Migration of Offshore
Bars.* — After offshore
bars have attained con-
siderable size, they become
the objects of greatest
wave attack. In their early
history they may be built
seaward by deposits from
incoming waves. Erosion
on the outer side of the
bar eventually brings the
sea or lake floor to *wave-
base. Wave-base is the
depth beyond which sedi-
ments are not stirred by
waves.* When this condi-
tion is reached the outer
slope of the bar becomes
steeper due to wave at-
tack, and the bar is driven
landward and cut away in
similar fashion to the retreat of sea-cliffs. As the
bars migrate landward,
they become smaller, for
part of the original ma-
terial is carried away by
undertow and currents,

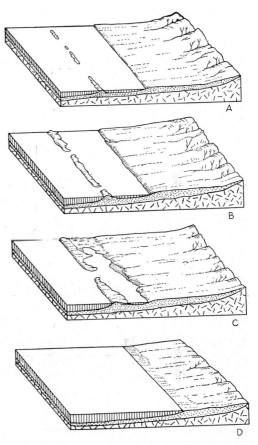

FIG. 278. — Four stages in the history of a shoreline of emergence. A represents an early
stage, B and C intermediate stages, and D
a late stage when the offshore bar has been
removed and the original shoreline is retreating landward due to the attack of
waves.

and part is washed over the bar toward shore by the advancing
waves. The lagoon behind the bar gets narrower until it may be
undercut and entirely obliterated.

Mature Stage. — In this stage of development of the shoreline of emergence, the lagoon, marshes, tidal inlets, nips and offshore bars have been destroyed. The original, gently sloping, subaqueous plain has been cut down to wave-base, and the waves in the deepened water are vigorously attacking the coastline, which is a low sea-cliff. The irregularities of youth have given way to simple outlines of maturity. Apparently few regions have reached this stage of development, but Gulliver cites the southeastern "toe" of Italy as an example, and Johnson regards the cliffs at Long Branch, New Jersey, as "bordering a mature shoreline."

Old Stage. — Theoretically the topography of old shorelines of emergence would not be very different from that of maturity. The coastline would continue to retreat before the wave attack. The resulting waste from the land would be transported by currents and deposited in deep water. Actually, no good examples of shorelines of this type are known.

Accidents in Shoreline Development

In discussing the cycle of stream erosion, it was noted that many conditions may interfere with the normal development of the topography. The same thing is true of cycles of shoreline development. Local uplifts or downwarpings of the land may occur at any stage. A good illustration of this is the Island of Crete, where the east end of the island has been sinking steadily for many years, while the west end has been emerging from the water. Volcanoes may pour lava or throw vast quantities of fragmental materials onto a shore; rivers build deltas in seas and lakes, defying the attack of waves and currents; therefore, the foregoing statements set forth general theoretical principles that in practice are subject to many modifications.

Submarine Canyons

While submarine canyons are not at present visible topographic features of coasts and shores, their distribution, origin and history are of interest to every physiographer, therefore, a brief discussion is included here.

Distribution. — Submarine canyons occur on both the Atlantic and Pacific continental shelves of North America and on the continental slopes off the seaward edge of the shelves. Thirty have been located off the coast of New England; others are found between Cape Cod and Cape Hatteras and in the Gulf of Mexico. About forty occur off the west coast between southern Mexico and Vancouver Island. Others are found on the shelf of eastern Asia from Korea to Formosa, around the Hawaiian Islands, off the mouth of the Ganges and Indus rivers of India, off the eastern, southern and western coasts of Africa (a particularly notable one being opposite the mouth of the Congo), off the coasts of Portugal, France and the British Isles. Altogether more than 100 are now known, and with the present development of *sonic sounding* many more, undoubtedly, will be discovered.

Characteristics. — The great majority of known canyons lie along the prolonged axes of present great river valleys. In 1863 Dana, in his *Manual of Geology*, described a great trough which can be followed from the mouth of the Hudson River to the outer edge of the continental shelf, a distance of

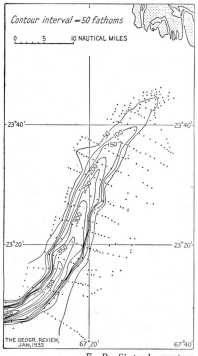

F. P. Shepard, courtesy Geographical Review, N. Y.

FIG. 279. — The submarine valley off the Indus Delta. Each dot represents a sounding. The apparent straightness of the course of the bottom of the valley may be due to an error in coordination of the soundings which were taken out of sight of land.

approximately 150 miles. Many other great trenches are similarly located. However, some do not appear to be the prolongation of present river valleys.

The canyons vary in width from less than one mile to more than three miles. The depths below the canyon rims usually range from

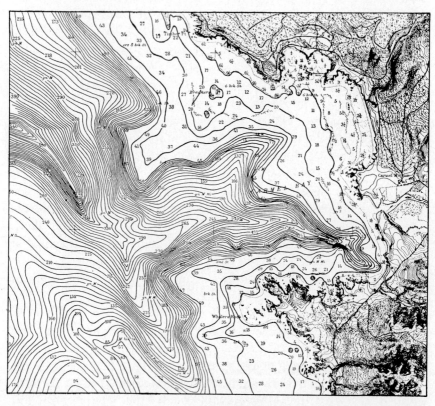

F. P. Shepard, Courtesy Geographical Review, N. Y.

FIG. 280. — The dendritic valley pattern of a submarine canyon off the Carmel River, California.   Contour interval 10 fathoms.

a few feet to about 3,000 feet, but some are very much deeper. Shepard has described canyons off the New England Coast 7,000 to 8,400 feet deep, with maximum depths not determined. Others more than 10,000 feet deep have been reported. Most of the trenches are V-shaped, the sides varying in slope from 3 to 45 degrees. Most of the canyons are sinuous, like many present-day river valleys, and many have tributaries with a dendritic pattern. The bottom gradients usually range from 5 to 50 feet to the mile, although in some cases the bottoms are hummocky as if partially filled by landslides. Dredging from the walls indicates that rocks of very different composition make up the sides of different canyons. Rocks recovered so far are granites, limestones, Cretaceous sandstones, Tertiary clays, and other clays and loess-like material of undetermined age.

Origin. — In considering the origin of these canyons, three types must be considered. First, there are some which *clearly* are drowned river valleys. Their origin is obvious. Second, there are comparatively shallow canyons which cross the continental shelf, and, third, there are the very deep, greatly submerged canyons that notch the continental shelf and extend down the continental slopes.

Various hypotheses have been advanced to explain the origin of the latter two types, not all of which can be considered here. For a more complete description of the canyons and discussion of their origin, the reader is referred to the references at the end of this chapter.

Recently Submerged River Canyons. — This hypothesis is the one most generally held by students of this subject. It seems to be valid in case of drowned river valleys, and the relatively shallow canyons that cross the continental shelves, but when applied to the great trenches on the margins of the continental shelves and on continental slopes, it leaves much to be explained. If emphasis is put on recent subsidence, it means that first the continental shelf must have been developed, then uplifted 6,000 to 10,000 feet. Canyons were then cut in the uplifted shelf some 6,000 to 10,000 feet deep; then general subsidence lowered the region by about the same amounts. This might happen in one region, but since it would have to apply to five continents, it seems improbable.

Ancient Submerged River Canyons. — When Shepard first studied these canyons, he offered the hypothesis that some of them might be very old canyons, possibly Paleozoic in age. He suggested that the canyons might have been filled by sea deposits and later emptied by sliding of the soft material down the continental slopes. Earthquakes were thought to have aided in opening the canyons by jarring the material loose. Pre-glacial canyons that were partially filled by sediment would almost certainly concentrate the currents that swept the continental shelves during the low sea water glacial epochs. These localized currents should have removed some of the filling and reopened the trenches. The discovery of late Tertiary sediments in the walls of canyons off both the New England and California coasts indicates plainly that many of the trenches are not so old as would be required by this hypothesis.

Structural Valleys. — It has been suggested by many people that the canyons may be sharply downfolded or faulted valleys, but the axes of many canyons are too sinuous to make this explanation reasonable, although it may hold in some cases. Also, most of the trenches are transverse to the coast rather than parallel as would be expected if they were structural valleys.

Counter Current Hypothesis. — In describing the great trench off the mouth of the Congo River, Buchanan advanced the hypothesis that a strong marine current ran landward to compensate for the seaward flow of the river. Lawson suggests that such a current might keep a trench open through a delta deposit made by a river. But the rocky nature of the sides of some canyons is not deltaic material and does not permit the application of this hypothesis to all canyons. Furthermore, the steep slope of the walls of many canyons is greater than the probable angle of rest of deltaic muds and silt. The lack of knowledge regarding deep counter currents also handicaps this hypothesis. The bottom of the Congo trench, cited by Buchanan, is reported to have quiet conditions rather than strong currents; in general, the deposits of fine silt and mud brought up by dredging from many deep canyon bottoms does not indicate the presence of strong scouring currents.

Density Currents. — In 1936 Daly suggested as a "working hypothesis" that the density of sea water might be increased by the receipt of silt from rivers. During the Pleistocene glacial epochs *when the sea level was lowered possibly as much as 300 feet*, storm waves and currents would stir up the mud on the continental shelves. The strong currents resulting from waves and tides weighted by the silt from the rivers and from the continental shelves would tend to dive under the cleaner, less dense water and move out across the continental shelf. On the continental slopes the velocity of these *density currents* might reach 1.2 to 1.8 miles per hour — an eroding rate — thus cutting trenches, particularly where pre-existing depressions concentrated the currents. Similarly, weighted water from the sides would accelerate the currents as the trenches were deepened.

The emphasis of this hypothesis on the lowering of sea level during glacial epochs, and the probability of storm waves and strong currents at those times is undoubtedly an important contribution to the discussion of the origin of these canyons. However, the rocky walls of many canyons, the deep trenches on the margins of the continental shelves far below the 300-foot level suggested in the hypothesis, the improbability of definite strong bottom currents at considerable depth, and the (so far) unknown general occurrence of density currents seem to leave the hypothesis still in the "working" stage. Some trenches may have been formed in this way, and Daly specifically states that the hypothesis does not apply to all types of canyons.

Glacial Control Hypothesis. — Recently, Shepard has elaborated the possible effects of Pleistocene glaciation. He postulates an ice cap over the Arctic Ocean, enlarges other areas of continental glaciation, and assumes that the ice in the central parts of the continental glaciers was four miles thick. Due to these conditions, he believes that the ocean surface was lowered at least 3,000 feet during the Pleistocene glacial ages. The idea that the glaciers were great enough to lower sea level by this amount is startling to the conservative investigators who have previously used 300 feet as a near maximum figure. However, if the ocean surface *was* lowered 3,000 feet, many canyons undoubtedly were formed by streams that carved trenches in the exposed continental shelves. Even then the origin of the very deep canyons is not yet explained. The supplementary hypothesis that Pre-Pleistocene lands stood higher than now, and that there has been general submergence of the borders of *all* the continents since the glacial epochs helps to explain the canyons on the present continental slopes, but this hypothesis is by no means proven.

Conclusions. — In spite of the fact that submarine canyons have been studied for more than half a century, the problem of their origin is not yet solved. Information obtained in recent years offers convincing evidence that *most* of the canyons were carved by rivers. Some of these are drowned valleys due to local subsidence of the land. Others formed during the Pleistocene glacial stages were submerged when the glaciers melted and the oceans were refilled. Some of the trenches may be of diastrophic origin. Density currents or other bottom currents may account for some shallow canyons cut in the unconsolidated sediments of the continental shelves. But it is inconceivable that such currents which at best must be feeble could cut the trenches in solid rocks, even granites, that have been described by Stetson and Shepard. However, such currents might be effective in opening or keeping open shallow canyons already in existence.

REFERENCES

1. Herbert A. Bauer: *The World Map of Tides.* Geog. Rev., Vol. 23, pp. 259–270, 1933.
2. Vaughn Cornish: *On the Dimensions of Deep Sea Waves, etc.* Geog. Jour., Vol. 23, pp. 623–645, 1904.
3. R. A. Daly: *Origin of Submarine Canyons.* Am. Jour. Sci., 5th Ser., Vol. 31, pp. 401–420, 1936.
4. W. M. Davis: *Geographical Essays.* Ginn and Co., 1909.
5. ———: *The Coral Reef Problem.* Am. Geog. Soc. Sp. Pub. No. 9, 1928.
6. N. M. Fenneman: *The Lakes of Southeastern Wisconsin.* Wisc. Geol. and Nat. Hist. Surv. Bull. 8, 1892.
7. G. K. Gilbert: *The Topographic Features of Shores.* U. S. Geol. Surv., 5th An. Rpt., pp. 69–123, 1885.
8. ———: *Lake Bonneville.* U. S. Geol. Surv., Mon. No. 1, 1890.
9. F. P. Gulliver: *Shoreline Topography.* Proc. Am. Acad. Arts and Sci., Vol. 34, pp. 151–258, 1899.
10. D. W. Johnson: *Shore Processes and Shoreline Development.* John Wiley and Sons, 1919.

11. ———: *The New England-Acadian Shoreline.* John Wiley and Sons, 1925.
12. ———: *Submarine Valleys.* Geog. Rev., Vol. 23, pp. 77–89, 1933.
13. ———: *The Underlying Causes of Submarine Canyons.* Geophys. Rev., Vol. 23, pp. 77–89, 1933.
14. ———: *Origin of Submarine Canyons.* Jour. Geomorph., Vol. 1, pp. 111–129, 230–243, 324–340, 1938.
15. I. C. Russell: *Lakes of North America.* Ginn and Co., 1900.
16. F. P. Shepard: *Canyons off the New England Coast.* Am. Jour. Sci., 5th Ser., Vol. 28, pp. 439–451, 1934.
17. ———: *Daly's Submarine Canyon Hypothesis.* Am. Jour. Sci., 5th Ser., Vol. 33, pp. 369–379, 1937.
18. ———: *Submarine Canyons. Distribution and Longitudinal Profiles.* Geog. Rev., Vol. 28, pp. 439–451, 1938.
19. National Research Council: *Oceanography* in Physics of the Earth, Vol. V, 1932.

CHAPTER XIII

TOPOGRAPHY DUE TO GROUND-WATER

Water in the cracks and pores of rocks of the lithosphere below the surface of the land is called *ground-water or underground-water*.

The presence of water in the ground is shown in many familiar ways. Nearly every one has seen springs in which water gushes from the ground. Wells, both drilled and dug, encounter water in many places. In many mines fissures are cut in the rocks through which water seeps or actually flows with a distinct current into the tunnels or shafts. Geysers periodically eject great quantities of water from the ground. Seepage water from the ground furnishes many lakes, swamps and rivers with a permanent supply of water. The total amount of water in the ground is unknown, but evidently is very large. It has been estimated that if all the water in the ground could be extracted and put on the surface of the lithosphere, it would be sufficient to form a layer more than 500 feet deep over the whole earth's surface. Some estimates are much greater; Slichter believes that the amount is sufficient to cover the earth to a depth of 3,000–3,500 feet.

SOURCES OF GROUND-WATER

There are three principal sources of ground-water. First and most important is water precipitated from the atmosphere, *meteoric water*, which falls as rain or snow. This water sinks into the ground through joints, faults, pores and cavities in the rock as well as along the stratification planes of folded sedimentary or meta-sedimentary rocks. The importance of this supply of water is clearly indicated by the fact that in many places in times of drought springs dry up, the water level in wells is lowered, and in mines seepage water disappears.

A second source of ground-water is *connate water*. This is water left in the pores of sedimentary rocks that were laid down in seas or lakes. It occurs chiefly in various kinds of sandstones and when encountered by drill holes is usually salty, having about the composition of sea water. Connate water apparently is sealed in these porous beds by surrounding impervious rocks, such as shales, and does not move freely through the rocks of the earth. In most cases such water has remained in the rocks for many thousands of years.

Another source of ground-water is *magmatic water*. Some minerals contain water as an essential part of their composition. When rocks become liquid due to internal earth processes and rise to or toward the earth's surface, magmatic water escapes from the liquid rock (*magma*) and spreads out through pores and fractures into the surrounding rocks. Most deposits of such metals as gold, silver, lead and copper are believed to be due to precipitation from highly mineralized magmatic waters.

Depth To Which Ground-Water Sinks

The amount of water in the ground and the depth to which it sinks vary greatly in different places. Wells have been drilled for water or oil in compact shales or certain types of igneous rocks thousands of feet deep without finding any water. In other regions where the rocks are porous or highly jointed or fractured, water has been encountered in large quantities at all depths up to more than a mile.

The limiting factors in determining the depth to which water may sink are the pore spaces or openings in rocks through which water may move. As depth increases, the weight of the overlying rocks becomes greater until finally a depth is reached where the strength of the rocks is unable to withstand the crushing weight of the overlying load. This depth is believed to be about 6 miles below the earth's surface where the pressure of the rocks must be at least 5 million pounds per square foot. This pressure is probably sufficient to close all pores and cavities in the rocks and thus limit the downward movement of water in the ground. As a matter of fact, very little water descends anything like this distance below the surface. Many deep mines are practically dry at the bottom, and it is probable that *most* ground-water (there are some notable exceptions) occurs within a few thousand feet of the earth's surface.

The Movement of Ground-Water

That water moves in the ground is plainly shown by many familiar examples. Wells are pumped dry, yet soon refill with water. Strong flows of water through fractures in rocks are frequently encountered in mine and railroad tunnels. Underground rivers have been discovered in great caverns. Except for the water that actually flows in such openings as fissures and caverns, the movement of ground-water is very slow. The exact rate depends upon the porosity of the water-bearing horizons, the head or height of the water column in the rocks, and other less important factors. The greater the head, the greater the amount of porosity, and the greater the size of the pores, the more rapid will be the movement. Different measurements that have been made indicate that the rate of movement of ground-water through average sandstone is from one to three miles a year. In open channels the rate is, of course, much greater.

Water may move very long distances underground. Artesian wells in western Kansas and Nebraska derive their water supply from a geologic formation known as the Dakota sandstone which outcrops on the east flank of the Rocky Mountains 200 miles or more away. The water which falls as rain and snow on the slopes of the mountains is carried out underneath the Great Plains in the porous sandstone which is underlain and overlain by impervious shales. In such cases it is estimated that it requires a fall of at least 1 foot per mile to overcome friction and keep the water moving.

The Water Table

Water is by no means uniformly distributed below the surface of the ground. In some humid regions that are underlain by porous, highly jointed or unconsolidated rocks, the ground is saturated to a great depth. In other regions where the underlying rock is imper-

vious or the climate is arid, the ground may be very dry both immediately below the surface and at great depths. However, water
may be carried underground into arid regions from more humid
regions a long distance away.

The water table is the surface or undulating plane below which
the ground for some distance is saturated with water. Figure 86
shows the relations of the water table and the surface of the land
in a moderately humid region.

Perched Water Table. — It often happens that porous or
cavernous beds are not continuous beneath the land surface. Lens-
like masses of rock capable of holding considerable water may be
more or less completely en-
closed by impervious rocks,
giving rise to conditions illustrated by Figure 281.
Water which seeps into the
porous beds yields a supply
for wells or springs while the surrounding ground is barren of
water.

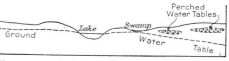

FIG. 281. — A diagram to show perched water tables.

Relations of Water Table to Lakes and Swamps. — When the
water table coincides with the surface of the land there is seepage
water which causes swampy ground, or if there are enclosed basins,
this water may give rise to lakes. Most swamps and many lakes
are supplied with water in this way.

Relations of Water Table to Streams. — As stated in Chapter
VIII most permanent streams depend directly on ground-water for
a constant supply. Where streams have cut their valleys below the
water table, seepage into the valley insures a permanent supply of
water (Fig. 86), while streams that have not so cut their valleys
may flow only seasonally or after heavy rains.

Springs

Springs are formed by water that issues from the ground with a
distinct current. Many kinds of springs are known: hot springs,
cold springs and mineral springs that contain various sorts of dissolved mineral matter.

The underground conditions that are favorable for the occurrence of springs are suggested by Figure 282. Any opening, usually a fault or more or less cylindrical fissure which connects the surface of the earth with the ground-water table may give rise to a spring. Since the amount of water in the ground fluctuates seasonally or through a period of years, the springs are likely to go dry or diminish their flow after periods of drought, or they may flow more freely than normal, as the famous hot springs of Yellowstone Park

FIG. 282. — A diagram showing the structure of one type of springs.

Philip Fix.

FIG. 283. — A hot spring, Yellowstone National Park.

did in 1938 when the ground-water table was raised, due to a series of years of excessive precipitation.

Wells

Wells may be dug or drilled. Permanent wells extend deep enough into the ground to penetrate the saturated rock below the water table. Artesian wells (named for deep-flowing wells at

Artois, France) are wells usually from 200 to several thousand feet in depth drilled into porous water-bearing formations (aquifers) that are underlain and overlain by impervious beds. The wells may flow due to the hydrostatic pressure or the water may be pumped to the surface of the land. Usually artesian water is pure, being well filtered and free from injurious solid substances, but many wells, contrary to popular belief, produce waters highly charged with chemicals. Therefore, "deep water" is by no means an assurance of "good water."

THE WORK OF GROUND-WATER

Both through its mechanical and chemical work ground-water profoundly alters the surface of the land. While neither activity is as widespread as are some other physiographic agents, the total results are very great, especially in humid regions where the amount of water in the ground is relatively great.

The Mechanical Work of Ground-Water

Water in the ground is one of the most important factors in causing or aiding *mass-movements* of the land. As a liquid it acts as a lubricant aiding gravity or earthquakes in causing rocks to split apart and to move. Although this work is more important in humid regions where mass-movements are common, it is also exceedingly important in semi-arid and even arid regions where the movements of great masses of the land are usually least likely to be prevented or reduced by vegetation. Meteoric waters are far more important than other ground-waters in causing or aiding landslides and related phenomena.

THE MASS-MOVEMENTS OF THE LAND

As indicated in previous chapters wind, streams, glaciers, waves and currents wear the land away a little at a time; while these types of erosion are relatively slow, the total geomorphic results are very great. We now come to very different types of erosion which occur locally and make immediate perceptible changes in the existing topography. Mass-movements of the land involve large masses of the land surface that move either slowly or quickly from one place to another. Usually they occur suddenly, and they may be repeated many times. Good examples of mass-movements are landslides, avalanches, earthflows, soil-creep, solifluction and mudflows. Mudflows have been discussed in Chapter IX, and will not be repeated here. Mass-movements range in type from mudflows which contain *much* water to rockfalls and avalanches which contain *usually very little* water. While ground water is not a contributing factor to *all* types of mass-movements, it is of such general importance in *most* types that the whole subject may appropriately be considered in this chapter.

Landslides

Landslides are by far the most conspicuous of all mass-movements; usually they involve the largest volume of rock material, and

Whitman Cross, U. S. Geol. Survey.

FIG. 284. — Landslip Mountain near Rico, Colorado.

their topographic effects are most pronounced. A landslide may be defined as a sliding or falling of a relatively *dry* mass of rock, earth, or both. Thus landslides are distinguished from mudflows, earthflows, soil-creep and solifluction by the small amount of water in the material that is moved. Varieties of landslides are slumps, debris slides, debris or rock falls, and rockslides. There are all possible gradations from one type to another. *Slumps* usually are masses of rock or earth displaced for only a short distance. *Debris slides* and *rockslides* may involve millions of cubic feet of material that has moved hundreds or thousands of feet. *Debris falls* and *rockfalls* are materials that have dropped from or over vertical cliffs under the influence of gravity.

Causes. — Landslides are usually caused by a combination of conditions which may be divided into (1) the inherent or passive nature of the material itself and (2) active or initiating factors. While ground-water is in part — perhaps chiefly — responsible for most great slides, many other factors may be involved.

Inherent Factors. — The basic conditions which favor landslides are classified by Sharpe [1] as lithologic, stratigraphic, structural and topographic. *Lithologic conditions* that are favorable to landslides are clay rocks that become slippery and act as lubricants or flow under pressure; decomposed rocks, such as volcanic materials, talc, serpentine, micaceous schists, bentonite, etc., all of which are easily lubricated by ground-water; rounded sand, pebbles and various soils, glacial till, alluvial deposits and lacustrine beds. Favorable *stratigraphic conditions* are alternating layers of sediments or any heavy massive layers overlying shales or other beds that slip when wet. *Structural conditions* that aid landslides include bedding planes that dip down steep slopes; highly jointed rocks, especially those that parallel steep slopes; faulted, slickensided or any crushed rock; steeply folded rocks.

The Active Causes. — The important factors that actually cause landslides are removal of support, overloading, lubrication, earth vibrations, wedging action, or the placing of materials on a slope steeper than its normal angle of repose through natural or artificial causes. *The removal of support* is most frequently accomplished by undercutting by streams or waves, although glaciers or wind may produce similar results. The ground may be saturated with water,

[1] C. F. Stewart Sharpe: *Landslides and Related Phenomena.* Columbia University Press, pp. 84–85, 1938.

allowing the land on higher ground to move; coal beds may be mined or burned, thus removing support. A famous sliding mountain at Durango, Colorado, was largely the result of weakening the rocks through coal mining. Soluble materials, such as limestone or salt, may be dissolved; man, in countless ways, such as mining, quarrying, digging canals, making excavations for roads, foundations of buildings or railroads, may remove support and cause landslides. The great slides of the Culebra Cut, Panama Canal, were directly caused by excavations made by man.

Overloading may be caused in several ways, such as saturation of the land by water or ice, avalanches or rockfalls from higher ground, filling for roads or dumping of waste from mines and quarries.

Lubrication is caused by the accumulation of water or ice in the ground. It is particularly likely to cause slides along faults, in ground composed of shales, decomposed volcanic rocks, schistose rocks, or others that are subject to rapid chemical decay. Notable small slides occurred a few years ago in Middle Park, Colorado, when road-builders cut into a great mass of talus whose openings were completely filled with ice. As the ice melted on exposure to the air, the material of the whole slope slid down. Many small slides are caused by saturating the ground through leakage from reservoirs, canals, irrigating ditches, etc.

Earthquakes, volcanoes, the collapse of roofs of caverns, blasting, or even the passage of trains and heavy trucks may cause *earth tremors* which start landslides. Howe believes that many of the great landslides of the San Juan mountains in Colorado were due to ancient earthquakes. There are numerous accounts of modern volcanic explosions in which landslides played a prominent part in the devastation of a region. Also, tremors due to thundering avalanches and snowslides or landslides may cause other land to move. *Wedging apart of rocks* on steep slopes by roots of trees, frost action, expansion due to chemical decay of minerals, swelling due to the formation of colloids, pushing apart of rocks by animals or man — all may cause landslides. The writer well remembers accidentally dislodging a rock that weighed perhaps 40 pounds while working his way along a narrow ridge (Fig. 72) on Mount Shavano in central Colorado. The rock, rolling down a talus channel, hit a second rock, then another and another; soon hundreds of tons of rocks were moving down the slope. Similar slides due to natural causes are of daily occurrence in high mountains all over the world.

Over-steepened slopes are not uncommon. Faults with steeply dipping planes frequently leave slopes so steep that slides occur. Man, often deliberately, makes fills for roads or throws out waste from mines and quarries on slopes steeper than the normal angle of

Whitman Cross, U. S. Geol. Survey.

FIG. 285. — Landslide topography in the San Juan Mountains, Colorado.

rest for the material. Under such conditions, slides continue until the angle of rest (about 35° for coarse material) is attained.

Landslide Topography. — The great variety of conditions caus-ing landslides implies a similar variety of topographic forms. Most slides occur on moderately steep to very steep slopes. Therefore, their topography usually is related to that of mountain slopes, valley walls or valley floors.

Scars. — Great scars on the sides of mountains (Fig. 286) with an irregular accumulation of debris at the base almost invariably indicate a landslide. However, many slides do not move very far; moreover, they do not move all at once. Therefore, a gigantic *rippled* appearance of a mountain side or valley wall (Fig. 70) also is characteristic of landslide topography.

E. G. Fine.

FIG. 286. — Landslide, or avalanche scars, near Telluride, Colorado.

Terraces. — Small terraces, many with a distinct backward surface slope, are common results of multiple slumping. When the slip or slump occurs, there is a tendency for backward rotation of the top as the bottom slides out (Fig. 287). On Grand Mesa, Colorado, there is a lava flow capping sedimentary rocks, consist-

ing of shales, sandstones and coal. Due to slumping, many narrow
lake basins have been formed with their longer axes parallel to the
edges of the mesa. Similar slumps are found on a grand scale in
the Columbia Plateau of Washington and Oregon.

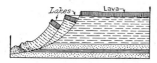

FIG. 287. — Lake basins due
to slumping, Grand
Mesa, Colorado.

FIG. 288. — Recession of canyon walls due to slump-
ing.

Recession of Canyon Walls. — In regions such as the Colorado
Plateau, there are thousands of small, deep, youthful canyons tributary to larger ones. In many places the plateau remnants between

A. J. Eardley.

FIG. 289. — Slumps in frozen muck on the bank of the Yukon River due to undercutting.

the canyons are capped by resistant sandstones which are underlain
by shales. Most of the small canyons have only tiny intermittent
streams in them, and many are dry practically all the time. The
rate of erosion and recession of the canyon walls is tremendously

increased by slumping which causes great blocks of the protective rim rock to break off. The same principle, of course, applies to all conditions both arid and humid where a cap or rim rock is underlain by shale or other rock that becomes slippery when wet.

Widening of Meanders. — Slumping is of especial importance in the widening of stream meanders. As the streams undercut their banks, the walls, particularly if composed of alluvium, slump down, thus aiding materially in the work of the stream. In regions where clays are thoroughly dried out and cracked open, then saturated by heavy rains, slumping is particularly common.

Hillside Terraces. — On many grassy hillsides, more commonly where the slopes are quite steep, one frequently sees small, nearly horizontal terraces which appear to be the paths of animals. Some undoubtedly are animal tracks, for most animals that feed on steep slopes move around rather than up and down the hills. But many such terraces occur where no animals are known to have grazed and are the result of innumerable small slumps of the soil.

Debris-Slides. — These result from the saturation by water and sudden sliding of unconsolidated mantle rock which may consist entirely of soil or a mixture of soil and boulders. The topography resulting from such a slide is a series of hummocks and depressions somewhat resembling a ground moraine; or it may simply be an irregular deposit on a hillside or valley floor. Slides involving thousands or millions of cubic yards of debris are not unusual.

Rockslides. — Rockslides are of daily occurrence in most high mountains of the earth. They differ from debris-slides in that solid rock is detached from its surroundings. The great talus cones and slopes (Figures 71 and 72) found near the base of bare mountain slopes indicate the prevalence of these slides. In addition recent catastrophic slides give some idea of the volume of material and extent of some of the great slides. In 1903 a rockslide at Frank, B. C., came down the north slope of Turtle mountain, covered more than two square miles of the valley floor, and ran up the opposite valley wall some 400 feet. It is estimated that more than 35,-000,000 cubic yards of rock were involved. The slide rock consists of boulders of all sizes up to ten or twelve feet in thickness which are now scattered irregularly over the region.

R. D. Crawford.

FIG. 290. — A great rockslide on Mount Keyes, Sawatch Range, Colorado.

George A. Grant, U. S. Dept. of the Interior.

Fig. 291.—The Gros Ventre Landslide, Wyoming, 1925.

The Gros Ventre slide in 1925 was a combined rock and debris slide. The volume of mantle rock and boulders involved in this slide is estimated at 50,000,000 cubic yards. The slide moved some 2,000 feet and made a dam more than 200 feet high across a valley, backing up water in the temporary lake thus formed for five miles.

Rockfalls and Debris-Falls. — These falls, which are due to rocks or debris that fall over or from vertical cliffs, give rise to irregular heaps or ridges at the foot of such cliffs. Loess bluffs, the vertical heads of cirques, rivers with high, steep banks, and canyon walls, particularly those rimmed by lava or resistant sandstone, are suitable places for such falls. The amount of rock fragments or unconsolidated debris that accumulates under such conditions often is surprisingly great.

Avalanches

Snow and debris-avalanches *"run"* frequently in nearly all high mountains where snow accumulates, or where thick mantle rock becomes saturated with water on steep slopes. The movement of the two types of avalanches is similar, but the debris-avalanche sweeps trees, houses, and everything in its path with it, leaving a deep, narrow scar on the mountain slope and an irregular or, in some cases, a fan-shaped mixture of rocks, earth and vegetation at the foot of the slope. Avalanches move so rapidly that they are catastrophic in nature.

Earthflows

Earthflows, usually accompanied by slumping, are not unusual in artificial fills, river banks, glacial drift, and on relatively low slopes where shales or other rocks of similar nature become saturated with water. One of the largest earthflows on record has been described by Dawson. The bank of Riviere Blanche in Quebec suddenly gave way, allowing some 3,500,000 cubic yards of clay and sandy silt to flow through a passage only 200 feet wide in about 4 hours. The area from which the flow came was about one-fifth of a square mile. The debris dammed the river and filled the channel for a distance of two miles. In this great earthflow, clays saturated with water lay beneath a sandy cultivated soil. When the flow started, the top layers "floated" on the saturated clay "like steamers on a river."

Earthflows of similar nature are known to have occurred in the St. Lawrence River Valley, in New York, Maine, Ohio, West Virginia, Pennsylvania, and in many other places. Irregular and usually shallow scars are left where the flows began, while the material of the flow forms irregular hummocks, ridges, etc., many of which are similar in topography to that of ground moraines.

Land-Creep

Mantle rock, soil, talus and rocks all have a tendency to creep down slopes. The creep is faster on steep slopes, but occurs on slopes whose angle is as low as 4 or 5 degrees. While the movement is much more pronounced in temperate and cold humid regions where water freezes in the ground, it is by no means confined to such regions. Noticeable creep may occur in both tropical and arid regions.

Soil-Creep. — Open, porous soils, particularly those that contain rounded grains and those that take up water easily are especially likely to creep. The evidence of creep is seen in fence posts out of alignment, curved trees, broken retaining walls, railroad tracks moved out of position, and lines of stones on gentle slopes that have been moved some distance from their source.

The principal causes of soil-creep are gravity, water in the soil, drying and cracking of the ground, wedging by roots, and particularly frost. Where open porous soils are filled with ice, small tufts of earth are lifted above the general surfaces of the land. When the ice melts, the earth moves down the slope. This process repeated many times causes a down-slope migration of vast quantities of material. Frost also causes wedging in the soil which tends to move down slopes. Water in the soil lubricates it and aids gravity in moving it down hill.

Topographic Effects of Soil-Creep. — The most important effects of soil-creep are (1) aiding erosion through sheetwash, streams and wind, (2) accumulation of earth at the foot of steep slopes, (3) peculiar low crescent-shaped scarps separated by small terraces — the whole sometimes called *stepped crescents* — that are particularly numerous in shallow arroyos on the High Plains, (4) shallow channelless depressions, such as have been described by Sauer in the Peninsular Range of California.

Talus-Creep. — Ordinarily talus is composed of coarse angular boulders without much soil. But there are all gradations in size from enormous blocks of rock to fine mantle rock which approaches soil in composition. Talus on steep slopes in mountainous regions is particularly likely to creep. As boulders fall due to frost-wedging and gravity from the cliffs above the talus, they build up heaps of rock whose surface slope may reach 35 degrees, which is the maximum angle at which the blocks will lie on the slope. At the foot of such slopes, the boulders tend to spread out in a fringe or sheet-like form.

Being composed chiefly of angular rock fragments, talus holds very little water. But in regions of heavy snow, the talus may acquire large quantities of ice. Due to repeated alternate freezing and thawing of the ice in the spaces between the boulders, the expansive force of the freezing water and the lubrication of water, the talus tends to creep down slopes. This process is aided by water in the upper part of the talus moving on the unthawed ice in the lower layers.

Topographic Forms due to Talus-Creep. — In Alaska, the San Juan Mountains and the Alps, great glacier or stream-like tongues of rock waste exactly like the material of a talus extend out from glacial cirques or from the foot of steep cliffs. These talus tongues have longitudinal ridges parallel with the sides of the mass and concentric ridges and depressions near the lower end. They have been given various names, such as *rock or talus glacier, rock stream, rock river,* etc. Several different explanations of their origin have been proposed, but apparently most rock glaciers fall into one of the following classifications: (1) Some may be the actual remains of true glaciers. In its dying stages the glacier melted until its surface was covered by boulders, but continued movement of the ice beneath the surface gave the characteristic form with concentric ridges and depressions and steep front. (2) Most so-called rock-glaciers seem to be the result of talus-creep due to causes described above.

Solifluction

Solifluction from *solum*, soil, and *fluere*, to flow, is a term proposed by Andersson to designate *the slow flowing from higher to lower ground of masses of soil or earth saturated with water*. This process differs from soil-creep in that it is faster, and differs from mudflows of semi-arid or volcanic regions in that the flow is not confined to channels. Through accepted usage solifluction has become associated particularly with cold climates of high latitudes or high altitudes. Favorable conditions are steep slopes, soil free from vegetation, an abundant supply of water in the soil, and frozen ground which thaws from the surface downward and remains frozen below a shallow depth, thus preventing rain or snow water from penetrating the ground more than a few feet. Under these conditions the soil over large areas may become saturated with water and actually flows down the slopes.

Topographic Effects of Solifluction. — The most important effect of solifluction is in aiding other forms of erosion. The earthy material that is almost "floated" down steep slopes is made easily available for removal by streams, glaciers, and, more rarely, by the wind. Locally, however, depressions are filled, small terraces are formed, especially above timber line, and broad summits are flattened. Local *sags* from which the soil has flowed are common in regions of solifluction. In many cases the lower ends of soil flows are steep and rampart-like in form. Bretz [1] has described many examples of solifluction in Greenland showing particularly the terraces with their typical characteristics.

THE CHEMICAL WORK OF GROUND-WATER

The chemical work of ground-water is extremely varied and geologically is very important. However, from a geomorphic point of view it is relatively simple.

As was stated in Chapter VI, ground-water is an active agent in causing the decay of rocks and thus preparing the land for erosion.

[1] J Harlen Bretz: *Physiographic Studies in East Greenland* (*in The Fiord Region of East Greenland*). Am. Geog. Soc., Special Pub. No. 18.

In addition, certain surface and underground forms are the direct result of the solvent action of ground-water that is charged with chemicals of various kinds.

Pure water is a poor solvent of most minerals or rocks, although it does attack salt beds readily; but when charged with certain substances, notably carbon dioxide, it becomes an active solvent of limestones and other rocks. Evidence of this action is shown by minerals that are dissolved in the waters of many springs, wells and mines. The walls of tunnels and shafts of some mines are coated with minerals that have been deposited recently by ground-water. The "hard" water of wells and springs is due to calcium carbonate, gypsum, or other chemical compounds taken into solution by water during its passage through the earth. For example, Silver Springs, Florida, brings to the surface of the ground 600 tons of mineral matter, mostly calcium carbonate, every day.

Caves

Caves and caverns have excited the interest of people from remote antiquity to the present time. They have provided shelter for man almost from the time of his advent on the earth. In Europe one still may find the implements and drawings made by men of the Stone Age who lived in caves during one of the Pleistocene interglacial ages. In the United States, modern men have set apart cave regions as National Parks and Monuments because of their great interest to scientists and other nature lovers.

The Formation of Caves. — Caverns are formed in several different ways, but here we are interested only in those made through the action of ground-water. The rocks in which most caves occur are salt, gypsum, dolomite and limestone, with the latter by far the most important.

Ground-water charged with the necessary chemicals seeps along stratification and joint planes or other cracks in the rock, and slowly dissolves the soluble rocks. Wholly stagnant ground-water soon becomes saturated with minerals and loses its effectiveness in the cave-making process. Therefore, it is necessary that there be such a condition of underground drainage that the saturated water can move away with its chemical load and be replaced with a new supply of water which is capable of continuing the solvent action. This

FIG. 292. — A diagram to show the formation of caves through the solvent action of ground-water.

underground drainage is most effective above the water table, but there is abundant evidence of ground-water movement well below this table. In fact, submarine springs of fresh water show clearly that water moves in the ground below sea-level.

As the solvent action goes on, the caves continue to grow; usually they are irregular in size and shape. Some are huge rooms; others are vast labyrinths of intricate branching passages. In some caves there are pools of

U. S. Geol. Survey.

FIG. 293. — The "Bottomless Pit," Arizona. The stream disappears, presumably into caverns below, through channels in limestone made through the leaching of ground-water along joint planes.

standing water; in others, there are large streams of moving water.

Stalagmites and Stalactites. — After limestone caverns have formed, it frequently happens that water seeping through the walls or the roof deposits calcium carbonate in the form of stalactites or stalagmites (sometimes called drip stones). The deposition from solution is brought about by (1) evaporation of the water, (2) reduction in pressure, (3) loss of gases. When the mineralized waters

George A. Grant, U. S. Dept. of the Interior.

FIG. 294. — A small cave in Wind Cave National Park, South Dakota. The white coating on some of the rocks is calcite deposited by ground-water.

ooze through the roof or side of a cave, any one or all three of these conditions may cause deposition of the mineral matter.

Stalactites are icicle-like forms that hang from the roofs of caves. Stalagmites are similar inverted forms built up from the floors of caves (Fig. 295). In many cases the two finally meet. Where the water emerges from the ceiling through a crack instead of a small hole, beautiful sheet deposits, curtain-like in form, are made. These often are called *drip stones.* An almost endless

George A. Grant, U. S. Dept. of the Interior.

FIG. 295.— "Drip stones" in the Queen's Chamber, Carlsbad Cavern National Park, New Mexico.

variety of beautiful and interesting adornments may be formed through deposition of calcite in limestone caves.[1] Timpanogos cave in Utah "floored with colored stalagmites and dripping ceilings studded with uncounted crystal stalactite formations" is said to be the most beautiful cave of its kind in America.

The Extent and Distribution of Caves. — It is wholly impossible in limited space to give an adequate conception of our knowledge of the caves of the world.   Hundreds of caves have been described in England, France and Greece.   The great Karst region on the east side of the Adriatic Sea is literally honey-combed with caves.   Limestone caves of great interest have been found in Africa and Southwestern Asia.   Scores occur in Bermuda and hundreds in Canada and Mexico.   In the United States at least thirty states have limestone caves of great size, beauty and general interest.   South Dakota, with its Wind Cave National Park; Tennessee, with more than 100 caverns; Oregon, with many caves in marble, beautifully decorated with stalactites and stalagmites; New Mexico, which has the world-famous Carlsbad caves with more than 21 miles of passages now explored; Missouri, which has hundreds of caves and remarkable underground drainage; Kentucky, with more than 100,000 miles of underground passages, many thousand sink holes and the Great Mammoth Cave as an outstanding feature; Indiana, one of the most important cave states of all; Colorado, California and Arizona — all with numerous caves, many unexplored, give some idea of the distribution of caverns in this country.

The Topography of Cave Regions

In some regions where the caverns are far below the surface of the ground, the topography gives no evidence of the underlying conditions, but where the caves are at shallow depths and where humid regions are underlain by a great thickness of limestone, salt or gypsum, the land surface includes many topographic features characteristic of cave regions.   Sinks, deep circular pools, disappearing streams, irregular basins with centripetal drainage, natural

[1] (See Willis T. Lee: *New Discoveries in Carlsbad Cavern.*   Nat. Geog. Mag., Vol. XLVIII, pp. 301–320, 1925.)

bridges and "Karst" topography, a maze of irregular elevations and depressions carved out of limestone, are all common topographic forms. Also local areas of subsidence, slumps and marshes may indicate the presence of caverns.

Sinks. — Limestone, salt and gypsum sinks are very numerous in cave regions. There are said to be between 60,000 and 70,000 sink holes in Kentucky alone.

A sink is an opening, usually more or less circular, which connects a cave and the land surface. It is formed by the roof of a

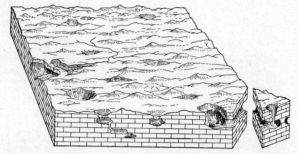

FIG. 296. — A diagram to show the formation of sinks and Karst topography.

cavern falling in. After the opening has been formed there is apt to be slumping of the soil or mantle rock around the rim.

Pools. — In some regions circular pools extend below the land surface to depths of several hundred feet. They are entirely solution cavities and are not necessarily bottomed in caves. Typical examples occur in Yucatan.

Centripetal Basins. — In regions where limestone caves occur at a moderate distance below the surface of the land, basins of irregular size and shape up to several miles in length are found, in which drainage is toward the center of the depression. Some of these were formerly sections of river valleys; others were plains or even hilly regions. In all cases the present basins are the result of subsidence of the land over caverns or over sedimentary beds that have become honey-combed by the solvent action of ground-water. Undoubtedly, the presence of ground-water in the rocks aids gravity in causing the subsidence of large land areas in this way. Sinks may or may not be found in the basins. Surface water that flows

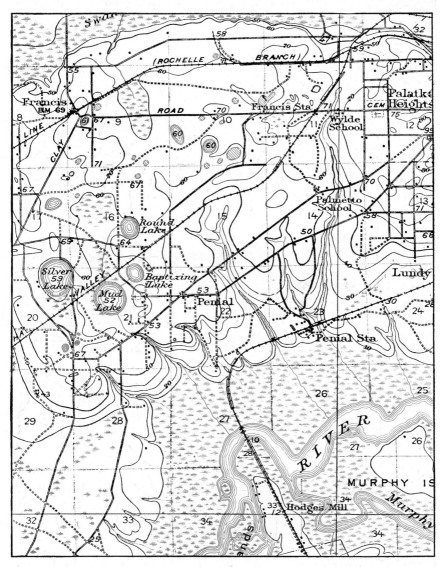

After U. S. Geol. Survey.

FIG. 297.—Part of the Palatka, Florida, topographic map. The circular lake basins are due to solution. Scale about 1 inch equals 1 mile. Contour interval 10 feet.

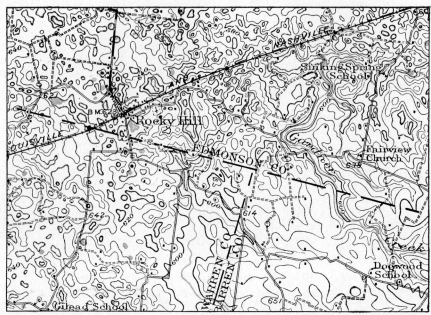

After U. S. Geol. Survey.

FIG. 298. — A section from Mammoth Cave, Kentucky, topographic map, showing Karst topography with sinks, depressions, disappearing streams and small hills. Scale approximately 1 inch equals 1 mile. Contour interval 20 feet.

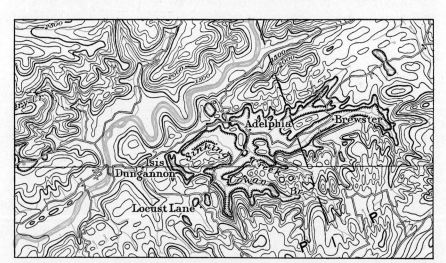

FIG. 298A. — A section from the Bristol topographic map, Virginia-Tennessee, showing, near the center, the subsidence of land due to the action of ground-water. Scale ½ inch equals one unit, contours intense 100 feet.

into the depressions disappears in sinks or cracks in the rock, and
descends into subterranean channels; some streams flow for miles
before they disappear. After flowing for some distance underground, the water may emerge again in the form of a stream.

Natural Bridges. — Natural bridges are formed in several different ways, but some types are the direct result of the chemical
work of ground-water and are of common occurrence in cave
regions. Where the roof at two ends of a cave falls in, leaving the
center in place, a natural bridge is formed. Also due to solution
along joint and bedding planes in limestones underlying a stream
valley, the water may be temporarily diverted underground where
it forms a new channel leaving a natural bridge.

Karst Topography. — In Karst on the east side of the Adriatic Sea, there is a region of very unusual topography that has developed through the solvent action of water both on and below the
surface of the land. The region is underlain by limestone in which
have been cut innumerable gullies, ravines, and short valleys. Sink
holes are scattered widely over the region, and many are very close
together. The narrow, irregular elevations that lie between the
depressions have steep slopes and fantastic forms. The surface of
the whole country is very rough. Because of its distinctive nature,
topography formed in this way is sometimes called *Karst topography*.

Hot Springs and Spring Deposits

Hot springs occur wherever ground-water sinks deeply into the
earth, remains long enough to be heated, and then finds its way
back to the surface through a natural opening. The depth to which
the water must sink in order to be heated depends upon the underground conditions. In Yellowstone Park, New Zealand and Iceland,
hot rocks lie comparatively near the surface of the land, and the
water is heated at a shallow depth. Hot water is a much better
solvent for most minerals than is cold water. Therefore, hot springs
may contain much mineral matter in solution. When the water
reaches the surface of the land, some of the minerals may be
precipitated through (1) reduction in temperature, (2) reduction
in pressure, (3) loss of gases that were in the water and tended

to keep the minerals in solution, (4) algae and other organisms that live in water and secrete mineral matter. In Yellowstone National Park alone there are more than 4,000 hot springs. Some have great deposits of travertine at their mouths; others deposit silica and still others deposit such materials as alum and sulphur.

Deposits. — The terraces at Mammoth Hot Springs in Yellowstone National Park are striking illustrations of deposits made by hot waters. The material of the terraces is chiefly travertine

F. E. Swisher.

Fig. 299. — Pulpit Terrace, Yellowstone National Park.

($CaCo_3$), which is dazzling white when fresh and pure, but which turns gray on weathering. Also algae that live in the water become imbedded in the travertine, giving red, brown or yellow colors to the deposits.

The terraces have been built up layer on layer from the bottom of the valley to a present height of about 1,000 feet. As the terrace building continues, the opening through which the hot water comes to the surface also rises so that the water is always emerging above the highest point of the terrace. As it flows over the shallow

basins on the surface of each little individual terrace, some travertine is deposited, thus increasing the height of the terrace. Some
water flows over the edge of one terrace and descends to the next
lower level. During this descent some precipitation of travertine
occurs on the outer side of the terrace thus making it wider. Not
all of the calcium carbonate is precipitated before the water leaves
the terraces. It is estimated that the Gardiner River, which receives the drainage from the Hot Springs, carries away 100 tons of
calcium carbonate in solution every day.

The hot springs are, of course, very old. In fact, they antedate the Pleistocene ice age, as is shown by the occurrence of glacial
boulders on Terrace Mountain, a great deposit of travertine situated 2 or 3 miles south of the present Mammoth Hot Springs. This
pre-glacial travertine deposit is more than 1,000 feet high, and
shows the stupendous amount of chemical work that has been done
by the springs.

Many of the Yellowstone springs do not build terraces, but like
some of the small geysers have funnel-shaped, small craterlike openings whose walls are encrusted with calcium carbonate or silica.
Some of these openings are beautifully colored by algae. Indigo,
Turquoise, Opal, Morning Glory and Emerald pools and Grand
Prismatic Spring are illustrative of these types. The color of Indigo
Pool is a deep blue, while that of Turquoise Pool is a delicate pale
blue. Opal Pool has a red and yellow border. In Emerald Pool
the water is a beautiful green, due apparently to a combination of
clear blue water and the reflected yellow from the algae that thread
through the mineral-coated walls. The colors of these and many
other pools are indescribably lovely.

Geysers and Geyser Deposits

Geysers are intermittent hot springs that from time to time spout
steam and hot water from their craters. More than 100 geysers
have been named and described in Yellowstone Park, and nearly
another hundred are known. Other fine examples are found in New
Zealand and Iceland. All known geysers are situated in regions of
present or recent volcanic activity, and are themselves an expression
of volcanism (Chapter XIV).

Geysers differ from ordinary hot springs chiefly in (1) their intermittent action, and (2) their ability to throw steam and water high (more than 300 feet in case of some of the Yellowstone Park geysers) into the air. One New Zealand geyser, Waimangu, is said to have spouted to a height of more than 1,200 feet.

The Nature of Geyser Action. — In Yellowstone Park many varieties of geysers are found. Nearly all are grouped in one of nine geyser basins, of which Norris, Upper, Lower, and Heart Lake

Fig. 300. — Norris geyser basin, Yellowstone National Park.

basins are perhaps the most noted. Nearly every year a new geyser appears in some one of the basins and almost as often another one ceases to erupt.

Most of the geysers fall into one of two broad groups: (1) those which erupt from open pools, and (2) those which have built up a cone and erupt through a small opening. The first group belongs to the "pool" type, and the second to the "nozzle" type. In eruptions from the pool type, tremendous sheets of water and steam are thrown into the air while in the second type only a thin column of steam and water is ejected.

New Zealand Government Photo, courtesy Canadian Pacific Railroad.

FIG. 301. — Pohutu Geyser, New Zealand.

Some geysers go into action with great regularity. Old Faithful, with an average interval of 64 minutes between eruptions, sets a standard for this type. Others are in almost constant but weak eruption. Many are very irregular in their activity, the intervals between eruptions varying from a few hours to many days. Some, like Excelsior and Old Faithful, eject immense quantities of water and steam 100 to more than 300 feet into the air, while others are so feeble that the water column is only a few inches, or at most a few feet high. When the Grand Geyser erupts, it plays for about 30 minutes; others complete an eruption in a few seconds. Peculiar mud geysers, lacking much water and steam, eject, almost constantly, small lumps of mud which rise a few feet into the air, then fall back into the pool and are thrown out again.

Philip Fix.

FIG. 302. — Vacuum Bottle Geyser, the "nozzle type," Yellowstone National Park.

Nearly all the larger geysers have their own characteristic whistling or roaring sound as the spouting begins. The sight and sound of a great geyser eruption with the magnificent column of steam and water which are thrown high into the air are things that no one is likely to forget! Of all the phenomena of Yellowstone Park, the geysers are the most interesting!

The Causes of Geyser Action. — In explaining the causes of geyser action, one must consider the various characteristics mentioned above. Apparently the necessary conditions are a source of water, heat, a critical balance between the amount of water and amount of heat, the geyser tube which connects the surface of the earth with the heated interior, and storage chambers for hot water within the earth.

Supply of Water. — The water supply is, of course, ground-water. Most of it is meteoric water that seeps into the earth from the land surface. Some, however, is believed to be magmatic water formed through the condensation of steam that rises from some deep-seated magma. In 1938, many of the Yellowstone geysers were erupting more than a normal amount of water. This is believed to be due to the greater precipitation of the preceding year which increased the supply of ground-water.

Heat. — The waters of the geysers and hot springs are scalding hot, even in the pools on the shores of the great cold Yellowstone Lake. Two holes drilled in 1925, one in the Norris Basin, the other in the Upper Geyser Basin, showed respectively a temperature of 401° F. at a depth of 265 feet and a temperature of 360° F. at a depth of 406 feet. These high temperatures at such shallow depths are very unusual and plainly indicate the presence of highly heated rocks

FIG. 303. — Old Faithful, 1936, Yellowstone National Park.

(magma) at a depth probably not greater than 5,000 feet. As this magma cools, it contracts and hot gases are ejected which rise through cracks and openings of various sorts to heat the overlying rocks and the ground-water that is percolating through these rocks.

The Balance between Water and Heat. — The constant eruptions of some geysers and the intermittent eruption of others indicates fundamental differences in water supply. The geysers that are in constant activity are really hot springs that have a constant supply of water through which steam is escaping. The periodically active geysers apparently must wait for a supply of water. After it has accumulated with the formation of sufficient steam to eject the water, the geyser erupts.

The Geyser Tube and Storage Chambers. — The geyser tube, only the upper end of which is visible, is believed to be irregular in size and position. It probably connects various caverns in which ground-water collects and becomes heated (Fig. 304). These are storage chambers for the water that is expelled during an eruption.

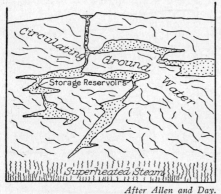

After Allen and Day.

Fig. 304. — A diagram to illustrate the cause of geyser action.

The tubes and chambers in Yellowstone Park probably do not extend more than 400 feet below the earth's surface.

The Cause of the Intermittent Eruptions. — It is evident that there must be some definite reason both for the intermittent activity of geysers and for the explosive nature of geyser eruptions. If there is a uniform opening from the ground surface to the zone of heated rock, and if the volume of water is small, one might expect to find either a boiling spring or a steam vent. On the other hand, if too much water stands in the geyser tube and storage chambers, it may not reach the boiling point, and there will be no geyser action. It appears evident then that there must be a critical rate and amount of accumulation of water in order to have part of it turned into steam, which is the propelling force in an eruption. The steps in the process of intermittent eruptions are believed to be as follows: (1) Some of the ground-water in contact with the hot rock at the bottom of the geyser tube turns to steam, which, as it expands, raises the column of water above it, causing the well-known surge or overflow of water at the surface of the ground. (2) Due to the overflow the water pressure decreases, allowing more steam to form, which raises the column still higher

New Zealand Government Photo, courtesy Canadian Pacific Railroad.

FIG. 305. — Waikite Geyser, New Zealand. The geyser cone is unusually large.

in the tube and storage chambers, possibly causing a second surge. (3) All this time the water in the tube is becoming more and more highly heated. Finally most of the water reaches the boiling point and becomes filled with steam bubbles that surge up from below, greatly reducing the pressure in the tube. (4) The expanding steam now starts an eruption which continues until all the water and steam are blown out of the tube and storage chambers. (5) Then the ground-water begins to collect in the geyser tube again, becomes heated, and the process eventually is repeated.

Geyser Deposits. — In Yellowstone Park silica (called *geyserite*) is deposited from the hot waters, both inside and outside the geyser vents. Algae which live in the hot water aid in the precipitation of the geyserite and give rich, very beautiful colors to many of the walls of the geyser pools.

Topography of Geyser Deposits. — The silica occurs in the water in very small amounts, nothing like so abundantly as does the calcium carbonate in the waters of Mammoth Hot Springs. Therefore, in case of the geysers, in spite of the fact that many are very old, only relatively small deposits of geyserite have accumulated. Some of these deposits are simply spread irregularly over the ground; others are in the form of low mounds, many of which are terraced like that of Old Faithful. Still others have accumulated in irregular columns, grottos and small castle-like forms. On the whole the topography due to geyser action is quite subordinate in interest to the marvelous coloring of the geyser pools and to the mechanics of the geyser action.

REFERENCES

1. W. C. Alden: *Landslide and Flood at Gros Ventre, Wyoming.* Am. Inst. Min. and Met. Eng. Trans., Vol. 76, pp. 347–361, 1928.
2. E. T. Allen and Arthur L. Day: *Hot Springs of the Yellowstone National Park.* Carnegie Institution of Washington, Pub. 466, 1935.
3. W. W. Atwood and K. F. Mather: *Physiography and Quaternary Geology of the San Juan Mountains, Colorado.* U. S. Geol. Surv., Prof. P. 166, 1932.
4. Clyde Max Bauer: *The Story of Yellowstone Geysers.* Haynes, Inc., 1937.

5. C. F. Becker: *Mechanics of the Panama Canal Slides.* U. S. Geol. Surv., Prof. P. 98N, 1916.

6. G. M. Dawson: *Remarkable Landslip in Portneuf County, Quebec.* Bull. Geol. Soc. Am., Vol. 10, pp. 484–490, 1899.

7. Junius Henderson: *Caverns, Ice Caves, Sinkholes and Natural Bridges.* Univ. Colo. Studies, Vol. 19, pp. 359–405, 1932, and Vol 20, pp. 115–158, 1933.

8. G. E. Ladd: *Landslides, Subsidences and Rock-Falls: As Problems of the R. R. Engineer.* Am. R. R. Eng. Assn. Proc., Vol. 36, pp. 1091–1162, 1935.

9. Nat. Acad. Sci.: *Report of Committee on Panama Canal Slides.* Memoir 18, 1924.

10. C. F. Stewart Sharpe: *Landslides and Related Phenomena.* Columbia Univ. Press, 1938.

11. Charles S. Slichter: *The Motion of Underground Water.* U. S. Geol. Survey, W. S. Paper No. 67, 1902.

CHAPTER XIV

VOLCANISM AND VOLCANOES

A great explosive volcanic eruption is probably the most spectacular and certainly one of the most terrifying of all natural phenomena. Early in the eruption a thick cauliflower or mushroom-shaped cloud composed of gases and dust is likely to gather over

U. S. Army Air Corps, courtesy of the Philippine Bureau of Science.

FIG. 306. — Eruption of Mayon, Philippine Islands, June 8, 1938. Gases are escaping into the air, frothy lava is moving down the mountain side.

the crater. Soon more dust, lapilli, bombs, great blocks of rock, and possibly streams of molten lava are ejected. Earthquakes, thunder crashes, and the noise of escaping gases and lava deafen the ears. Sunlight is obscured by the clouds and dust. Water, condensed from the steam of the rising cloud, mingles with dust to form mudflows which block stream courses and overwhelm cities.

Flashes of lightning and burning gases illuminate the region. The
total effect is stupendous but appalling.   In the more quiet types
of eruption, lava seethes and froths in its fire pit for days, then
possibly wells over the rim or bursts through the cracks in the
crater walls and flows down the surrounding slopes. At night the
burning gases give vivid-colored flames, but aside from this the
eruption may go on without much display or confusion.

   The literature of volcanoes is full of descriptions of different

Philippine Bureau of Science.

Fig. 307. — Mount Taal in eruption, Jan. 29, 1911.

types of eruptions and their results, many of which are covered by
the references at the end of this chapter.

   Volcanism results in a wealth of physiographic forms.   In general, detailed study of each form helps one to understand its origin.
In other words, there are usually definite relationships between the
mechanism which causes volcanism and the resulting topography. On
this account geologists find volcanism a fascinating study, but due
to inherent difficulties, research in this field has not kept pace with
that in many other divisions of earth science.   Within the last forty
years, three great volcanic observatories (Vesuvius, in Italy; Vol-

cano on Kilauea, Hawaii; Mt. Pelée, Martinique) together with detailed work in many other parts of the world, particularly in Japan, have added tremendously to our knowledge of volcanism. However, much is yet to be learned!

Definitions. — *Volcanism* includes all phenomena connected with the movement of heated material from the interior to or toward the surface of the earth. It may be divided into (a) intrusive and (b) extrusive phenomena. Intrusions include such things as batholiths, laccoliths, stocks, bosses, sills and dikes which were described in Chapter V. Extrusions, as the name indicates, have to do with heated materials that are thrown out of the earth upon the surface of the land. The chief types are *volcanoes, fissure flows, hot springs, geysers* and *fumaroles*.

Hot springs and geysers, distinctly phenomena of volcanism, depend on ground-water for their existence; therefore, they were discussed in Chapter XIII, and need not be considered in this chapter.

Volcanoes of the Central Type. — A volcano is a vent, or opening, usually circular or nearly circular in form, through which heated materials consisting of gases, water, liquid lava and fragments of rocks are ejected from the highly heated interior to the surface of the earth. The vent, which is seldom more than a few hundred feet in diameter, is often called a *pipe*. Volcanoes of this type are frequently called *volcanoes of the central type of eruption* to distinguish them from *fissure* types. Usually cone-shaped mountains, domes or mounds enclosing the vents, stand above the general surface of the ground, but some volcanoes are known that do not have such associated topographic forms.

Fissures. — Although actually a volcano, a fissure is distinguished from those of the central type by the form of the vent and by the absence of large amounts of gases and fragmental materials ejected from it. Only a very few large fissure eruptions have occurred in historical times, at least on the land. In Iceland in 1783, a fissure 17 miles long was opened through which lava poured out, covering more than 218 square miles of the adjacent territory. One-fifth of the inhabitants of Iceland were destroyed. It is believed that the vast lava plateaus of India, France and the northwestern

United States were built up by successive flows of lava from great fissures of Tertiary age.

Minor fissure flows are of common occurrence in connection with modern volcanism. In 1935 a crack opened on the side of Mauna Loa. From this fissure, lava flowed down the slope of the mountain, endangering the water supply of Hilo and possibly the city itself. An attempt was made to divert the flow by dropping explosives from airplanes. Whether or not this was effective is an open question. At any rate, the flow stopped before doing serious damage.

Fumaroles. — These are openings in the earth through which steam and other hot gases reach the surface. They are often called solfatara. The Valley of Ten Thousand Smokes in Alaska and Roaring Mountain in Yellowstone Park are good examples.

Classification of Volcanoes

Active volcanoes exhibit many variations in their periods and nature of eruptions. Some eject entirely basic rocks, while in others intermediate or even acidic magmas rise to the surface. Some are violently explosive; others are violent at some times and quiet during other eruptions; still others are relatively quiet at all times during an eruption.

Lacroix has divided volcanoes into four groups, each represented by an actual modern example.

Hawaiian Type. — In this type violent eruptions are rare; the magmas are very fluid and are expelled usually without

Am. Museum of Nat. History, N. Y.
FIG. 308. — Vesuvius in eruption.

explosive liberation of gases or the ejection of fragmental material. The Hawaiian Island volcanoes are the best known examples of this type.

Strombolian Type. — This group is named for the famous volcano Stromboli which is situated in the Mediterranean Sea north of the island of Sicily. The lavas are basaltic, but less fluid than in the Hawaiian type. Violent explosions sometimes occur, apparently due to resistance in the release of gases. Fragmental materials, such as dust, pumice, scoria, bombs, etc., are ejected. Liquid lava, hurled high into the air, drops back into the fire pit of the crater.

Stromboli is in almost constant eruption, but not all volcanoes of this type are so active.

Vulcanian Type. — This type also is named for the volcano Vulcano, near Stromboli, in the Lipari islands. The lavas of this type are very viscous and crust over between eruptions. Each new explosion breaks the crust of the last magma and tears out fragments of rocks from the crater. Dark, dust-filled clouds of steam and other gases hang over the volcano during an eruption. Violent explosions are

Philippine Bureau of Science.

FIG. 309. — A boulder weighing more than 500 pounds thrown out of Mount Taal in the eruption of June 30, 1911.

common; all magmas from acidic to basic are found in volcanoes of this type, but not, of course, in a single volcano.

Peléean Type. — This is the most violently explosive of all types. Gas expansion and explosions are great. The clouds may be illuminated by the burning gases. Dust and other fragments are ejected in enormous quantities. In the Pelée eruption of May 8, 1902, a tremendous black, dust-filled cloud of gases broke through the side of the mountain beneath the plug that filled the crater and swept *down* the mountain side to the adjacent lowlands, devastating everything in its path. The force of the advancing dust cloud was so great that the bark was pulled from green trees, and the wood was etched as if by a sand blast.

When eruptions of either the Vulcanian or Peléean type occur, the explosions may be so violent that the old cones and craters are largely demolished. In the Krakatau (also spelled Krakatao and

Krakatoa), Java, eruption of 1883, more than one-third of a cubic mile of the old cone was blown away. In 1911, Mt. Taal in the Philippine Islands went into violent eruption. The old crater walls were partly blown away, and a new inner crater was formed. Hovey states that in the Pelée eruption of May 8, 1902, many enormous blocks of lava, one measuring $22 \times 24 \times 30$ feet (more than 100 tons in weight) were thrown far from the crater.

Number and Distribution of Volcanoes

Number. — There are about 500 volcanoes that can be classed as active in the world today. Some have been dormant for a long time, but not long enough to be called with certainty extinct. It is probable that there are other active submarine volcanoes, but there is no way of determining their number.

Geographic Distribution. — Figure 38 shows the distribution of active and recently active volcanoes of the earth. The strikingly close agreement between volcanic and earthquake zones is of more than passing importance. It indicates plainly a definite relationship between these two great groups of phenomena.

The prevailing location of volcanoes on steep continental borders near great ocean deeps (for example, note the relations of volcanic areas to the Japanese, Philippine and Puerto Rican troughs) and in or near youthful mountains correlates them definitely with zones of weakness in the earth's crust. The submarine conditions in the vicinity of such regions as the Aleutian and the Hawaiian Islands are not known; but they also probably represent similar zones of weakness where fractures extend far down into the earth.

The remarkable chains of volcanoes that are found in so many parts of the earth indicate locations over single fissures or closely spaced parallel fissures. In Iceland an actual example of such associations has developed within historic times. The Laki fracture opened in 1783. Although it was a typical fissure flow, many small craters and mounds were formed on the fracture. Not all volcanoes, however, occur in chains. Some are in groups and some are isolated and apparently have independent vents.

Distribution in Time. — Historical geology shows us that volcanism is no mere accidental or temporary phenomenon. Volcanoes have been active in all eras and probably in all periods of earth history. From their widespread distribution both in time and geographically, it is evident that volcanism has a definite place in the orderly development of the earth.

Jaggar's studies of Hawaiian volcanoes indicate cycles of approximately eleven years' length in the details of their eruptions. Longer cycles of 65, 130 and 260 years' length, also, seem to be recognizable. Still longer cycles, millions of years in length, are indicated by geologic history. The last world-wide time of intense volcanism seems to have ended with the Miocene Epoch perhaps 10 million years ago. Since that time activity has been declining all over the world. Sometime in the future, possibly thousands or a few million years from now, the earth will undergo renewed paroxysms comparable to those of the Miocene when there probably were thousands of active volcanoes for every one in existence today! The results of Miocene volcanism are shown in our present topography both by great volcanic mountains and by enormous fissure flows.

TOPOGRAPHIC FORMS DUE TO CENTRAL ERUPTIONS

The topography of volcanoes is likely to change with each eruption. This is especially true of explosive volcanoes of the Vulcanian and Peléean types. High perfect cones are rare and usually are subject to rapid erosion after an eruption. Most volcanic mountains of the earth were formed long ago, and are now extinct. Their cones and mounds have suffered from erosion by glaciers, streams and wind. Long volcanic chains like those of the Aleutian, Hawaiian and Japanese islands include both active and dormant or extinct types. One of the most remarkable groups of volcanoes on earth is in Ecuador where there are 22 great mountains, 15 of them more than 15,000 feet high, with Cotopaxi (elevation 19,613 feet) the highest active volcano in the world.

Elevated Forms

Composite, cinder and spatter cones; domes and mounds; lava, cinder and ash plains, are the major elevated topographic forms produced by volcanoes of the central type. Among the minor forms are mudflows, plugs, spines and cliffs of great variety.

Philippine Bureau of Science.

FIG. 310. — Mayon, Philippine Islands, March 24, 1907. The cone shows the effects of rapid erosion. Immediately after a great eruption it is the most perfect cone known.

Composite Cones. — These also may be called *stratocones*. Most of the largest, highest and most symmetrical volcanic mountains of the world are of this type. Shasta, Hood, Rainier, in western United States, Popocatepetl in Mexico, Mayon in the Philippine Island, and Fujiyama in Japan are good

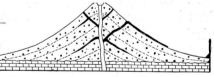

FIG. 311. — A composite volcanic cone.

representatives. They are built up by alternate layers of lava and fragmental material (Fig. 311) due to explosions. The sheets of solidified lava give strength to the edifice, while the rock fragments that are ejected from the crater and fall from the air build up the magnificent cones. These fragments of all sizes from dust to enormous blocks lie on slopes whose angles, measured from a horizontal plane, may be as much as 35 degrees, which is the maximum *angle of rest* for such material. At higher angles the rocks tend to roll down the slopes. A cross-section through a composite cone shows a roughly stratified structure. The materials include dense felsitic or basaltic lava flows, sheets of obsidian, breccias, tuffs and agglomer-

G. R. Johnson. From "Peru from the Air."
Pub. by Am. Geog. Soc., N. Y.

FIG. 312. — El Misti, Peru.

ates. Usually these are cut by dikes formed by the solidification of lava in cracks in the sides of the cone, made by the volcanic explosions.

The arrangement of these materials has much to do with the rate and amount of erosion of the mountains. Slopes that are covered with fragmental material are eroded relatively rapidly. Where they are covered by sheets of solidified lava, erosion is much slower. In fact, protective coatings of *glassy* lava reduce chemical weathering to a negligible factor.

Cinder Cones. — These are relatively low cones composed of fragments thrown out of vents by small explosive volcanoes. Many have relatively large craters which are cleared and enlarged by successive eruptions. The loose, unconsolidated rock fragments lie on the outer slopes at their angle of rest. In humid regions the fine material is soon washed away from cinder cones, often making fans at the foot of the slopes. Due to the resistant nature of the coarser

U. S. Geol. Survey.

FIG. 313. — A cinder cone on an eroded lava plain. San Franciscan volcanic field, Arizona.

material, bombs, scoria, etc., the form of the original cone may be preserved for a long time.

Spatter Cones. — Small cones called *spatter* or driblet cones are abundant on many lava flows from both central and fissure eruptions. They are formed by gas bubbles which accumulate and burst through the lava raising small irregular cones only a few feet high.

Domes or Mounds. — These are steep-sided masses of lava that develop in more or less dome-shaped forms around volcanic vents. Williams divides domes into three groups: (1) *plug domes* which represent upheaved conduit fillings; (2) *endogenous domes* that grow essentially by expansion from within; and (3) *exogenous domes or shield volcanoes* built by surface effusion, usually from a

U. S. Geol. Survey.

FIG. 314. — A dissected ash cone, Arizona.

central summit crater. The Hawaiian volcanoes are of the latter type, which is probably the most common of the three.

Mt. Pelée on the Island of Martinique represents a dome largely of the second or endogenous type. Before the 1902 eruption Mt.

U. S. Geol. Survey.

FIG. 315. — A spatter cone, Arizona.

Pelée was a great cone composed chiefly, possibly entirely, of fragmental material. At the top there was a crater one-half mile in diameter and 1,000 to 2,000 feet deep which contained a lake. The eruptions began late in April, 1902, and reached a climax on May 8 of that year when the dust-filled cloud of gases wiped out the town of Saint Pierre. Many minor and some violent explosions followed, continuing for several months.

Meanwhile a dome of thick viscous lava began to rise in the crater. On May 21st it had a rounded crest and had attained a height of 400 feet above its apparent base; there was a "deep moat" between the sides of the rising dome and the crater walls. Early in July, according to Jaggar, a great monolith (spine) shaped like the dorsal fin of a shark projected 200 feet above the surface of the dome. Other smaller ones stood on the lower slopes. These were soon destroyed by melting or explosions, but later, as the dome continued to grow, a new greater spine appeared which in July, 1903, stood nearly 1,000 feet above the surface of the dome.

FIG. 316. — Peléean type of dome. The crater of a composite cone filled with lava.

E. A. Hovey,
Am. Museum of Natural History, N. Y.

FIG. 317. — The spine of Mount Pelée, July, 1903, squeezed through cracks in the dome like toothpaste issuing from a tube.

Many somewhat similar types of endogenous domes have been described in France, Japan, South America, the Ascension Islands, Greece, Mexico, Alaska, California, and in many other regions. The surfaces of all domes of the endogenous type are much fractured and many show spines. After the first lava cools and crusts over it is broken by fresh rising magma from below. Through the cracks, gases and fragmental material may be ejected, lava may stream or spines may be pushed up.

Exogenous Domes or Shield Domes. — These are formed by volcanoes that emit chiefly lava from their craters or through cracks in their sides. Fragmental material may be present in relatively small amounts, but the main structure is a series of lava flows. The fluidity of the lava as it comes from the volcano is usually great; therefore, the flows may extend to the base of the mountain and out over the surrounding country. On this account the slopes of these domes usually are much more gentle than those of composite cones or endogenous

domes. The volcanoes of the Hawaiian type best illustrate shield domes.

FIG. 318. — A shield dome built up by successive lava flows.

Lava, Cinder and Ash Plains. — Many explosive volcanoes of the central type scatter dust and other fragmental material over large areas. The fine dust, often incorrectly called *ash,* may be heaped up by the wind "like snow drifts." Falls of dust and small fragments several feet deep are not uncommon; thus extensive plains are built up. The materials include, in addition to dust, pumice, scoria and breccias of many different kinds. Successive eruptions and partial consolidation due to the weight of the overlying load and to some cementation

Junius Henderson.

FIG. 319. — Pahoehoe lava, Kilauea, 1919.

of the fragments by minerals introduced by ground-water give a crudely stratified structure.

FIG. 320. — A volcanic plug, Huerfano Park, Colorado.

Lava plains also may form from volcanoes of the central type as has been indicated above. After recent eruptions the surfaces of flows may exhibit remarkable forms, depending on the composition, viscosity and constituent gases of the lavas. Many surfaces are *vesicular* (sponge-like) in texture; others are billowy in appearance often with ropy, corded surfaces and are called *"pahoehoe"* lavas. Still others develop cindery, blocky or other extremely irregular surfaces of the *"aa"* type.

Mudflows. — Mudflows occur in the early stages of violent explosions and usually continue until eruptions are over. The dust blown out of a volcano mingles with condensed steam and with rain water which frequently falls during an eruption. Also, such water picks up fragmental material from previous eruptions. Alluvial fans and plains are formed at the base of volcanoes; stream courses are blocked; great boulders are carried long distances by the mud; cities are overwhelmed. Where lavas flow over large snowfields, or glaciers, as has happened in Ecuador, Iceland and many other places, melting takes place rapidly. Great quantities of water rush down the sides of the mountains accumulating fragmental materials of all sorts and causing devastating mudflows. Avalanches and snow slides also may be caused by the meltwater which the soil cannot absorb.

Fig. 321. — Rabbit Ears Peak, Colorado. A very old, much-eroded, composite volcanic cone.

Plugs. — When volcanoes of the composite type become extinct it often happens that their vents are filled with solidified lava. As the cones are worn away, the more resistant plug is finally exposed. In many places a plug is all that is left of a once good-sized volcanic cone. These plugs which filled *vents, pipes or necks* are sometimes called *volcanic necks*.

Cliffs and Crags. — As already indicated, explosions of great violence accompany intense eruptions of the Strombolian, Vulcanian or Peléean types. Mountain tops are blown away, the sides of cones are blown out, old craters are destroyed. Even in lava flows gases accumulate in sufficient amounts to blow masses of the lava away, leaving caves, cliffs and other irregular forms after erosion.

Depressed Forms

Craters. — A crater is a pit at the top of a volcanic vent. Most craters are funnel-shaped with flaring walls which may be interrupted in places by steeper slopes or vertical cliffs. As cones and mounds

U. S. Geol. Survey.

FIG. 322. — Aniakchak Crater, Alaska. The diameter of the crater is about 6 miles. Note the subsidiary cone. Compare with Fig. 238.

grow, there is a tendency for craters to widen at the top. Usually both the inner and outer slopes are mantled with loose fragments and boulders, although in craters of the Hawaiian type most of the material is solid with only a relatively thin covering of rock fragments.

Craters differ greatly in size, ranging from tiny craterlets to enormous pits several miles in diameter. The crater of Aniakchak, an extinct volcano in Alaska, is about six miles in diameter and has walls from 1,200 to 3,000 feet in height. If Crater Lake, Oregon, is in a true crater, it is an even more impressive example, for its walls are 4,000 feet high.

Nested Craters. — Many volcanoes have craters within craters. There are three in Mt. Taal, in the Philippine Islands. Vesuvius at times has had three distinct craters. Early in the last century Mount Etna had two small craters, each surrounded by a small cone within a much larger old crater. Such a condition indicates a diminution of the volcanic forces after the first crater was formed.

Philippine Bureau of Science.

FIG. 323. — Mount Taal, showing parts of three craters after the 1911 eruption.

Adventive Craters. — Small craters sometimes are found on the sides of old volcanic cones. They result from the fracturing of the older rocks; then gases and lava working through the fractures reach the surface with explosive violence leaving *adventive craters.*

Caldera. — Considerable confusion exists in geologic literature and apparently in the minds of geologists and physiographers regarding the proper use of the term *caldera.* Many writers use the term to designate any very large volcanic pit or crater completely or largely walled in. This usage is purely physiographic, and there are no implications as to the origin of the basin.

In the literature published by the United States Geological Survey a *caldera* is defined as a volcanic crater that has been enlarged by subsidence. All basins of explosive origin are called craters. Daly suggests that subsidence basins be called *volcanic sinks*, and that caldera be used to designate any *large* volcanic crater due to explosion. This simplifies the usage of the term, for in many

Geo. R. Johnson. From "Peru from the Air."
Pub. by Am. Geographical Society, N. Y.

FIG. 324. — The double crater of El Misti, Peru.

cases (see discussion of the origin of Crater Lake, Chapter XI), it is difficult and may be impossible to determine whether a basin is due to explosion or subsidence.

One definite characteristic of a caldera, regardless of its origin, is that the diameter of its floor is much larger than that of the volcanic vent. Nested calderas, similar to nested craters, have been found in many places.

Volcanic Rents. — Some cones or mounds exhibit large irregular depressions in their sides, due apparently to explosions. These may be called *rents*.

TOPOGRAPHIC FORMS DUE TO FISSURE ERUPTIONS

While the topographic forms due to central eruptions are varied and of great interest, they do not represent the *magnitude* of volcanic forces as do the forms produced by fissure flows. In France, Iceland, New Zealand, west-central India, South Africa, northern and southern Argentina, Brazil, Siberia and the northwestern part of the United States, there are great lava plains or plateaus made by successive fissure flows. Others of smaller size are found in many other regions. In most cases it is impossible to locate the fissure from which any particular sheet of lava came, but the total thickness and areas covered by the combined flows of a region may be very great.

Lava Plateaus. — The Columbia Plateau region of northwestern United States is the best American example of a lava plateau. This region is bounded by the Rocky Mountains on the east, the Basin and Range Province on the south, and the Cascade Mountains on the west. On the north it merges into the Plateau of British Columbia. The total area is more than 100,000 square miles. The thickness of the lava which underlies the plateau varies considerably; in some places it is more than 5,000 feet, in others less than 2,000 feet. It averages now at least one-half mile for the whole region, and it has been estimated that at least 1,000 feet have been removed by erosion from much of the region. As many as 20 distinct individual layers of lava can be counted on some canyon walls where the flows have been deeply dissected by streams. The thickness of the individual flows varies somewhat, but is usually from 10 to 20 feet.

In this region the fissure eruptions started in the Eocene Epoch and continued intermittently until the Pliocene (at least in western Wyoming). During this long time some 50,000 to 60,000 *cubic miles* of lava was transferred from the interior to the surface of the earth, building a plateau whose surface is believed to have been not less than 4,000 feet above sea level and probably higher.

Since the plateau was formed it has been folded and faulted in many places. Parts have been uplifted and large areas have been depressed from 1,000 to as much as 4,000 feet. The region is cut by the deep valleys of the Snake and Columbia and other large rivers, and is less deeply dissected by hundreds of smaller streams.

The Deccan region of India is another fine example of a lava

Junius Henderson.

FIG. 325. — Lava flows of the Columbia Plateau, Washington.

plateau built up by a great series of flows from fissure eruptions. The basalts of this region are both thicker and more widespread than are the Columbia Plateau lavas. The total amount of lava extruded from these fissures was at least 100,000 cubic miles. Like the Columbia Plateau this region has been subject to great earth movements with parts of the area elevated and other parts depressed.

Lava Plains. — Lava plains differ little from lava plateaus except in the total thickness of the lava and in the depth of erosion that has taken place since the fissure eruptions ended. Plateaus that have subsided may not be distinguishable from plains.

The surface characteristics, except for the depth of valleys, are the same. Small rounded knolls due to the escape of gas bubbles, caves, scoriaceous or glassy surface of the upper and lower surfaces of the individual flows are almost universally present.

Lava-Capped Mesas and Buttes. — In many regions relatively thin lava flows have spread out from fissures over older rocks. Later streams have cut valleys through the lava well down into the underlying formations. The land between the valleys is protected from erosion by the relatively resistant layers of lava. The resulting topography is a single mesa or butte or a whole group of mesas and buttes separated by river valleys of varying depth.

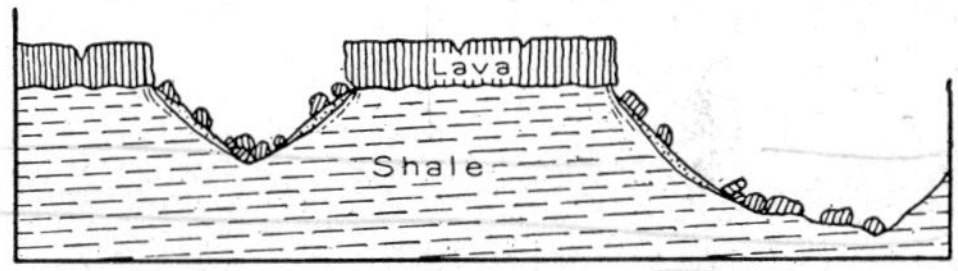

Fig. 326. — A lava flow that protects the underlying softer rocks from erosion.

Remarkably fine examples of such buttes and mesas are found in southern Wyoming, Colorado (Fig. 140) and New Mexico. Some of the mesas are so large that they may appropriately be called plateaus. Grand Mesa in west-central Colorado is of this type. It joins the Rocky Mountains on the east, but stands 5,000 feet above the Colorado and Gunnison rivers, which have eroded it on the north, west and south. Raton Mesa on the boundary between southeastern Colorado and New Mexico is another good example. Here the lava cap is only about 1,000 feet thick, yet the west end of this great tableland stands 6,000 feet above the adjacent valley floor.

Rim Rocks. — The vertical or near vertical cliffs that mark the sides of lava-capped mesas are frequently called *rim rocks*. The steep cliffs are perpetuated by the columnar jointing of the lava which permits blocks to drop down when the underlying, less resistant materials are worn away by water and wind.

The Causes of Volcanism

Any discussion of the possible causes of volcanism leads directly
to the fields of highly theoretical geology that deal with the interior
of the earth. The chemical and physical conditions that exist even
a short distance below the land surface can not now be determined
with accuracy. All our ideas regarding the earth's interior are deductions based on very limited information; this explains the general
lack of agreement among competent geologists regarding the
various theories.

In explaining volcanism many factors must be considered.
Among the more important ones are (1) the distribution of volcanoes; (2) the prevalence of basaltic rocks in fissure flows; (3)
the great variety of rock compositions in volcanic eruptions of the
central type; (4) the sources of the material; (5) the great heat;
(6) the origin and accumulation of gases including, particularly,
steam; (7) the ascent of magmas to the earth's surface which involves the whole mechanism of volcanism of all sorts.

Distribution. — The close association of volcanoes to regions
of crustal unrest has already been noted. The arrangement of most
active volcanoes in great chains, such as those of the East and West
Indies; Aleutian, Hawaiian and Japanese islands; Andes and Iceland, is too definite to be ignored.

Composition of Fissure Flows. — While various types of rocks
are known, Daly states that "for all the world as a whole, basalt
probably constitutes as much as 90 or 95 per cent of the total volume
of fissure eruptions."

Variable Composition of Central Type Lavas. — Practically
all rock classes are represented in the compositions of rocks that are
ejected from volcanoes of the central type. Some have the composition (but not the texture) of granites; others are of dioritic
composition; still others, including most of the lavas of the Hawaiian type of volcanoes, belong to the gabbro-basalt class. This
variable composition is important when considering the origin of the
lavas and the mechanism of eruption of the fissure flows as compared with the central types.

Sources of the Lava. — Three quite distinct, immediate sources of lava are recognized by different authorities. Complete statements of the theories in this connection are too complicated and too detailed to be included here.

Basaltic Substratum. — There is a growing belief among geologists and geophysicists that at an average depth of about 36 miles below the land surface, shallower under the ocean basins and deeper under the continents, there is a thick stratum or envelope of basalt which completely surrounds the core of the earth. The preponderance of basalt in world-wide fissure flows leads to the somewhat general belief that the lavas of nearly all fissure eruptions and many central type eruptions are conducted, without important changes in composition, through great fractures in the earth's crust from the basaltic substratum to the earth's surface.

It is held that this substratum is always in the *potentially liquid state.* That is, the temperature is great enough to liquefy the rock under normal atmospheric pressure, but at a depth of 20 or 30 miles the *pressure is so great* that the rock is actually solid. However, due to stresses within the earth, fractures are formed which extend into the basaltic substratum; pressures are reduced; some of the rock becomes liquid; gases accumulate, and the lava rises to the surface, pouring out in long linear fractures, fissure flows, or, in localized vents, central eruptions.

Local Reservoirs. — Many scientists do not believe that the lavas, particularly in central type eruptions, come from a basaltic substratum. Rather, they think that there are many localized regions *nearer* the earth's surface which are reached by fractures which reduce pressures and cause the magmas to form and rise to the surface.

Batholithic Reservoirs. — Batholiths have been described briefly in Chapter V. Their distribution in association with folded mountain regions is notable. Without going into the complete mechanics of the injection of batholiths, it may be stated that as the hot liquid magma of a batholith rises, it melts and assimilates much of the rock with which it comes in contact, thus changing its own chemical composition.

The top of a batholith is believed to be a very irregular surface

(Fig. 24), with depressions between elevated masses. The elevations are called *cupolas*. Convection of both gases and liquids causes superheated lava to accumulate in the cupolas. Where the crust is thin, fractures occur, and volcanoes, chiefly of the central type, are formed over the cupolas. When the batholith has completely solidified, naturally the overlying volcano becomes extinct.

Sources of Heat. — It is held by some people that the internal heat of the earth is residual heat from the sun. This assumes that the earth has not yet entirely cooled since it left the sun. Others believe that the high temperatures within the earth are due to the disintegration of radio-active minerals and the consequent production of heat. Chemical reactions within the earth and friction due to earth movements also may produce heat. It is probable that more than one of these conditions contributes to the internal heat of the earth.

Origin of the Gases. — Gases are the chief propelling force in volcanic eruptions. Steam forms from 80 to 95 per cent of volcanic gases. Other important ones are hydrogen, sulphur, carbon dioxide and various hydrocarbons. All are believed to be constituents of the original magma, but in addition to this source, much steam — in fact, probably most of the steam — is derived from ground-water which seeps into volcanic vents or down to heated rocks several hundred feet below the surface of the earth.

In case of volcanoes situated in or on the borders of the ocean basins, sea water almost certainly contributes to the supply of steam. The bases and even the cones of numerous volcanoes are well below sea level. Most cones, mounds and domes are greatly fractured by repeated explosions; therefore, the penetration of sea water into the regions of hot lava should be an easy thing to do.

In some places rising magmas assimilate limestones, thus becoming charged with carbon dioxide, with consequent great internal pressure. This may explain the abundance of this gas in some volcanic regions.

The Ascent of Lava in Volcanic Eruptions. — Jaggar [1] concisely explains this phenomenon in the following words:

[1] T. A. Jaggar: *Volcanology*. Physics of the Earth—1. National Research Council, p. 54, 1931.

"The ascent of lava, then, is actuated by the release of pressure on magma when a fracture plane over the magma yields, and the dissolved gas starts vesiculation and consequent liquefaction. The fixed gases react with each other and with air. This heats the system and increases mobility. The heating and frothing find outlet through the fracture. The result is lava outflow."

The quiet eruptions of volcanoes of the Hawaiian type, the rise and fall of molten lava in fire pits that apparently are immediately over the vents indicate open pipes connecting the lava reservoirs and the craters. Violent explosions, breaks through the sides of cones, etc., indicate plugged pipes, which may or may not eventually be blown out or melted. In all explosive eruptions, steam is of greatest importance.

The great fissures, many miles in length, indicate open fractures through which the lava moves freely. However, in some places, as in Iceland in 1783, a chain of local cones and mounds similar to those of the central type of eruption developed on the 17 mile-long fracture.

Where very large lava flows, such as those of the Columbia Plateau, central Africa and the Deccan of India, have overloaded the surface of the land, subsidence has occurred. This downward movement *may have been* a factor in forcing out more lava, although this is not known to have been the case.

REFERENCES

1. R. A. Daly: *Igneous Rocks and the Depths of the Earth.* McGraw-Hill Book Co., 1933.
2. J. D. Dana: *Characteristics of Volcanoes.* Dodd, Mead and Co., 1891.
3. Arthur L. Day and E. T. Allen: *Volcanic Activity and Hot Springs of Lassen Peak.* Carnegie Institution of Washington, Pub. 360, 1925.
4. J. S. Diller and H. B. Patton: *The Geology and Petrography of Crater Lake National Park.* U. S. Geol. Surv., Prof. P. No. 3, 1902.
5. E. O. Hovey: *Observations on the Eruptions of 1902 of La Soufriere, St. Vincent, and Mt. Pelée, Martinique.* Am. Jour. Sci. 4th Ser., Vol. 14, pp. 319–358, 1902.
6. J. P. Iddings: *The Problem of Volcanism.* Yale Univ. Press, 1914.

7. T. A. Jaggar: *The Evolution of Bogoslof Volcano.* Bull. Am. Geog. Soc., Vol. 40, pp. 385–400, 1908.
8. A. Lacroix:*La Montagne Pelée.* Paris, 1904.
9. Frank A. Perret: *The Vesuvius Eruption of 1906.* Carnegie Institution of Washington, 1924.
10. I. C. Russell: *Volcanoes of North America.* Macmillan and Co., 1897.
11. Karl Sapper, Immanual Friedlander and T. A. Jaggar: *Volcanology.* In Physics of the Earth—1. Nat. Research Council, 1931.
12. Howel Williams: *The History and Character of Volcanic Domes.* Univ. Calif., Dept. Geol. Bull., Vol. 21, pp. 51–146, 1931.
13. *Volcano News Letter.* Pub. weekly. Volcanic Observatory, Hawaii.

CHAPTER XV

ISLANDS AND CORAL REEFS

Islands and coral reefs are considered together in this chapter, partly for convenience, but chiefly because all coral reefs except *fringing* reefs are special forms of islands. As will appear later, fringing reefs may be changed into other reef forms, or islands.

ISLANDS

Islands are masses of land surrounded by water. They are found in oceans, lakes, rivers and swamps; the water that surrounds them may be salt, fresh or brackish. Some islands, like Greenland with an area of 826,000 square miles, or Madagascar, area 228,000 square miles, are very large and retain their island characteristics for a long time; others are mere ephemeral dots of land surrounded by water. Large islands, such as the British Isles or New Zealand, exhibit all sorts of topographic forms found on continents with well-developed mountains, plains and plateaus and minor relief features. Other islands standing only a few feet above sea level are constantly washed by surf and tides.

Classification

Islands are classified in many different ways. They are *continental* or *pelagic,* depending on their situation on continental platforms or in oceans far from the mainland; they may be classified according to the composition and structure of their component rocks. Probably the best classification is on the basis of their origin. Even on this basis, the classification is, admittedly, incomplete, for the origin of many islands is not known. In some cases several modes of origin have been ascribed to the same island.

479

The origin and history of coral islands constitute a problem that has been debated for a century. It deserves and will receive special consideration in this chapter.

Islands other than coral barrier reefs and atolls have been mentioned more or less incidentally in the preceding chapters. The following statements, which summarize and systematize their classification, are, therefore, partly in the nature of a review.

Diastrophic Islands. — Earth movements of various kinds are responsible for most of the large and many of the small islands of the world. The land may subside; sea floors may rise; continents and ocean basins may be torn apart by great faults or possibly by the drifting of land masses.

Islands Due to Land Subsidence. — It is generally believed that the group of large islands situated between the mainland of North America and the Arctic Ocean are the result of a broad but relatively shallow subsidence of the land. The composition and structure of the rocks and present topography of these islands are similar to those of the adjacent lands. The British Islands are attributed to subsidence which separated them from the rest of Europe. Off the coasts of British Columbia and Maine there are hundreds of small islands made by the recent subsidence of hilly or mountainous regions. There has been some re-elevation of the land since most of the Maine islands were formed, but the general shoreline is still one of submergence.

In this and future discussions only a few typical examples from many possible ones will be given.

Islands Formed by Elevation of the Sea Floor. — In many places folding or faulting of the sea floor has brought land above the water. Cuba and most of the other West Indian islands were formed in this way, although volcanism has modified their forms. In the Pacific Ocean many islands, including scores of coral reefs, have been raised as much as 3,000 feet in recent times. It is probable that the Azores, which stand on a plateau in the Atlantic Ocean, are primarily the result of a broad uplift. Although three modes of origin have been ascribed to Madagascar, Willis regards this island as a great upthrust block bounded on the east by a steep fault scarp more than 700 miles long, and on the west by a very

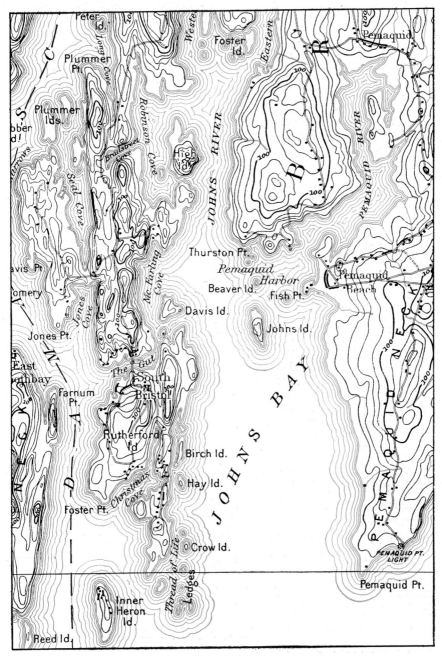

After U. S. Geol. Survey.

FIG. 327. — A section from the Boothbay, Maine, topographic map. The region was intensely scoured by the Labrador continental glaciers. Submergence and some emergence followed the glaciation. The islands which during glaciation were part of the mainland are due to subsidence.

deep, steeply downward area which underlies the Mozambique Channel.

Islands Due to Rifts. — An older explanation of the origin of Madagascar holds that the island was separated from Africa by a great rift valley (graben). If so, the graben is an enormous one, for the Mozambique Channel, which is supposed to occupy the rift valley, is 150 miles wide and 1,000 miles long.

Islands Resulting from Continental Drift. — Although it has many advocates, the theory of continental drift, discussed in Chapter 11, is by no means established. According to some of its proponents, Ireland, Greenland and the great groups of islands west of Greenland are land masses that became detached from one another and from the mainland when North America migrated westward from its former position against Europe. Madagascar, according to this theory, was once in contact with both Africa and India, but was separated from them when southern Asia drifted to the northeast.

Volcanic Islands. — Among the large islands of the world those resulting from volcanic activity are second only in size to diastrophic islands. Scores, including the Aleutian, Hawaiian and Japanese islands are in reality great chains of volcanoes. Many of them rise thousands of feet above the ocean floor. These islands are far more numerous in the Pacific Ocean than in all the rest of the earth combined. They include several hundred volcanoes that have been active within recent geologic times, and many more that have been dormant or extinct for a long time.

Bogoslof Islands. — Jaggar [1] has written a vivid account of land in the making in his description of Bogoslof Volcano. In 1796, a violent volcanic eruption, just north of and at the east end of the Aleutian Islands, lifted a new island, Bogoslof, above the sea. Another land mass one and one-half miles northwest of old Bogoslof appeared above the water in 1883. In March, 1906, there was renewed activity which resulted in two new hills appearing above water midway between the older islands. The last one to appear in the winter of 1906 was examined while it was still hot. The four

[1] T. A. Jaggar: *The Evolution of Bogoslof Volcano.* Bull. Am. Geog. Soc., Vol. 40, pp. 385–400, 1908.

islands represent projections of a great volcano that heaped itself up 6,000 feet above the floor of Bering Sea.

Islands due to Gradation. — The processes both of aggradation and degradation give rise to many relatively small islands. Glaciers, streams, waves and currents may be involved in these processes.

Islands Resulting from Glacial Erosion. — The Pleistocene continental glaciers wore down many coasts, for example those of

Geological Survey of Canada.

FIG. 328. — Pierced Rock, Gaspé, Quebec, at high tide. An island separated from the mainland by wave erosion. At the far end of the island an arch large enough to permit the passage of ships through it has been cut by waves out of the vertical limestone beds.

Greenland and northeastern North America. When the ice melted and sea level rose, due to the return of the meltwater to the oceans, hills and ridges became islands. Other islands were formed in a similar way in the Great Lakes and in thousands of other lakes where erosion was followed by filling of the basins by glacial meltwater.

Islands Due to Glacial Deposits. — Drumlins, kames and other irregular glacial deposits now occur in lakes and on shores that were once covered by glaciers. Usually such islands are small and be-

cause of the unconsolidated nature of their material are rapidly
worn away by waves and currents.

Islands Formed by Stream Erosion. — The most common form
of islands due to stream erosion are the meander "necks" found on
flood-plains. These necks may be cut off by streams in times of flood
or may be made by lateral cutting. Islands formed in these ways
at first are surrounded by ox-bow lakes. Soon the ends of the lake
fill up with sediment and vegetation, thus attaching the neck to the
adjacent floodplain.

Other islands on deltaic plains are made where distributary
streams cut new channels. They are likely to change form and size
with each passing whim of the stream.

Islands made by Stream Deposits. — All overloaded streams
and most mature and old streams deposit alluvium here and there
which may grow into islands.

Other small islands are likely to form where streams undercut
their banks, dislodging trees which are carried down stream and
finally come to rest against sand bars. The accumulating vegetation catches sediment causing island growth.

Islands made by Waves and Currents. — These islands have
been described at some length in Chapter XII, and need be discussed only briefly here. Narrow points of land may be cut through
by waves, leaving islands. Wave attack on rocks of quite different
composition removes the weaker materials, leaving the more resistant rock as small islands. Offshore bars not attached to the mainland are, of course, islands. Spits or bars formed by littoral currents may be cut apart by storm waves and the inlets perpetuated
by tidal currents leaving islands between the inlets.

CORAL REEFS

Coral reefs are masses of limestone and dolomite accumulated
by various lime-secreting organisms, chiefly corals. *Fringing reefs*
are attached to the shores of continents or islands. *Barrier reefs,*
which may be from a few feet to more than 1,000 feet in width,
are separated from the shores by lagoons usually less than 250 feet
deep and from half a mile to many miles in width. They usually

occur as single reefs, but double reefs, one inside the other, are known. *Atoll reefs* are low, roughly circular reefs which enclose a central lagoon. Most atolls are broken by one or more inlets. The *lagoon* waters of barrier and atoll reefs usually are very clear. The

From W. M. Davis, "The Coral Reef Problem." Pub. by Am. Geographical Society, N. Y.

FIG. 329. — Emerged, wave-cut coral reef, Fiji Islands.

bottoms of the lagoons are nearly flat. The slopes from the lagoon floors to the enclosing reefs may be very steep in some places, but more commonly are gradual. Marvelous branching corals, growing in profusion in the quiet, clear waters of many lagoons, explain why such regions are often called "coral gardens."

Corals

Coral polyps are small marine organisms that thrive in warm (temperatures above 68° F.) sea water, at depths of less than 150 feet. Sediment-free water and gentle currents favor coral growth. Violent wave action breaks up the delicate coral structure and retards reef-building processes. Under favorable conditions the corals multiply rapidly, and the larvae produced on living reefs are swept by the ocean currents from one place to another. If they land on firm rocks or solidified shell beds, they quickly attach themselves and proceed to branch out, soon making reefs. Through their ability to secrete calcium carbonate, their structures are built up in an amazing variety of forms. Large masses of limestone, matted together and enclosing both living and dead corals, make up the reefs.

The work of the coral polyps is augmented by algae, *nullipores,* that, living in a similar environment, also extract calcium carbonate from the sea water. The reef building processes of both algae and polyps seem to be most effective between depths of 60 and 120 feet of water. The upper limit of growth is the high tide line, although waves and wind may pile fragments of coral limestone much higher.

Coral Seas

The regions of luxuriant coral growth are limited to the tropical ocean waters. The western half of the South Pacific Ocean is the great "coral sea" of the earth. Other important reef regions are the east side of the Indian Ocean and the Caribbean and Gulf of Mexico areas of the North Atlantic Ocean. Wherever cold ocean currents penetrate far toward the equator, corals are absent. A notable example of this condition is the east side of the South Pacific, which is chilled by the cold Peruvian current.

Marginal belts of coral growth occur, where conditions are favorable, some distance from the three great coral sea centers. Hundreds of islands, chiefly of volcanic origin, in the Pacific Ocean are bordered by fringing and barrier reefs. Atoll reefs are far more numerous in this region than in any other.

Characteristics of Coral Reefs

The three types of reefs have certain common characteristics. Elevated, depressed and sea-level reefs are known. Naturally the elevated reefs give opportunities for examination that are not afforded by the other types. All reefs are founded, as far as is now known, on relatively firm rock, not on unconsolidated sand. All, apparently, grow more rapidly on the *seaward* than on the landward or lagoon face. This seems to be due to several conditions. The currents and waves on the seaward side bring oxygen and calcium carbonate which are necessary for the growth of both polyps and algae. Also this side at shallow depth is washed free of broken bits of limestone, while the inner face becomes clogged with such debris. Where lagoons are encircled by reefs, the lagoon floors are built up by debris washed in over the reef and by coral growth. Reefs are almost invariably better developed on the windward rather than on the leeward side of islands. This seems to be due to a more active circulation of water on the windward side, and, consequently, a better food supply. Some reefs are several hundred feet thick, a fact that bears directly on the mode of origin, for coral growth is limited to a maximum vertical range of 150 feet. The seaward side of typical reefs of all types is characterized by a gentle slope, 15 to 25 degrees at the top, with a much steeper pitch up to 45 degrees below. This, apparently, represents a balance between the growth of the reef and the degrading processes of waves and currents in the upper zone where both processes are most active. Some reefs seem to be thin "veneers" on broad, smooth, wave-cut plains; others, judging from rather unsatisfactory bore holes, are much thicker and are built on irregular foundations.

The great barrier reef northeast of Australia is the largest one known. It is more than 1,000 miles long and encloses a shallow lagoon from 20 to 70 miles wide. Other great barriers are found in many places, with particularly notable ones on the north side of Cuba and in the Philippine Islands.

The Origin of Barrier Reefs and Atolls

The origin of fringing reefs is generally accepted as being due to normal growth through the secretion of lime by corals and algae that attach themselves to rocky shores.

Barrier reefs and atolls are not so easily explained, and many theories have been proposed to account for their origin; the following have been most widely accepted, and Darwin's subsidence theory, with certain modifications, seems to explain best the known conditions.

Darwin's Subsidence Theory. — This theory first proposed by Charles Darwin in 1837 and slightly modified by later work has been accepted by Dana, Davis and many other investigators. The fundamental principles are indicated by Fig. 330, which represents a slowly subsiding volcanic island. If the original fringing reef grows as fast as the island subsides, it is transformed into a barrier reef. But the island is worn down by erosion as it subsides; therefore, embayments (drowned valleys) will appear on the borders of the island. The debris eroded from the island will be washed into the lagoon, the fine material eventually being carried out to the ocean through channels that cut the reef.

Continued subsidence of the island and upgrowth of the reef

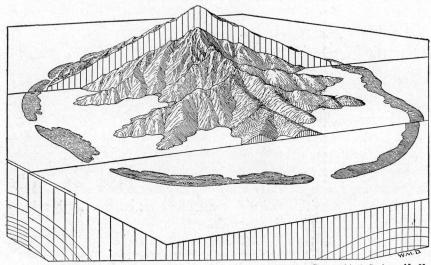

W. M. Davis, "The Coral Reef Problem." Pub. by Am. Geographical Society, N. Y.

Fig. 330. — Diagram of a subsiding volcanic island in an ocean of constant level, showing the conversion of a fringing reef on the background block into a barrier reef in the middle block and an atoll in the foreground block. The embayment of the island in the middle block is an inevitable consequence of the subsidence by which the upgrowing fringing reef is converted into a barrier reef.

will result in the formation of an atoll. If subsidence is more rapid than the growth of the reef, there may be a time when the reef is entirely submerged; but if the downward movement ceases, the reef, continually growing, will eventually reappear at the water level. As stated above, the reef widens chiefly by growth of the corals on its seaward side, but waves may also widen it at the expense of the lagoon by depositing coral fragments on the inside of the reef. The complete disappearance of the original island indicates a probable subsidence of several thousand feet.

Agassiz' Submarine Platform Theory. — This theory, advo-
cated by Alexander Agassiz and other students of coral reefs, holds
that barriers and atolls grow on submarine platforms made by wave
erosion. The platforms are believed to stand still. No submergence is involved. In case of atolls, the platforms must represent
completely truncated islands. With no subsidence the thickness of
the reefs could be no greater than the maximum depth of water

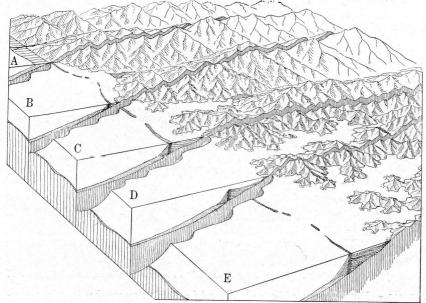

W. M. Davis, "The Coral Reef Problem." Pub. by Am. Geographical Society, N. Y.

FIG. 331. — Diagram illustrating the development of a barrier reef, blocks (B, C), its
submergence, block (D), and its later upgrowth (E).

(about 150 feet) in which corals can grow. The lagoons between
barriers and the adjacent shorelines or enclosed by atolls are believed to be scoured out and deepened by wave action. The inside
margins of dead reefs of all types are believed to crumble and decay
due to solution and to the boring by marine organisms; the products
of such disintegrating processes are washed away by tides and currents.

This theory does not satisfactorily explain the thickness of some
reefs, the presence of many submerged barriers and atolls which

have been located by soundings, or the complete truncation of islands which are supposed to form the floors of atoll lagoons.

Daly's Glacial Control Theory. — A brief statement of this theory is as follows. During the Pleistocene glacial period, the whole ocean was chilled. Over large areas corals were exterminated or greatly weakened in their reef-building power. Benches and plateaus were cut and built by waves on the old reefs and on land formerly protected by reefs. At a climax of glaciation the

W. M. Davis, *"The Coral Reef Problem."* Pub. by Am. Geographical Society, N. Y.

FIG. 332. — Diagram of a still-standing island in a rising ocean, showing the conversion of a fringing reef in the foreground block into a barrier reef in the middle block and an atoll in the background block.

water level was reduced (a) by the amount locked up in ice sheets, and (b) by the attraction of sea water into the northern oceans due to the greater mass of the ice-loaded continents. The total effect was to reduce the water level of the tropical oceans by some 250-300 feet.

When a warmer climate caused the ice to melt, the oceans were warmed, and corals not entirely exterminated began to colonize the wave-cut and built benches and platforms. Reefs of all sorts grew higher as the water-level rose due to the return of the glacial melt-waters. Since coral growth is greatest on the seaward side of reefs, the barriers and atolls would widen in this direction and the dominant reefs would finally be found near the edges of the wave-formed platforms. The age of all important present-day reefs, then, does not antedate the Pleistocene glacial epoch.

The theory holds that much of the erosion that produced the wave-formed benches and platforms was Pre-Pleistocene; the finishing touches were put on in the glacial epochs when the water level was low. Post-Pleistocene elevations and subsidences are recognized and accounted for, but most of the platforms originated at a time when the ocean floor was very stable.

Many facts and observations are offered in support of this theory. The fall and rise of ocean water due to the growth and melting of continental glaciers is generally accepted as a fact, al-

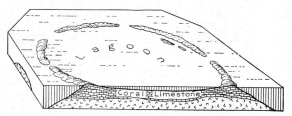

FIG. 333. — An ideal cross-section of an atoll.

though there is some doubt regarding the total amount of change in sea level. The remarkable agreement between the depth of water in lagoons behind barriers and in lagoons within atolls seems to demand platforms, terraces and benches that were formed at a very uniform depth below present sea level. No lagoon depths much below 300 feet are known. The puzzling problem of forming and keeping the lagoon floors rather flat and shallow seems to be best solved by the glacial-control theory. Another significant thing is the general accordance in depth of submarine shelves, *outside the coral sea areas,* with the broad lagoon floors *within the coral seas.*

Summary. — It is impossible to cover in limited space the controversial problems that arise from these different theories. The stand-still of the ocean floor long enough to allow the development of broad wave-formed platforms is doubted by many investigators. On the other hand, a subsidence of islands by as much as several thousand feet, yet so balanced by the growth of reefs that the enclosed lagoon floors are seldom if ever more than 300 feet deep, may equally well be questioned. Some borings in reefs have already been made in an attempt to determine the thickness, structure and composition of the material. The results have not been very satisfactory. If, in the interest of pure science, *many* borings could be made both on the reefs and especially on the lagoon floors, much help would be given in solving these perplexing problems.

Davis in *The Coral Reef Problem,* a book of 596 pages, discusses 12 different theories, not all wholly independent, but with some specific differences in principle or application, and concludes that the subsidence theory, supplemented by the changes in sea level and the sea temperatures in the Glacial Period, best fits the known facts regarding all types of reefs. His conclusions, however, are by no means universally accepted by students of the problem. Davis' statement that *"coral reefs should nevertheless be still regarded, especially in their barrier and atoll forms, as among the most marvelous of natural structures,"* is indeed true!

The Life History of Islands

It is evident from the preceding statements that the life history of islands will depend largely on their size, location, and composition, and on the physiographic processes that act on and around them. The borders of all islands are, of course, subject to the attack of waves and currents. Small islands in seas, lakes and rivers usually are short-lived. Coral reefs, as a rule, are exceptions to this statement, for coral growth is likely at least to balance and, in many cases, exceed the agents of destruction. Volcanic islands may be destroyed by the forces that created them. Also, due to their composition and high degree of jointing, they are subject to rapid erosion.

Many islands in seas and lakes are tied to the mainland by connecting bars, thus destroying their island form (Fig. 274); or are tied to one another, increasing their size. Islands in rivers are quite as likely to grow through deposition of sediment as they are to be destroyed by river erosion. This is particularly true of islands on flood-plains and deltas. Meander necks usually do not remain long as islands, for sediment deposited by the streams fills the ends of the ox-bow lakes that at first surround them, thus attaching them to the adjacent flood-plain. Later, the lakes may become so filled with sediment and vegetation that the original island form is entirely obscured, except perhaps for old meander tracks which support a different vegetation from that of the adjacent land. Large islands have a history similar to that of mainlands in similar geo-

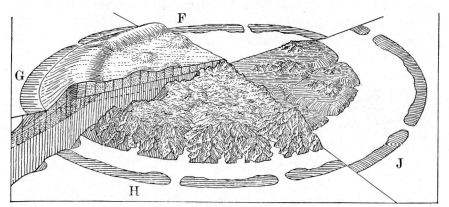

W. M. Davis, "The Coral Reef Problem." Pub. by Am. Geographical Society, N. Y.
FIG. 334. — Sector diagram, illustrating elevation and dissection of an atoll based on an abraded volcanic platform.

graphic positions, with the appropriate agents, such as streams, glaciers, wind and waves performing their normal functions.

Since many islands are located on continental borders they are particularly instructive in showing the evidence of uplift or submergence due to diastrophism. Irregular, youthful shorelines, or old uplifted wave-cut plains, sea caves and wave-cut cliffs, now well back from the shore — all are unmistakable evidence of earth movements. Even isolated islands far out in oceans show evidence of uplift or subsidence, thus indicating definitely the instability of the ocean floor.

REFERENCES

1. R. A. Daly: *The Glacial-Control Theory of Coral Reefs.* Proceed. Am. Acad. Arts and Sci., Vol. 51, pp. 158–251, 1915.
2. W. M. Davis: *The Coral Reef Problem.* Am. Geog. Soc. Sp. Pub. No. 9, 1928. (Contains a very complete bibliography on coral reefs up to date of publication.)
3. Alfred Wegener: *Origin of Continents and Oceans.* Methuen and Co., London, 1924.
4. Bailey Willis: *East African Plateaus and Rift Valleys.* Carnegie Inst. Wash., Pub. 470, 1936.

CHAPTER XVI

PLAINS, PLATEAUS AND MOUNTAINS

The details of the earth's composition, structure, processes and resulting topography have been considered at some length in the preceding chapters. It is appropriate now to focus these details in a comprehensive view of the origin and history of relief of the second order, namely, plains, plateaus and mountains.

PLAINS

Plains are the lowlands of the earth. They may be very flat, moderately rolling, or even hilly. They are formed both by internal earth forces and by external processes of aggradation or degradation. They range in size from very small to very large areas. They are situated in a great variety of places: on the borders of or well within the continents, and at all latitudes where land is known. All sorts of climates from the hot, humid climate of the Amazon Basin to the cold, dry climate of the Arctic borders occur over plains.

The great centers of population of the world are on plains. Far more people live on plains than on plateaus and mountains combined. There are many reasons for this: most of the largest and richest agricultural regions of the world are on plains; also the relatively low relief of plains makes communication and transportation facilities easier to develop than in mountains or plateaus.

The Origin and Classification of Plains

Like other major relief features, plains are best classified according to their origin. One rarely finds any large plains whose origin and present topography can be attributed to a single cause.

495

FIG. 335.— Mount McKinley, Alaska, elevation 20,300 feet. Air view from 10,000 feet.

Usually several processes have contributed to the final results, often in such fashion that it is difficult to discriminate between them. However, one of the chief functions of a physiographer is to work out the history of land surfaces, and the following statements indicate some of the principles involved in such studies.

Diastrophic Plains

Nearly all the *great* plains of the world are regions that were once submerged by epicontinental seas. Some were uplifted long ago and have been modified by many agents of gradation. Others have been raised above sea level in comparatively recent times, and have had a correspondingly shorter and less complex life history.

Great Plains Province of the United States. — This plains region (Fig. 336) extends eastward from the front of the Rocky Mountains to the Central Lowland Province, and from the Rio Grande River on the south to the Canadian boundary. (If extended northward it would continue to the Arctic coastal plain.) The western boundary is distinct; the eastern is rather indefinite, but is more or less arbitrarily placed at the 1,500 foot contour line.

This whole area was long submerged beneath the Upper Cretaceous Sea (Fig. 337). Sediments of great thickness were spread over the sea floor in a nearly horizontal position. Toward the end of the period, the land began to rise, due to *diastrophism*. For a long time much of the region stood only slightly above sea level. Swamps and marshes in which great quantities of vegetation accumulated, eventually making coal, covered several thousand square miles of the newly uplifted plains. In the Tertiary Epoch, the Rocky Mountains rose high above the plains. Vast quantities of alluvium were washed away from the highlands and deposited on the lowlands by the mountain streams that became sluggish as they spread out over the plains. Much of this thick alluvial cover still remains over the Late Cretaceous marine sediments.

In the Pleistocene glacial ages, continental ice sheets covered the parts of this province that lie in North Dakota and Montana, leaving, when they melted, their characteristic morainal deposits, marshes, small lakes, now largely drained, and lacustrine plains.

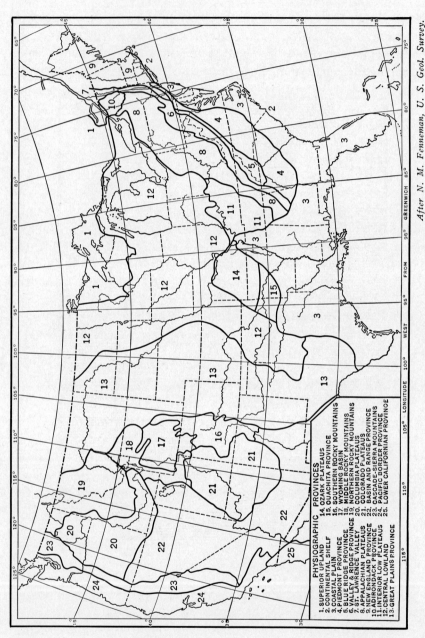

PHYSIOGRAPHIC PROVINCES
1. SUPERIOR UPLAND   14. OZARK PLATEAUS
2. CONTINENTAL SHELF   15. OUACHITA PROVINCE
3. COASTAL PLAIN   16. SOUTHERN ROCKY MOUNTAINS
4. PIEDMONT PROVINCE   17. WYOMING BASIN
5. BLUE RIDGE PROVINCE   18. MIDDLE ROCKY MOUNTAINS
6. VALLEY & RIDGE PROVINCE 19. NORTHERN ROCKY MOUNTAINS
7. ST. LAWRENCE VALLEY   20. COLUMBIA PLATEAUS
8. APPALACHIAN PLATEAUS   21. COLORADO PLATEAUS
9. NEW ENGLAND PROVINCE   22. BASIN AND RANGE PROVINCE
10. ADIRONDACK PROVINCE   23. CASCADE-SIERRA MOUNTAINS
11. INTERIOR LOW PLATEAUS   24. PACIFIC BORDER PROVINCE
12. CENTRAL LOWLAND   25. LOWER CALIFORNIAN PROVINCE
13. GREAT PLAINS PROVINCE

FIG. 336. — The Physiographic Provinces of the United States.

After N. M. Fenneman, U. S. Geol. Survey.

At the same time the rest of the province to the south was dissected by scores of glacier-fed streams from the Rocky Mountains. In very recent times wind has scoured out hundreds of shallow lake basins on the surface of the plains and has left many scattered

Early Upper
Cretaceous
Benton
C. Schuchert 1930

By permission of Charles Schuchert.

FIG. 337. — The Benton (Upper Cretaceous) seas of North America.

deposits of loess and dune sand. Streams have modified the glaciated topography in the northern part of the province.

Summarizing this very brief outline of the origin of these plains, it is evident that diastrophism of several different ages, stream erosion and deposition, glacial action and wind all have played important parts in the development of the present topography.

The Great Plains Province now is divided into ten *sections,* each with its characteristic landscape. Not all these sections can be described here, but a few examples may be given.

The High Plains Section. — This section with portions in eastern Wyoming, Colorado and New Mexico, and in western Texas, Oklahoma, Kansas and Nebraska, is noted for its few streams and *wide, very flat intervalley areas,* which are parts of the great alluvial plain referred to above.

The Colorado Piedmont Section. — This region lies wholly in Colorado between the Rocky Mountains and the High Plains. It is crossed by many streams which have maturely dissected the region. The relief is relatively great (as much as 1,000 feet). The valleys are broad, divides are narrow; buttes, mesas and erosion remnants of various sorts abound.

The Missouri Plateau Section (unglaciated). — This region is situated in southeastern Montana, northeastern Wyoming and in the adjacent areas of North and South Dakota. It is characterized by badlands, broad valleys, terraces and isolated mountains, giving the impression of a much-dissected plateau.

Coastal Plains Province. — Referring again to Fig. 336, the Coastal Plains Province is another good example of a plains region primarily due to diastrophism. It has all been uplifted since Miocene and much of it since Pliocene times, as is shown by marine beds of these ages which underlie most if not all of the plain. While, at present, the Atlantic Ocean is its outer boundary, actually the Coastal Plain is continuous with and divides its width with the continental shelf. Together they are some 300 miles wide, but where the plain is narrow, the shelf is wide, and the opposite is equally true.

In most parts of the plain the seaward slope is very gentle, being in few places as much as 10 feet to the mile. The lowest slope of all is from the mouth of the Ohio River to the Gulf of Mexico, where it averages only slightly more than one foot to the mile.

Since the original uplift, various parts of the plain have had quite a different history. From New York to the Gulf of Mexico a series of marine terraces is a distinctive feature of the topography of the Coastal Plain. Where best developed there are at least seven terraces, the younger ones, those nearest the present shoreline, being most distinct. Over wide areas they exist as slightly eroded plains. The older higher terraces, as a rule, are much more eroded, and, consequently, in many places are less easily recognized. There is remarkable uniformity in elevation between the successive terrace levels. The terraces are due to intermittent oscillations of

D. F. Higgins.

FIG. 338. — A view of the High Plains, northeastern Colorado.

land or sea level, probably largely the latter, and are believed to be correlated, at least in part, with withdrawals and rises in sea level during Pleistocene glacial and interglacial ages. In the region from Cape Hatteras north, recent submergence has produced embayed valleys, of which Chesapeake Bay is an excellent example. Florida stands barely out of water, and represents a young marine plain. Solution lake basins made in limestone dot the northern part of the Peninsula, while the Everglades cover the southern third of the state. The region including the Mississippi delta and west, according to Russell, has been slowly subsiding, due to the weighting down of the area by the delta deposits.

Peneplains

Although there are few large peneplains at base-level today, many *uplifted* peneplains, some of which were originally true plains, have been recorded. Examples may be seen in the Scottish High-

James Johnson.

FIG. 339. — Uplifted remnants of the Flattop peneplain, near Montezuma, Colorado.

lands, Appalachians and Rocky Mountains. One of the most perfect uplifted peneplains yet described is in east-central Africa.

Flood-Plains and Delta Plains

These types are closely associated in origin and in present geographic position. The plains of the Mississippi, Orinoco, Nile and Yellow rivers are good examples. Unless one considers deltaic plains to be the lowlands between the *present* distributary channels of rivers on deltas, it is difficult to say where flood-plains end and delta plains begin. On both types of plains, rivers build natural levees and broad flood-plains. Distributary streams, swamps, oxbow lakes, and abandoned channels are common to both. As a rule the soils are extremely fertile, but flood dangers are great.

Glaciated Plains

In general the great glaciated plains of central North America and western Europe were plains before they were glaciated. However, the glaciers superimposed a new topography on the old. Drumlins, moraines of various kinds, lake basins, marshes, and lacustrine plains dominate the present relief. Important changes have been made in the pre-glacial drainage. Contrasts between the glaciated and non-glaciated plains are nowhere better shown in North America than in the "Driftless Area" of southwestern Wisconsin and adjacent states and the glaciated regions that surround this area. The driftless area exhibits a well-drained, matured topography, (Fig. 223), while the surrounding glaciated regions are distinctly youthful (Fig. 218).

Minor Plains

In this group may be included the wind-swept plains of bolsons, playas, bajadas, pediments, lava and ash plains, lacustrine, lagoon and marsh plains, and uplifted wave-cut plains, all of which are distinctive in their mode of origin and present characteristics.

The Life History of Plains

Something of the past history of plains has been indicated in the preceding paragraphs. Their future, in most cases, will be a long one. Coastal plains are somewhat temporary features that may be submerged or elevated by local diastrophism, but the great interior plains of the earth are likely to endure for a very long time with only minor changes of their surfaces. Plains now existing near baselevel are not subject to rapid erosion by streams. In humid regions chemical weathering may be rapid with considerable material removed by solution, but corrasion may be approximately balanced by deposition. Usually plains may be expected to survive adjacent mountains or plateaus, for the rate of erosion is much more rapid in the highlands. As was suggested in Chapter II, if all diastrophism and volcanism ceased for a sufficiently long time, any one of the continents would eventually be worn down to plains; and at the same time, wave-cut plains would be developed on the borders of the continents.

Plateaus

Plateaus are highlands with large summit area. Usually there is an abrupt rise or drop from the surface of a plateau to the adjacent land. The term *highland* is entirely relative for many plateaus are higher than some mountains, while many plains are higher than some plateaus. The surfaces of plateaus may be plains-like

Royal Canadian Air Force Photo.

Fig. 340. — Dore Lake, Quebec. A view characteristic of the glaciated surface of the Plateau of Quebec.

in quality, very flat, rolling or hilly, or they may be so dissected by streams and glaciers that it is difficult to recognize their original plateau characteristics. Great plateaus and some small ones are closely associated with mountains and are primarily the products of diastrophism or volcanism. Many small plateaus, not sharply distinguished from mesas, are merely remnants left standing above the surrounding land as a result of erosion.

Diastrophic Plateaus

All the highest plateaus of the earth are the direct products of diastrophism. Since their uplifts they have been modified by various agents of erosion and in many cases by volcanism and minor earth movements. For convenience they may be classified as (1) *intermontane plateaus*, (2) *mountain border plateaus*, and (3) *domed plateaus*.

Intermontane Plateaus. — These include the highest, largest and in many respects most complex plateaus of the earth. Their surfaces show an extraordinary variety of topographic features.

Plateau of Tibet. — The great highland of Tibet, called the "Heart of Asia," is the largest and highest plateau known. Its area is between 700,000 and 800,000 square miles. Its average elevation is more than 12,000 feet, with many parts rising to more than 18,000 feet above sea level. It is bounded on the north by the Kunlun Mountains, the longest mountain system in Asia, on the south by the mighty Himalayas, the highest and one of the greatest systems of the world. These two systems meet to make the western boundary of the plateau, while on the east there is a less sharp demarcation between the plateau proper and the lower mountains of western China.

The whole highland may be divided into four physical divisions: (1) the northern plains, a jumbled mixture of plains, valleys and some mountains — the whole with an average elevation of 16,000 feet. Hundreds of enclosed basins containing salt lakes, one more than 1,000 square miles in area, are scattered over this region. (2) Southern Tibet flanks the Inner Himalayas. Here, close together, rise the Indus and Brahmaputra rivers, one flowing west and the other east. On the southern side of this section are three long, high folded mountain ranges paralleling the Himalayan structures and indicating their common origin. (3) Eastern Tibet is considerably lower than the first two sections. Within its borders rise four of the great rivers of eastern Asia, the Salween, Mekong, Yangtze and Hwang-Ho. The first three leave the plateau in magnificent, roughly parallel gorges that are among the grandest features of their kind on earth. (4) In the northeastern part of Tibet are great closed basins with playas, salt lakes and the enormous Tsaidam swamps.

The Plateau of Bolivia and Peru. — This is another excellent example of an intermontane plateau. It lies largely in Bolivia at an average elevation of more than 12,000 feet above sea level. There is abundant evidence that the highland was uplifted during the Tertiary Period when the Andes were formed. Great mountains, many more than 20,000 feet in elevation, surround the plateau. Part of its surface is a plain, with broad expanses of gently rolling land. Other parts are mountainous. Several large basins are included in the plateau surface, in one of which lies Lake Titicaca, a very deep, fresh-water lake 165 miles long and 60 miles wide. Its surface elevation is 12,370 feet above sea level. The lake is fed by melting snows from the Andes. Its waters drain into lake Poopo, a large shallow salt lake. During the Pleistocene the two lakes were part of one much greater lake which drained east to the Amazon River. In this respect the region has much in common with the Basin and Range Province of western United States.

At present the main part of the plateau has no exterior drainage, although several streams rise on its eastern side, with the waters eventually reaching the Atlantic Ocean through the Parana and Amazon rivers. The gorges of the headwaters of these rivers are, like those on the edge of the plateau of Tibet, noted for their grandeur.

Mexican Plateau. — Another typical intermontane plateau, also a product of tremendous uplifts, is the Plateau of Mexico, which stands between the eastern and western Sierra Madre Mountains. The surface of the plateau slopes gently northward from near Mexico City, elevation 7,410 feet, to the United States boundary, elevation about 4,000 feet. The land exhibits strange contrasts with many rich fertile valleys and intervalley deserts. Scores of low mountain ranges due to *block faulting* stand on the plateau. Some of these mountains have been largely buried by alluvium washed from their own slopes or from nearby higher mountains. Great bolsons (one, the Bolson of Mapimi, more than 50,000 square miles in area), containing playas, salt lakes and marshes are found here and there on the plateau. Large areas, however, are very dry plains. Several volcanic mountains stand on the south end of the plateau near Mexico City.

Border Plateaus. — Many plateaus border mountain ranges and owe their present position to the same uplifts that raised the mountains. This does not mean that the whole history of the plateaus and adjacent mountains has been the same. In fact, as a rule, the two histories have been quite different. But most diastrophic mountains have been raised vertically after the first stages of mountain building were completed, the border plateaus sharing in the later movements.

The Piedmont Plateau. — This plateau, Fig. 336, is a strip of land that stands between the Atlantic Coastal Plain and the Appalachian Mountains. Its eastern side is marked by a more or less definite *fall line*, where the gradients of most of the streams that descend from the edge of the plateau to the plain are steepest. On the west it terminates against the mountains of the Blue Ridge and Valley and Ridge provinces. The plateau surface slopes gently to the east and also slopes northeast from central Georgia, where the elevation is 1,800 feet, to New Jersey, at an elevation of only 200 or 300 above sea level.

The rocks that underlie the plateau are chiefly highly folded metamorphic rocks of rather great and uniform resistance to erosive agents. The gently rolling plateau surface is the relic of one or more peneplains with many monadnocks standing above the general level of the land. Hundreds of streams in this very humid region have cut valleys up to about 400 feet in depth below the general surface of the plateau; therefore, its original character is recognizable only through the accordant heights of the intervalley hills and ridges. That the region was once peneplained is plainly indicated by the truncated folds below the plateau surface.

Plateaus of the Colorado Front Range. — In Colorado a long plateau borders the Front Range throughout its length of more than 150 miles. At the Colorado-Wyoming state line the plateau surface has an elevation of about 8,000 feet, therefore is only about 1,000 feet above the Great Plains which flank it on the east. West of the city of Colorado Springs, the plateau surface is at an elevation of 9,500 feet or 3,500 feet above the plains and 4,000 feet below the summits of the adjacent mountains. This highland, which rises abruptly above the plains, is an uplifted peneplain that was formed during late Miocene and early Pliocene times at about the level of the Great Plains. It was raised to its present position by several uplifts that also raised the whole mountain region. This plateau, usually called the Rocky Mountain Peneplain, is now much dissected, many canyons more than 1,000 feet deep having been cut below its general surface. It is surmounted by scores of monadnocks of varying heights, the greatest of which is Pikes Peak.

T. S. Lovering.

FIG. 341. — A border plateau north of Colorado Springs, Colorado. A portion of the uplifted and dissected Rocky Mountain peneplain that lies between the plains and the crest of the Colorado Front Range.

The Colorado Plateau. — The Colorado Plateau, which is bounded on the north and east by the Rocky Mountains and on the south and west by the Basin and Range Province, probably belongs to the *border type* of plateau; although it could be classed almost equally well as *intermontane.* Its mountain border is sharply defined, but it grades without clear-cut demarcation into the uplands of the Basin and Range region. Actually there are a whole series of plateaus in this province.

The region ranges in altitude from 5,000 to 11,000 feet. Numerous small mountain ranges, several groups of laccolithic mountains, as well as volcanic mountains, are included within its borders. The greater part of the rocks of the plateau are sedimentary and

are very flat, although near the mountain borders folding and faulting are extensive, and great faults are found in the center of the
plateau.   The plateau was formed by a nearly vertical continental
uplift in the latter part of the Tertiary Period.

The large number of very deep canyons is one of the outstanding features of the region.   The Grand Canyon is, of course, the
most notable example, but scores of others are scarcely less remarkable.   The thick nearly horizontally bedded rocks erode in
such a way that vertical cliffs and terraces are dominant features

U. S. Geol. Survey.

FIG. 342. — A portion of the Colorado Plateau. Echo Cliffs, an eroded monoclinal fold,
and the Colorado River in the center.

of the canyon walls.   As the canyons widen, the cliffs retreat, still
preserving their steep faces.

Within the parts of the plateau that are situated in Colorado,
New Mexico and Utah, there are many broad valleys, some of which
are very fertile.   These, however, are not characteristic features
of the plateau as a whole.   The high, steep cliffs that border the
valleys and the great fault scarps that are most abundant in the
western half of the province are fine illustrations of the "retreating
escarpments" so common to arid regions.

In its erosional cycle the region is distinctly youthful.   Due to
the prevailing aridity of the climate, it is destined to remain youthful for a long time to come.   The broad divides supported by

underlying resistant beds remain flat, or at most only slightly sloping, to the very rims of the canyons.   In no other region of North
America are "rim rocks" so remarkably developed.

Comparatively few streams rise on the general surface of the
arid plateau.   The streams that are present either flow across the
region from the adjacent mountain provinces or rise on mountains
within the plateau that are high enough to have more than the
normal amount of precipitation for the region as a whole.

Domed Plateaus. — A good example of this type is the Ozark
region of southern Missouri and northern Arkansas.   Here, according to Fenneman, is one of the oldest land areas in the United States.

Fig. 343. — The south side of the Yampa Plateau, Colorado.   Note the steeply tilted
sandstones on the edge of the plateau and the horizontal beds (same formation)
above.

The region was uplifted by folding and faulting into a broad dome
some 40,000 square miles in area during the *Appalachian Revolution,* which occurred at the close of the Paleozoic Era.   Since that
time the original highlands have been peneplaned.   Three notable,
somewhat separated plateaus, the Springfield, Salem and Boston
surfaces, are now recognized in this region.   The elevation of the
Boston Plateau is 2,000 feet above sea level and from 1,000 to
1,600 feet above the surrounding plains.   Aside from this surface,
the general height of the plateaus is about 1,600 feet above the sea.

Streams which flow radially outward from the center of the
dome have cut only shallow valleys in the general plateau surface,

but on the borders many valleys are 500 or 600 feet deep, and on the southeast flank deep gorges have been cut back into the dome for a distance of 30 to 60 miles from the edge. Entrenched meanders are significant features of many of the upland streams. Inner gorges have been cut below the old meander loops as a result of rejuvenation due to comparatively recent uplift.

The whole physiographic history of the region is too long and complex to record here. Briefly, the region was up-domed at the close of the Paleozoic Era, peneplaned some time during the Tertiary, uplifted again about 1,000 feet and again partly peneplaned in the late Tertiary. Renewed uplifts have introduced two incomplete cycles of erosion, the last represented by the gorges of the entrenched meanders that were formed since the last stage of peneplanation.

Volcanic Plateaus

Several varieties of plateaus are formed through volcanism. The largest are built up by lava flows (Fig. 325). Smaller, degraded plateaus are formed by resistant lava caps that protect the land from erosion and maintain its high elevation after the surrounding land has been worn away. Both of these types have been described in Chapter XIV and need not be discussed here.

Plateaus Formed by Central Eruptions. — Around the bases of many volcanic mountains of this type are found curious mixtures of fragmental materials, lava and mudflows, all more or less interstratified, that have been ejected from the volcanoes. Usually the plateau surfaces are quite irregular; often they grade into surrounding plains. Usually such plateaus are small and unless they are covered with sheets of lava they are short-lived. The plateau that surrounds Mount Mazama in Oregon (Fig. 240) is a good example.

Erosional Plateaus

Stream-formed Plateaus. — Low plateaus are formed, particularly in semi-arid regions where streams have cut away portions of high plains, leaving broad, nearly flat intervalley highlands. Scores are found in the United States in the Colorado Piedmont

Province. Many stand 1,000 feet or more above their surroundings and have surface areas from 1 or 2 up to 40 or 50 square miles.

Plateaus due to Glaciation. — Continental glaciers may remove hills, leaving a rather uniform rolling plateau surface. The surface of the plateau of Quebec apparently has been modified in this way, although the pre-glacial topography is not well known.

It has been suggested, although authentic examples are lacking, that valley glaciers may form plateaus through headward erosion. Let us assume that three or four valley glaciers rise from snowfields at about the same elevation on different sides of a large massive mountain. As the cycle of glaciation develops, the glaciers will form cirques with floors at about the same height. The heads of the cirques will retreat, eventually forming a pyramid-shaped mountain or *horn* (Fig. 193). If glaciation continues, the horn eventually will be worn away, the divides between the cirques will disappear, and the cirque floors will unite to make a small, high plateau in place of the former mountain.

The Life History of Plateaus

The life history of plateaus like that of any other highlands depends upon a great number of factors, of which diastrophism and climate are the most important. Assuming that the land stands still, plateaus of humid regions will pass through the typical successive stages of a cycle of erosion and will be reduced to peneplains. Plateaus of arid regions, although worn away much more slowly, must eventually go through the various stages of an arid erosional cycle. The ultimate results will be dissection and loss of all the original characteristics. Plateaus on coasts are subject to the attack of both *subaerial* agents and of waves and currents.

As is shown in case of the Ozark plateaus, repeated uplifts along old structural lines will recreate plateaus or perpetuate them longer than their normal life history otherwise would permit. Renewed volcanism has a similar effect.

Royal Canadian Air Force Photo.

FIG. 344.—Mount Assiniboine, Canadian Rockies. The view affords marvelous examples of rock composition and structure, glaciers, cirques, hanging valleys, Cyclopean stairs, moraines, and stream erosion.

Mountains

It is quite appropriate to end this book with a brief discussion of mountains. Nowhere else does the physiographer find such a marvelous variety of rocks, structures, processes and resulting topographic forms. When all mountains are considered, one has an epitome of most of the subject matter of geomorphology. No two mountains are exactly alike. Every range presents a challenge to the student who would determine its history. In a textbook of modest proportions it is impossible to indicate all types of mountains to say nothing of describing them adequately. The following discussion can only summarize our knowledge of a few important mountain regions.

The Age of Mountains

Studies of historical geology show clearly that mountains have been formed during every era and probably in every period of earth history. Those of the oldest eras have been completely worn away, but their roots indicate their former positions.

As we come into the middle ages of earth history, we find evidence of world-wide mountain growth toward the close of the Paleozoic Era. The Brazilian highlands and the Appalachians, representatives of this time, are among the oldest existing mountains on earth. All would have been eroded away long ago had it not been for repeated uplifts since their first periods of growth. Large "Ancestral Rocky Mountains" were formed in Colorado and New Mexico at about the same time the Appalachians began to rise. The western mountains soon disappeared and their sites were covered later by sediments deposited in epicontinental seas during the Cretaceous Period (Fig. 337).

The Sierra Nevada Range was first uplifted in the Jurassic Period. Its history, which includes peneplanation and repeated rejuvenation, is complex; but the range still endures today as a great barrier more than 500 miles long culminating in Mount Whitney (elevation 14,501 feet), the highest mountain in the United States.

A period of tremendous mountain growth, world-wide in its extent, began late in the Mesozoic Era and continued well into the

Cenozoic. The Andes, Rockies and many Asiatic ranges were formed at this time, while the Alps, Appalachians and other older mountains were re-elevated.

The Coast Ranges of western United States and several ranges in central Asia are the products of late Tertiary and Quaternary diastrophism; also most of the older mountains of the earth again were uplifted at this time. In general the growth of volcanic mountains has accompanied the rise of diastrophic mountains.

Volcanic Mountains

The various types of volcanic mountains have been discussed in Chapters V, VI and XIV, and little need be said about them here. Although the origin of volcanoes is not well understood, the nature

George A. Grant, U. S. Dept. of the Interior.

Fig. 345. — Mount Rainier, Washington. An extinct volcano now largely covered by glaciers.

of volcanic mountains, such as cones, domes and mounds, after they are formed is relatively simple. They occur as independent isolated highlands, in chains, and in groups. Their heights vary from low mounds to great elevations that rival the highest diastrophic ranges on earth. Composite volcanic mountains are relatively short-lived unless the up-building processes continue or unless the cones are strengthened by lava flows. Many extinct volcanoes, like Acon-cagua in Chile, and Hood, Rainier and Shasta in the western United States, are noted both for their great height and for their remark-able forms.

The base of a volcanic mountain may be the ocean floor, a plain, a plateau or a mountain range formed in another way. The great volcanoes of the Andes are striking examples of mountains that have been superimposed on ranges that were formed by uplifts.

The correlation in the positions of present active volcanoes and earthquake zones (Fig. 38) cannot be accidental. Clearly, zones of crustal weakness are indicated by both phenomena. If we apply the fundamental physiographic principle "that the past is to be inter-preted in the light of the present," we may conclude that through-out earth history there has been a similar arrangement of volcanic and earthquake belts.

Laccolithic mountains are widely scattered over the earth, but are seldom closely associated with active volcanoes. The intrusive rocks arch up the overlying sediments (Fig. 27) forming low domes. Many have been at least partially uncovered, showing the igneous rock core and the uptilted sedimentary rocks on the flanks. In western Montana fine examples of laccoliths rise above the great plains, while in western Colorado and eastern Utah there are single mountains and laccolithic groups on the Colorado Plateau.

Residual Mountains

Every plateau, even every high plain, is a possible site for future residual mountains. This fact is well illustrated by the walls of the Grand Canyon of the Colorado River. There one may see today mountains in the making. Remnants of the walls between tribu-taries and the main canyon are favorable places for mountains to be carved out; but even on the sides of the main canyon, due to superior resistance of certain rocks or due to accidents of erosion, mountains are being formed.

FIG. 346. — The Grand Canyon of the Colorado, depth more than 6,250 feet, showing mountains in the making.

U. S. Dept. of the Interior.

Older residual mountains formed through dissection of plateaus are found in the Ozarks of southern Missouri and the Catskills of New York. Those of the Ozarks are in a more youthful stage of development than are the Catskills. In the latter case the parent plateau out of which the mountains were carved has nearly disappeared, but its former surface can be reconstructed from the accordant summits of the present mountains.

Diastrophic Mountains

In this group are included most of the great mountain ranges and systems of the earth. The Himalayas, Andes, Alps, Appalachians, Rockies and Sierra Nevadas are good examples. The structures of all give evidence of tremendous earth movements; high and low angle faults, broad upwarps and long anticlines are present in one or another of these systems. In most cases *both folding and faulting* contributed to the present mountain structures. Often it is difficult to decide which was the dominant process because of the complexity of the present structures.

As noted above, volcanic mountains may be superimposed on fold or fault mountains. Erosion by streams, wind and in many places by glaciers always has modified the original forms. Both folds and faults, especially when they are in sedimentary or metamorphic rocks, guide erosion and to a marked degree determine the resulting local topographic forms.

Geosynclines. — It is interesting to note that the sites of diastrophic mountains are determined long before there is any visible growth. This statement applies with particular force to folded mountains, but is generally true for fault mountains as well. *All great folded ranges stand on the sites of former geosynclines.*

The Appalachian geosyncline of Paleozoic age was repeatedly downwarped from early Cambrian to late Mississippian times. In it were deposited sediments thousands of feet thick. Most of the rocks indicate shallow or at most only moderately deep water; therefore, in North Carolina where the accumulated sedimentary rocks were more than 35,000 feet thick, there must have been a downwarping of approximately the same amount. The Appalachian Mountains now stand on the site of that former greatly subsiding region which extended from central Alabama to New England.

The mountains of eastern Mexico and the whole Rocky Mountain System grew out of a geosyncline of Mesozoic age. These examples are indicative of the similar conditions that existed for all diastrophic mountain ranges.

The evidence of the geosynclinal sites is found in the uplifted, highly folded or faulted sedimentary rocks, such as conglomerates, sandstones, shales, limestones and, in some cases, coal, that either flank or completely cover the tops of the present mountains. This condition will be more fully explained in later sections of this chapter where different systems or ranges are described.

It is evident that the continued downwarping of geosynclines causes deformation of the relatively weak rocks that are being deposited within these areas. Crumpling, folding and faulting of the beds must occur. The zones of weakness thus developed pave the way for the mountain building forces that come later. Just how geosynclines are formed is a matter of conjecture. Several theories have been formulated to explain their origin, but none have met with general acceptance. The downwarping of a basin by thousands of feet, thousands of miles long and hundreds of miles wide is in itself a crustal deformation of major proportions. The positions of such basins within the hearts of continents as well as near the borders indicate forces that are effective beneath or within the continental platforms; therefore, the whole problem of geosynclines is definitely related to the even greater problems of orogenic and epeirogenic movements.

Fault Mountains. — Mountains formed primarily by faults are found in many parts of the earth. Blocks of land may be lifted up along two roughly parallel fault planes, giving rise to a *horst* (Fig. 55); or there may be an upthrust on one side with warping or tilting on the other. In either case the direct movements seem to be vertical or near vertical in nature. It is possible that some fault-block mountains are *left up* between down-faulted blocks. If such movements occurred in a high plateau or broad domal uplift, the results would be the same as in the case of horsts.

The following brief descriptions give some conception of the variety of structures and topography that are associated with different types of fault mountains.

The Basin and Range Province. — Within this province (Fig. 336), some 215,000 square miles in area, there are scores of roughly parallel mountain ranges separated by intermontane valleys. The individual ranges and valleys vary in width from a few hundred

Spence Air Photos.

FIG. 347. — The San Andreas Fault, California.

yards to many miles, and in length, usually from a few miles to 50 or 75 miles (a few are longer).

Excluding the Wasatch and Sierra Nevada mountains, which are arbitrarily regarded as the eastern and western boundaries of this province, the ranges rarely stand more than 3,000 to 6,000 feet above the adjacent valley floors. The crests are narrow but remarkably continuous. The outlines of the bases of the various ranges are rather straight, without deep valley embayments or pronounced projecting ridges. Some slopes are very steep from summit to base, but most are probably less than 600 feet to the mile.

The slopes, however, are remarkably uniform for any particular range, and in nearly all ranges there is an abrupt meeting of the mountain slope and valley floor. The intervening basins are mostly bolsons with floors at many different levels.

It should be noted that many of the rocks of this region are intricately folded, but most of this was done long before the present mountains were formed.

Although several explanations of the Basin Ranges and inter-

Spence Air Photos.

FIG. 348. — Butte Valley and Panamint Range, California. The view shows several ranges and bolsons illustrating on a small scale the larger forms of the Basin and Range Province. The banded beds in the middle-ground are in a fault block.

montane valleys have been proposed, the following quotation from Louderback [1] concisely summarizes the present geological opinions regarding their origin.

"In the western part of the Great Basin from which most of the examples cited in this paper are drawn, the present topography received its dominant characteristics from the breaking up of the preexistent terrane into a number of earth blocks. This action followed or was coincident

[1] George D. Louderback: *Morphological Features of the Basin Range Displacements in the Great Basin.* Univ. of Calif. Pub., Bull. Dept. Geol. Sci., Vol. 16, p. 3, 1926.

with a general movement of uplift. The resultant blocks underwent important differential movements. Some of them became differentially elevated, or remained at a high stand, thereby forming a new system of mountain ranges, while others were differentially depressed, or lagged behind in the upward movement, and became the seats of intermont valleys or valley plains. The range blocks are commonly sharply separated from the adjoining blocks, on one or both sides, by steep scarps that rise abruptly from the intermont valley plains. In many cases evidence is obtainable that these steep scarps were primarily fault scarps, which, although more or less modified by erosion, are frequently even now very striking features of the landscape. The dominance of faulting in the differential movements of the earth blocks that produced the new topography has given rise to the term block-faulting for the process, and the mountain blocks so produced are commonly called fault-block mountains, or mountains of the Basin Range type."

The recognition of the faults that bound the mountain blocks on at least two sides may or may not be an easy matter. In certain cases the material on top of the mountains can be correlated with that of the valleys below, and the steep fault planes that separate the two actually form the mountain slopes. Faceted (triangular-shaped) spurs also indicate faulting (Fig. 371), as does an abundance of slickensiding on the suspected fault plane. Where the criteria are definite, it can be shown that some of the fault blocks are in their first cycle of erosion.

Blackwelder [1] has shown clearly the need for careful study in order to determine whether these and similar mountains are actually uplifted fault blocks or instead may be only residual mountains left standing above excavated valleys that were bounded by old faults. In other words, the present scarps may be old *fault-line scarps* from which softer material (of the valleys) has been removed. There has not been sufficient work done on all the individual ranges to determine their history, but certainly some are uplifted fault blocks, and it is probable that a great many are of the fault-line scarp type and represent a second cycle of erosion.

The topography within the mountains is characterized by steep

[1] Eliot Blackwelder: *The Recognition of Fault Scarps.* Jour. Geol., Vol. 36, pp. 289–311, 1928.

V-shaped valleys between narrow crested ridges. Abnormally small alluvial fans (if any) are found at the mouths of the valleys. The ends of the spurs are faceted. The angularity of ridges and valleys coupled with rather mature erosion is common to arid regions, but would be most unusual in humid climates.

The Northern Rocky Mountains. — Some of these mountains situated in Montana and Canada afford good examples of low-angle

Copyrighted by Spence Air Photos.

FIG. 349. — East side of Cuyama Valley, California, showing typical erosional forms of the mountains of the Basin and Range Province. Note the stream course in the foreground with its abandoned loops and over-steepened bluffs due to undercutting. Also note the dissected pediment between the stream channel and the mountains.

overthrust faults. The structures vary from place to place, and two sections only a few miles apart may differ materially.

The Lewis Range near the International Boundary shows a magnificent overthrust. The region was part of a geosyncline during most of the Paleozoic and Mesozoic eras. Late in the Cretaceous Period, mountain movements began. The region was uplifted, folded into broad anticlines and synclines and greatly eroded. After the first folding, continued lateral compression resulted in the move-

ment of a great block to the east along a westerly dipping low-angle
fault plane. The total maximum displacement was at least 15 miles.
The fault can be traced along the mountain front for many miles.
Figure 350 indicates the main stages in the development of this
range, and shows the present abrupt contact of mountains and plains
with Pre-Cambrian rocks overlying Cretaceous beds.

Near the North Saskatchewan River in Alberta the mountain
front is more complex. Here an outer range has been formed by

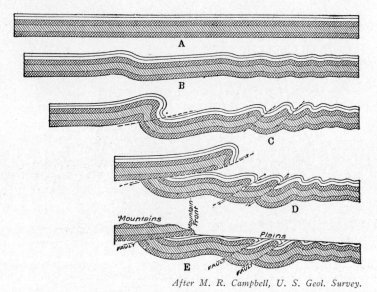

After M. R. Campbell, U. S. Geol. Survey.

FIG. 350. — Diagram illustrating the pressure from the northwest that produced the
low-angle thrust fault of Lewis Range, Montana.

a nearly vertical upthrust of a tightly compressed, folded block,
while the inner range to the west is sharply defined as in Montana.
The steep slope of the main range (Fig. 352) evidently has receded
some distance, although at the base, the fault contact with Cretaceous rocks can be seen. It should be noted that in both of the
ranges just mentioned there has been considerable folding as well
as extensive faulting.

Many similar examples of mountains made by thrust faults could
be cited. In eastern Idaho one great fault, the *Bannock overthrust,*

has been traced for about 270 miles; the maximum displacement along the fault plane is 35 miles.

Folded Mountains. — In these mountains folding of the rocks is the *dominant* structure. However, faults, some of great size, almost invariably occur in strongly folded ranges, and volcanism expressed both by intrusions and extrusions usually accompanies or follows the uplift of the mountains. In many folded mountain systems the activities of faulting and volcanism have been so great that the combined structures are exceedingly complex, hence the term *complex mountains* is often applied to the so-called folded type.

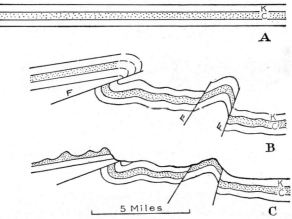

Fig. 351. — Diagram illustrating the faults and folds of the mountain front northwest of Calgary, Alberta.

The folding may result in simple elongated domes, such as the Black Hills uplift; a long series of anticlines and synclines which make up the Appalachian structure; or exceedingly complicated overfolds whereby a single layer is repeated several times in vertical section, as in the *decken* or *nappe structure* of the Alps. Naturally, the resulting mountain topography reflects strongly the underlying structures. This is especially true where, as is usually the case, sedimentary rocks of varying thickness and composition are involved in the folding.

The Black Hills of South Dakota. — The "Black Hills" are really domed mountains that rise abruptly above the Great Plains.

The length of the uplift, which in ground plan is oval, is about
120 miles, the width is about 45 miles. Figure 353 shows an ideal
cross-section. A longitudinal section would be similar, but longer.

FIG. 352. — The inner mountain front indicated in the last figure. The rocks are
shales and limestones. The valley parallel to the mountain front has been cut
along the fault.

The uplifted, eroded sedimentary rocks that flank the mountains
give rise to a series of cuestas and strike valleys that completely
encircle the central region. Consequent streams flow radially out-

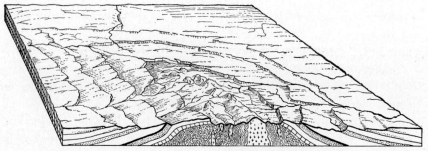

Modified after Newton, U. S. Geol. Survey.
FIG. 353. — A cross-section of the Black Hills, South Dakota.

ward from the top of the dome with fine examples of subsequent
and obsequent streams developed on the flanks. As indicated by
the cross-section, part of the top of the dome is quite flat and
plateau-like where thick, nearly horizontal beds have not yet been

eroded away. Other parts, where erosion has been greater, are rough, with deep canyons and mountains carved out of igneous, metamorphic and sedimentary rocks.

Either accompanying or immediately following the Black Hills folding, there were many small laccolithic intrusions. Due to differential erosion the igneous cores of these intrusions now stand high above their surroundings.

The Alps. — In sharp contrast to the relatively simple domed mountains of the Black Hills, the Alps represent the most complex mountain structures known. One would need a whole book and a long one at that to describe them adequately. The structures are a confused mixture of simple anticlines and synclines, tremendous recumbent anticlines, *nappes*; faults of many varieties, but particularly low- and high-angle thrusts, involving igneous, sedimentary and metamorphic rocks of great variety from Pre-Cambrian to Tertiary in age.

Some conception of the development of the Alps may be gained by the following outline:
(1) In middle and late Paleozoic times the site of the Alps was a geosyncline in which were deposited beds of sedimentary rocks including very thick layers of limestone, which are dominant factors in the development of the present topography. (2) In the Pennsylvanian Period, the geosyncline was compressed by lateral movements of the earth from the north and south. (*Imagine the region in a vise of which Europe is the northern and Africa the southern jaw.* As the jaws moved inward, great folds were formed which trended east and west forming the first Alps.) (3) Growth continued to Middle Jurassic times with some uplift of the original mountains, but with most of the geosyn-

Junius Henderson.

FIG. 354. — Devils Tower, Wyoming. This great mass of igneous rock stands fully 600 feet above its surroundings. It is believed to be laccolithic in structure, although the evidence is not entirely clear. The columns average 6 feet in diameter.

cline still under water. (4) In Upper Jurassic times pressure from the vise was released and most of the region was submerged. (5) By the Upper Cretaceous Period the mountains were rising again

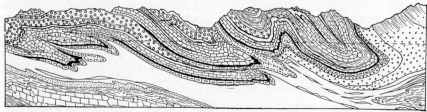

After A. Heim, "Geologie der Schweiz." Verlag Willibald Keller, Leipzig.

FIG. 355. — Structures of the Alps.

due to renewed lateral compression, although some regions remained under water. (6) During the Oligocene, mountain growth was rapid, culminating in *intense* folding as the African and European jaws ap-

Courtesy French Government Tourist Bureau.

FIG. 356. — A view in the Alps showing different types of erosional forms in the horizontal and tilted beds.

proached one another. In this period the intensity of the uplifts varied from time to time and from place to place. The *decken or nappe structure*, that is long recumbent folds with the same beds overlapping one another so that they are repeated several times in vertical section, reached its greatest development at this time. (7) Tremendous igneous intrusions occurred in the Upper Oligocene and in the Miocene. (8) Erosion resulting in widespread peneplanation occurred in the Miocene; a second less extensive planation period is recognized in the Early Pliocene. (9) The last major uplift, which was largely vertical, occurred in the Pliocene.

The present topography of the Alps is the product of erosion on the complexly folded, faulted sedimentary and metamorphic rocks, and on the various types of intrusions. On the borders of the uplift there are simple folded mountains, such as the Juras. Within the main highlands are horns, massive mountains, plateaus that are remnants of uplifted peneplains, "mountains without roots," serrated ridges, glaciated valleys, lakes and waterfalls in marvelous array — all the results of stream and glacial erosion.

The History of Mountains

A brief outline of the history of some mountains has already been given in connection with their structural development. In this section a somewhat more detailed account of the history of two typical mountain systems will be given.

The Appalachian System. — This region extends some 2,000 miles northeasterly from central Alabama to Canada. It is bounded on the east by the Atlantic Coastal Plains and on the west by the Central Lowlands. The average width is between 250 and 300 miles; the total area is more than 500,000 square miles. The history begins with the Cambrian Period about 500 million years ago, and ends (without regard for the future) at the present moment.

Hundreds of scholarly articles have been written on this region. Scores of long-studied but still unsolved problems await further investigation. The whole region includes folded and faulted mountains, plateaus, great valleys, peneplaned surfaces, abandoned valleys, streams both in and out of harmony with their structural surroundings, continental glaciated areas, regions that show evidence of repeated uplifts, and a still further array of physiographic subjects.

While the principal events in the history of the region are well established, scores of details are subject to more than one interpretation. The following statements are of necessity dogmatic, for space does not permit discussion of debated problems. For the most comprehensive treatment of the whole region that is available in a single volume, the reader is referred to Fenneman.[1]

The Appalachian Geosyncline. — This geosyncline, during nearly the whole Paleozoic Era, occupied the site of the present Appalachians. In it were accumulated sediments that ranged in thickness from less than 5,000 feet on the west to more than 35,000 feet in North Carolina. The average thickness throughout the deepest part of the trough was about 20,000 feet. The sediments that were deposited were sandstones, shales, limestones and coal. At no time is the geosyncline believed to have been excessively deep. It was warped downward repeatedly (or steadily) as it filled.

The history of the trough was not everywhere the same. The southern end was more continuously a geosynclinal tract than was the northern end. In the Ordovician and again in the Devonian there were mountain-making movements in New England and adjacent regions, while on the west the great Cincinnati Arch was uplifted in the Ordovician and repeatedly re-elevated during middle and late Paleozoic times.

Appalachia. — During the Paleozoic Era an ancient highland stood on the east side of the geosyncline. It covered most of the present Piedmont and Coastal Plains areas and extended for an unknown distance over the Atlantic Continental Shelf. The sediments deposited in the geosyncline are much coarser in texture, and also are thicker on the east, thus indicating the position of the former highland. By the end of the Paleozoic it apparently was worn down essentially to baselevel, and is, of course, a good example of a mountainous region that has entirely disappeared.

The Appalachian Revolution. — The great period of mountain building, which reached its climax in eastern North America in the Permian, is appropriately called the *Appalachian Revolution*. It was heralded in the Canadian Maritime Provinces by four moun-

---

[1] N. M. Fenneman: *Physiography of Eastern United States*, pp. 121–448. McGraw-Hill Book Co., 1938. The book includes an excellent bibliography.

FIG. 357.—A photograph of a relief model of part of the Appalachian System.

After U. S. Geol. Survey.

FIG. 358.—A cross-section of a moderately folded region showing the development of monoclinal ridges on the massive, resistant Tuscarora (St.) sandstone. *After U. S. Geol. Survey. Mercersburg Quadrangle, Pennsylvania.*

tain-forming movements in Mississippian and two in Pennsylvanian times. Also in Alabama, Texas and Oklahoma, mountains of Pennsylvanian age were raised, but the Permian orogeny climaxed all the preceding movements and raised the whole Appalachian System from Newfoundland to Alabama. At this time the epi-continental seas were drained from the eastern part of the continent. Since then they have returned only locally.

The Original Appalachians. — The area covered by the original mountains is determined by noting the structures referable to the Permian folding and faulting. The height of the mountains is not known. By reconstructing the (now eroded) folds, it is evident that ranges would have towered 20,000 to 25,000 feet above the sea *if there had been no erosion.* But, of course, erosion must have begun with the first uplifts. The mountain growth undoubtedly was very slow; therefore it is improbable that the mountains ever attained heights much, if any, greater than the Rocky Mountains are today.

The crustal shortening due to compression was tremendous. The whole central mountain region was wrinkled by great anticlines and synclines, and beds were overlapped by thrust faults. Chamberlin [1] has shown that in the folded region of central Pennsylvania *a block originally 81 miles in width was compressed into 66 miles.*

Volcanism. — Both intrusions and extrusions of great magnitude accompanied or immediately followed the mountain-building. Granite batholiths as much as 350 miles long and 30 miles wide were intruded into the highlands. "Thousands of dikes lead off from the batholiths and hundreds of sills are as-

[1] R. T. Chamberlin: *The Appalachian Folds of Central Pennsylvania.* Jour. Geol., Vol. 18, pp. 228–251, 1910.

sociated with them." (Arthur Keith.) That they were intruded under great pressure is shown by the shattering of the country rock. In the Triassic Period a great number of dikes and surface flows were formed along the Atlantic coast all the way from Georgia to New Brunswick. The influence of all these rocks in the development of the present topography obviously has been very great.

The Lost Interval. — Comparatively little is known about the Appalachian region during the Mesozoic Era. Triassic volcanism already has been noted. Also sediments of this age were deposited in New England. Tremendous block faults are recorded. It is assumed that by the close of the Jurassic much, probably most, of the original highlands had been reduced to low subdued hills with broad bordering peneplains. On the Coastal Plain, sediments of Lower Cretaceous age were deposited on a peneplaned surface. Undoubtedly there was time enough in the Mesozoic Era to reduce the whole region to baselevel; but, judging by the more legible history of other younger mountains, many uplifts followed the main period of mountain growth, and it is probable that, especially in the northern and southern parts of the region, some mountains escaped destruction. Sometime, or more likely at various times, after the Jurassic planation, local movements lowered the region in some places and raised it in others. Cretaceous sediments which indicate subsidence may still be found in Pennsylvania and on the Piedmont from New Jersey to Alabama.

The Late Cretaceous and Early Tertiary history of the region is almost unknown. It is assumed that Cretaceous sediments were deposited over much of the peneplaned area. When Post-Cretaceous uplifts occurred, consequent streams superimposed by these sediments began to flow toward the east and northwest. These became the transverse streams of the present which now cross the folded and faulted areas without regard for the underlying structures.

The Present Appalachians. — One finds a bewildering number and variety of opinions interwoven in the interpretation of the modern history of this region. The chief problems center in the ages and numbers of erosional cycles. Some investigators recognize as many as twelve distinct peneplains, while others find only a single widespread one with at most a second incipient one. Some consider the oldest general peneplain (after the Jurassic) as Cretaceous in age, while others place it in the Pliocene. The ages of many transverse streams, such as the Potomac and James rivers, which flow entirely out of harmony with the underlying structures, are referable only to erosion cycles; therefore, the whole question of peneplanation is of outstanding importance.

U. S. Dept. of the Interior.

FIG. 359. — Mt. LeConte, Great Smoky National Park.

Except for relatively small areas of high mountains, the topography of the whole region is characterized by level-crested mountains, plateaus and hills of accordant heights at various levels, separated by deep valleys. The remarkable agreement in height and the many broad divides suggest at once an uplifted, dissected peneplain which constitutes a *summit* plain for all but the highest mountains that stand irregularly above it. Below the summit peneplain are broad areas consisting of even-crested ridges or accordant-topped hills representing a second erosional surface, which has been dissected by streams that now flow in deep relatively narrow valleys. The Piedmont and Allegheny plateaus on the two sides of the present mountains proper also are peneplaned surfaces younger than the summit peneplain.

Locally many other regions between or below the two erosional surfaces just described have reached an incipient peneplain, *strath* stage. The number of these local surfaces is not known, and they have not yet been correlated in age.

The Schooley Peneplain. — This was first described in New Jersey where it is the summit peneplain. Later it was extended

George H. Ashley.

FIG. 360. — View in northern part of Clearfield County, Pennsylvania, showing surface usually described as a remnant of the Schooley peneplain.

into Pennsylvania, New England and New York, where it is a subsummit peneplain. Now it is generally, although by no means universally, regarded as the same erosional surface as the Kittatinny and the Cumberland peneplains which embrace the *highest* accordant ridges and mountain summits of the Appalachian region. As noted above, discordant residual mountains rise above this surface, particularly in the northern (New York and New England) and in the southern (Tennessee and Carolina) parts of the region. The Schooley peneplain has been traced westward well into the flat-lying sedimentary rocks of Ohio.

The age of the Schooley peneplain is not known. It was once supposed to be Cretaceous, but now is generally regarded as Mid-Tertiary. Ashley, however, considers it to have been formed during the Pliocene. Much of the Appalachian region was reduced to baselevel during this erosional cycle and the major transverse streams ignored attempts at structural control, yet tributary streams probably developed strike valleys with cuestas that were not entirely peneplaned. When the Schooley peneplain was uplifted, the main streams persisted in their courses, but the smaller ones began to etch out their valleys along the strike of the softer beds, thus beginning the great system of trellis drainage that is seen today.

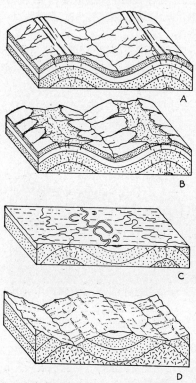

FIG. 361.—Diagram to show "inverted drainage," the consequence of folding, peneplanation, uplift, and a second cycle of erosion.

The Harrisburg Peneplain. — The cycle of erosion that produced this surface began with the uplift of the Schooley peneplain. The Harrisburg cycle was much shorter and baseleveling was much less complete than in case of the Schooley cycle. The Harrisburg surface is tentatively correlated by Fenneman with the Lexington and Allegheny peneplains on the south and west and with the Ashville and Piedmont peneplains on the south and east. There are other *local* peneplains younger than the Schooley and older than the Harrisburg that have not yet been correlated. There is considerable difference in the present altitude of the remnants of the Harrisburg surfaces, but no more than can be explained by different heights of the local baselevels at which they were formed and by differential uplift since they were formed.

During the Harrisburg cycle many streams were captured leaving great wind gaps, some as much as 1,500-1,800 feet deep, that are notable features in the present Appalachian topography.

Later Erosional Cycles. — Uplift of the Harrisburg peneplain, which, of course, means an uplift of the whole region, again rejuvenated the streams. Many incompletely baseleveled areas lower than the Harrisburg remnants are scattered over the region. Most of these are tentatively correlated with the incipient Somerville peneplain of New Jersey. It does not follow that all were formed

George H. Ashley.

Fig. 362. — Wind gap near Archbald, Pennsylvania, from the north.

at the same time or at the same level, but all are of relatively recent origin.

Straths. — In his discussion of Appalachian physiography, Fenneman uses the term *strath* (first used by Archibald Geikie) to designate "an incipient peneplain, a surface whose interstream areas have been worn down, not planed off." Many straths up to 10 or 12 miles in width are found in this region. Some are above and some below the Harrisburg peneplain remnants. They are essentially broad valleys with irregular borders and nearly flat floors. Uplifts since the straths were formed have rejuvenated the streams permitting them to cut deep narrow gorges below the old valley floors. In many places *strath terraces* have been left, but in some cases the whole valley floor has been removed. Also in the Blue Ridge region straths are found with gorges in their lower ends, but with the upper parts undissected showing that the rejuvenation has not yet extended up that far.

Adjustment of Streams. — The adjustment of streams to the underlying rocks and their structures seems to have started with the uplift that preceded the Schooley erosion cycle, and it has continued to the present. The east and west-flowing transverse streams have persisted to a marked degree in their positions, although their

George H. Ashley.

FIG. 363. — Plain north of Gettysburg. The divide between the Potomac and Susquehanna rivers. Interpreted by Dr. Ashley as a plain due to local baseleveling and of rather recent age.

headwaters have been captured. The longitudinal subsequent streams have cut valleys on the softer folded or faulted beds during each cycle or subcycle of erosion. Obsequent drainage is now well developed. Every uplift has modified the positions of the smaller streams. Some have been captured, leaving only wind gaps through ridges where water formerly flowed. The increased volume of water of the capturing stream naturally allowed it to do more work. The present trellis drainage pattern, the result of four cycles of uplift and erosion, has undergone many changes from that of each previous cycle. The present great number of synclinal and monoclinal hills and ridges, as well as anticlinal valleys, are products

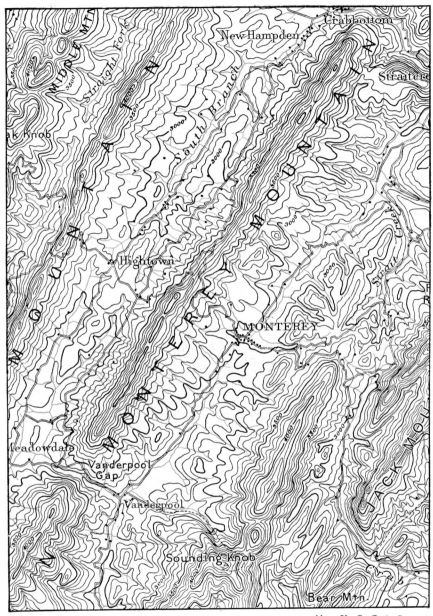

After U. S. Geol. Survey.

FIG. 364. — A section from the Monterey, Virginia-West Virginia topographic map. The long ridges with elevations of about 4,000 feet are remnants of the Schooley peneplain. Another large group of accordant hills at an elevation of about 3,000 feet represent another erosional surface. The trellis drainage is well adjusted to the structure of the region. Scale approximately ½ inch to the mile. Contour interval, 100 feet.

of an "inverted drainage system" established after baseleveling, as a new cycle of erosion was inaugurated by uplift. The etching by the streams has now gone so far that the long ridges and cuestas, such as are shown in Figure 364, are almost invariably composed of the more resistant folded rocks, while valleys are cut in the softer beds.

The control of erosion by resistant and non-resistant rocks is shown even in peneplanation. The Harrisburg peneplain on the Piedmont Plateau was cut largely on the softer rocks. Igneous rocks have played a comparatively small part in the development of the present topography. Locally, as in the case of the Palisades of the Hudson River valley, they give conspicuous features to the relief.

The Southern Rocky Mountain Province. — The history of these youthful mountains is much simpler than that of the Alps or Appalachians. The province lies largely in the State of Colorado with short extensions into Wyoming and New Mexico (Fig. 336). It includes 17 mountain ranges and groups, the latter being chiefly volcanic mountains. Between the mountains in Colorado there are six great intermontane valleys whose origin and history are linked with those of the surrounding highlands. The total area of the province, including the intermontane valleys, is approximately 50,000 square miles.

Fifty-one peaks in Colorado stand 14,000 or more feet above sea level. The elevation of Mount Elbert, the highest of all, is 14,424 feet. Three hundred other summits are more than 13,000 feet high. From the central highlands, streams flow out into all adjoining states. The continental divide, which winds irregularly from south to north through Colorado, has a length of nearly 500 miles. In many places this divide is very narrow and very high.

The mountains are composed of many different kinds of rocks, but the cores of all the principal ranges are granites or other Pre-Cambrian rocks, many of which are metamorphic. Flanking the ranges and in many places topping them are uptilted Paleozoic and Mesozoic sedimentary rocks of great thickness and great variety. Tertiary intrusions, batholiths, sills and thousands of dikes cut the older rocks. The whole western side of the mountain belt is dotted with remnants of lava flows and fragmental volcanics. A few such

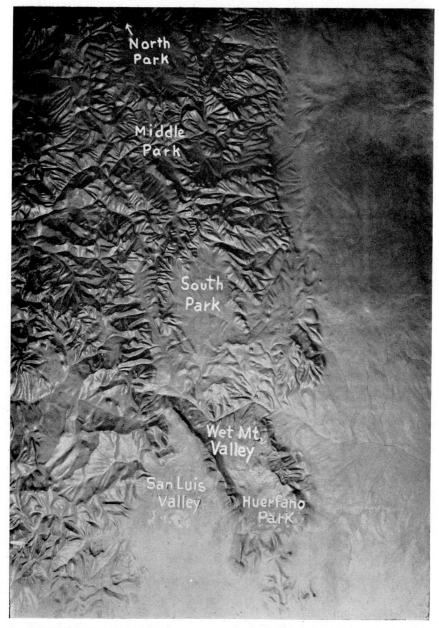

FIG. 365. — A relief model showing part of the Southern Rockies and the great inter-mountain valleys (some are locally called "parks") in Colorado.

remnants occur within the ranges and on the east side of the province. It is estimated that in late Miocene times at least 25,000 square miles of Colorado was covered by extrusive volcanics. While erosion has removed them from large areas, one still finds in the San Juan Mountains an area of some 6,000 square miles largely covered by these rocks.

The Late Jurassic Peneplain. — The history of present mountains really begins in late Jurassic times, when the whole region

Infra-red Photo.   R. L. Ives, courtesy Am. Phil. Soc.

Fig. 366. — Middle Park, Colorado, from the crest of the Front Range. The Park Range in the distance is more than 50 miles away.

seems to have been peneplaned. Streams wandered aimlessly over the region, swamps and shallow lakes were numerous. Doubtless many low monadnocks, remnants of the Paleozoic "Ancestral Rockies," stood above the peneplain surface. This condition seems to have continued on into the Cretaceous Period.

The Cretaceous Geosyncline. — Early in the Cretaceous Period the region near the Gulf of Mexico began to warp down letting ocean water come in over the land. By early Upper Cretaceous times, the downwarping of the continent had reached Colorado and

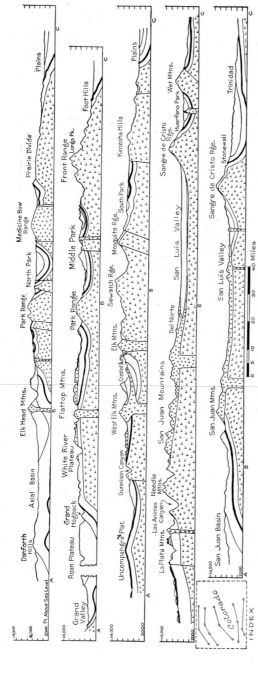

FIG. 367.— Mountain structures of Colorado. The index map shows the position of each cross section. The check pattern represents Pre-Cambrian rocks; the cross pattern shows Eocene or later intrusions and extrusions; the lined pattern represents sedimentary rocks. The heavy black line is the Dakota formation of Upper Cretaceous age. Faults are shown by solid black lines, most of which are vertical or nearly vertical in position.

the epi-continental sea had occupied the depression. Slightly later, much of western North America was covered by this sea, as is indicated in Figure 337. The borders of the sea shifted from time to time, but for at least 60 or 70 million years it stood over the site of the present mountains. As sediment was washed into the sea, largely from the west, subsidence of the floor continued. The total thickness of Upper Cretaceous sediments deposited in the geosyncline

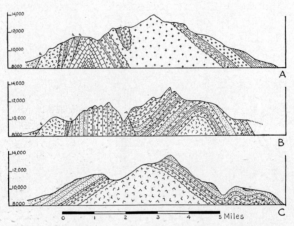

FIG. 368. — Cross-sections of the Sangre de Cristo Range, Colorado. Section A is near the north end; section B is near the town of Crestone; section C is near the New Mexico State line.

varied from less than 5,000 feet to more than 14,000 feet. The average for the region now occupied by the mountains was about 8,500 feet.

The Laramide Revolution. — Late in the Cretaceous Period the land began to rise. At first there seems to have been a general uplift of the continent which drained the sea back to the Arctic and Atlantic oceans. Soon orogenic movements began and by early Eocene times the mountains were outlined in ground plan much as they are today.

The growth, although slow in terms of years, was, geologically, relatively rapid, for erosion, even on the cracked and broken arches composed of sedimentary rocks, could not keep pace with the uplift. The height of the mountains after this first period of growth is not known. Some people have assumed that they were 15,000 to 20,000 feet in elevation, but, in the author's opinion, they were not as high as they are today.

Structures. — Usually these mountains are classified as *folded mountains,* but there also was *much faulting.* Some of the folds are broad open anticlines. The Front and Park ranges, each more than 100 miles long, consist of long arches (with many subordinate folds on their lower flanks). In the San Juan Mountains there was a broad, low domal uplift. In the Sangre de Cristo Range, a broad anticline occurs at the south end, but farther north tightly com-

Fig. 369. — The west side of the Sangre de Cristo Range, Colorado, showing close folding and faulting.

pressed folds and many great faults make up the whole highland structure. (Fig. 368 A and B).

The faulting is represented chiefly by low and high angle thrusts, the latter predominating. Faults occur both on the flanks of the mountains and in all possible positions within their borders. These great fractures paved the way for the deposits of gold, silver, tungsten, molybdenite and other minerals for which Colorado is famous.

Eocene Volcanism. — Tremendous volcanism accompanied the Laramide orogeny. Laccoliths, batholiths, stocks, sills, dikes and great lava flows are of widespread occurrence within and on the borders of the mountains.

Eocene Glaciation. — Atwood and Mather [1] have found evidence of rather extensive glaciation of Eocene age in the San Juan Mountains. Further evidence has been found a short distance north of these mountains, but none elsewhere in this province.

Eocene Erosion. — During the first period of mountain growth, erosion must have been very great. Thick beds of sedimentary rocks of Eocene age derived from the mountains are found in most

F. Fortson.

FIG. 370. — Pikes Peak, Colorado, elevation 14,107, an old dome-shaped mountain before it was glaciated. The rock is a very homogeneous coarse-grained granite.

of the intermontane valleys and on the plains and plateaus that border the mountain province. The Cretaceous sediments in some places were completely removed from the mountain tops. By late Eocene times the highlands were greatly eroded and there is considerable evidence of peneplanation. The surface so produced has been called the Flattop peneplain (Fig. 339). Whether there was only local or quite general baseleveling is an open question. Many

[1] W. W. Atwood and Kirtley Mather: *Physiography and Quaternary Geology of the San Juan Mountains, Colorado.* U. S. Geol. Survey, Prof. Paper 166, 1932.

flat-topped, plateau-like erosion surfaces now stand at elevations of 11,800 to 12,200 feet. Their wide distribution through the mountain region has led to the conception of general peneplanation, but the evidence is not conclusive. The arguments for and against this theory are too long to be discussed here. There is abundant evidence that erosion did not reduce all the highlands to baselevel, for between 300 and 400 mountains stand above the so-called peneplain remnants. They must have been monadnocks on that surface during Eocene times.

Oligocene and Miocene Uplifts. — Sometime during the Late Oligocene renewed uplift began. There was attending volcanic

Fig. 371. — A recent fault scarp on the west side, at the north end, of the Sangre de Cristo Range, Colorado. The truncated ridges and high hanging valleys with large alluvial fans at their mouths are good evidence of the fault. In addition the smooth-faceted ends of the ridges are beautifully slickensided.

activity, both intrusive and extrusive. This orogeny lasted until late in the Miocene. The uplift varied in amount in different parts of the province and is assumed to have reached a maximum of 4,000 feet, but the evidence is not entirely clear.

The Rocky Mountain Peneplain. — After the second uplift, there was another long period of stability when erosion again became dominant. Much of the mountain region was finally reduced to a peneplain which is called the Rocky Mountain or the South Park peneplain. It is of late Miocene and early Pliocene age. When formed its eastern edge must have coincided with the Great Plains at an elevation then of perhaps 6,000 feet above sea level.

Now broad plateau-like remnants of this erosional surface are found at elevations of 8,000 feet near the Wyoming State line, at 8,000-8,500 feet west of Boulder, at 9,500 feet west of Colorado Springs (Fig. 341), and at 10,000 feet in South Park. Remnants of the Eocene erosional surface and the higher mountains all stand above this peneplain. Also there are on it hundreds of low monadnocks, many cored by resistant dike rocks. The mountains that stand high above the Rocky Mountain peneplain are interesting. Their structure and composition vary greatly, but those that are

Fig. 372.—A bench 200 feet above the valley floor shows rejuvenation. The surface of the bench bevels steeply tilted sedimentary rocks of varying lithology. White River, Colorado.

made up of homogeneous granite evidently had been eroded to broad relatively subdued domes, "*old mountains*," before they were attacked by Pleistocene glaciers. Pikes Peak and James Peak in the Front Range are good examples. Other mountains composed of sedimentary or metamorphic rocks were less uniformly eroded, although in terms of years they must be of the same age.

The interpretation here given, that the Rocky Mountain peneplain is a single, much warped and faulted erosional surface, is not held by all physiographers. For example: Van Tuyl[1] and Lovering find evidence of six peneplains and three other less complete

[1] F. M. Van Tuyl and T. S. Lovering: *Physiographic Development of the Front Range.* Bull. Geol. Soc. Am., Vol. 46, pp. 1291–1350, 1935.

erosional surfaces—all formed during Oligocene, Miocene and Pliocene times below the Flattop, which they divide into two peneplains and consider to be Eocene in age. They do not recognize one definite Rocky Mountain or South Park peneplain.

E. G. Fine.

FIG. 373.—The Black Canyon of the Gunnison. Note the old well-eroded surface above it.

Late Pliocene and Pleistocene Uplifts.—Sometime late in the Pliocene, mountain growth became active again. This time the uplifts were fitful and variable. There was very little movement in the northern part of the province, but at least 3,500 feet of

FIG. 374. — Treasure Mountain, west-central Colorado. A fine example of a greatly eroded anticlinal dome. The thick beds on the right and left sides have been almost completely removed from the top of the dome. Glacial-polished granite is shown in the right middle ground.

J. W. Vandervelt, U. S. Geol. Survey.

uplift in the central and southern parts.[1] This estimate is based on the average height of the Rocky Mountain peneplain above the Great Plains, and assumes equal rate and amount of erosion of both the peneplain and the Great Plains since the uplifts began.

The movements continued intermittently through the Pleistocene with halts long enough to allow the rapidly cutting streams to reach temporary baselevel and to form valley flats, some a mile or more in width. Four distinct levels of benches and spurs on many of the present canyon walls now mark these old valley flats.

The Canyon-Cutting Cycle. — Canyon-cutting began with the late Pliocene uplift and has continued, except for the interruptions noted in the last paragraph, to the present time. Wherever the Rocky Mountain peneplain has been recognized, the canyons are below it. Magnificent examples of deep, steep-walled canyons separated by relatively broad, flattish divides are striking features of this province. They are best developed near the outer parts of the various ranges and are particularly marked in the Colorado Front Range.

[1] If, as some geologists believe, the Flattop and Rocky Mountain peneplains are really one erosional surface, the Flattop remnants being simply up-warped or up-faulted portions of the Rocky Mountain peneplain, the uplift was double this amount.

Glaciation. — Pleistocene glaciers left their unmistakable marks on the mountains. There were literally many thousands, although now less than a score remain. It is estimated that in Colorado alone a total area of 10,000 square miles of the mountains above 8,000 feet in elevation was covered by the ice sheets. The longest valley glaciers were in the San Juan Mountains, where one was 40 miles in length. Except in these mountains, none descended much below

E. G. Fine.

FIG. 375. — A glimpse of Estes Park and the Mummy Range, Colorado.

the 8,000 foot contour line. Cirques, Cyclopean stairs, hanging valleys, waterfalls, lakes and enormous lateral and terminal moraines abound throughout the mountains.

The Present. — Since the Pleistocene Epoch streams and wind have been the principal agents in changing the mountains. Within the highlands the topography is still youthful. It will be a long time before it becomes as subdued as that of old mountains such as the Appalachians.

Our Youthful Topography

The statements made in this chapter, which could be enlarged, if space permitted, to cover most of the earth's surface, are sufficient to indicate that much of the topography of the lands is very youthful—not only youthful in topographic development, but in actual years. The relatively recent uplifts of most of the mountains and plateaus, Tertiary or more recent volcanism, the widespread influences, both direct and indirect, of Pleistocene glaciation, and finally the ceaseless activities of streams, wind and waves—all have combined in comparatively recent times to develop most of the relief features that we see about us.

REFERENCES

1. W. W. Atwood and Kirtley Mather: *Physiography and Quaternary Geology of the San Juan Mountains, Colorado.* U. S. Geol. Survey, Prof. Paper 166, 1932.
2. George H. Ashley: *Studies in Appalachian Mountain Structure.* Bull. Geol. Soc. Am., Vol. 46, pp. 1395–1436, 1935.
3. E. B. Bailey: *Tectonic Essays Mainly Alpine.* Oxford Univ. Press, 1935.
4. Sir Charles Bell: *Tibet, Past and Present.* Oxford Univ. Press, 1924.
5. Eliot Blackwelder: *The Recognition of Fault Scarps.* Jour. Geol., Vol. 36, pp. 289–311, 1928.
6. R. T. Chamberlin: *Building of the Colorado Rockies.* Jour. Geol., Vol. 27, pp. 145–164 and 225–251, 1910.
7. L. W. Collet: *The Structure of the Alps.* Edward Arnold and Co. (London), 1927.
8. N. M. Fenneman: *Physiography of Western United States.* McGraw-Hill Book Co., 1931.
9. ———: *Physiography of Eastern United States.* McGraw-Hill Book Co., 1938.
10. James Geikie: *Mountains, Their Origin, Growth and Decay.* D. Van Nostrand Co., 1914.
11. G. K. Gilbert: *Studies in Basin Range Structure.* U. S. Geol. Surv., Prof. Paper 153, 1928.
12. Alb. Hiem: *Geologie der Schweiz.* Leipzig, 1922.
13. Wm. H. Hobbs: *Earth Features and Their Meaning.* The Macmillan Co., 1931.

14. George D. Louderback: *Basin Range Structure in the Great Basin.* Univ. Calif. Pub., Bull. Dept. Geol. Sciences, Vol. 14, pp. 329–376, 1923.
15. ———: *Morphological Features of the Basin Range Displacement in the Great Basin.* Univ. Calif. Pub., Bull. Dept. Geol. Sciences, Vol. 16, pp. 1–42, 1926.
16. F. M. Van Tuyl and T. S. Lovering: *Physiographic Development of the Front Range.* Bull. Geol. Soc. Am., Vol. 46, pp. 1291–1350, 1935.

INDEX

(Asterisks indicate illustrations)

African, faults, 113; lakes, 349; rift or ramp valleys, 348, 349
Agassiz, Alexander, 489
Agassiz, Lake, 317*
Age, of glacial topography, 328; of mountains, 514; of the earth, 9, 10
Agglomerate, 65*
Aggradation, 148
Alaskan glaciers, 268, 271*, 278, 279, 283, 284
Alden, W. C., 159
Algae, 383, 486
Algonquin, Lake, 365, 366*
Allison, I. S., 215
Alluvial fans, of arid regions, 240*-241, 247; of humid regions, 158, 169*, 170, 210, 211; profiles, 210*
Alps, 23*, 268, 527-529; structures of, 528*
Andes, 101
Aniakchak, crater, 468*
Animals, geomorphic work, 130
Antarctica, glaciation of, 264
Antevs, Ernst, 326, 327
Anticlinal, dome, 550*; valleys, 104, 536*
Anticline, 104, 105*
Anticlinorium, 106*
Appalachia, 530
Appalachian, 530; erosional cycles, 533-537; geosyncline, 530; mountains, 101, 529; peneplains, 535-537; revolution, 530; structures, 532*; system, 529
Arches, desert, 121*, 259*, 260; sea, 393*
Arid regions, 220; badlands of, 244; deflation in, 221; dunes of, 226; geomorphic cycle, 236-243; interior drainage, 237; land forms peculiar to, 243; mudflows, 234; streams, 220, 232-234; topography, 220-263; torrential storms, 237; weathering in, 220; wind work, 220-231
Arkose, 79, 80
Ash plains, 466

Assiniboine, Mount, 513*
Athabaska glacier, 283*
Atmosphere, 1; composition, 39; effects of on sun's heat, 40, 41; gases, 39, 41; movements, 39
Atolls, 485, 487, 491*
Avalanches, 431
Avawatz Mountains, 240*, 242*, 252

Badlands, 243, 244*, 245*
Baltic Sea, geosyncline, 103
Bajadas, 241, 242*, 247
Barchan, 230*
Barrett, Minnesota, topographic map, 339
Bars, barrier, 397*, 398, 404; bay, 401; connecting, 399*, 400*, 401; offshore, 397*, 398*, 404; migration of offshore, 407*
Basalt, 73, 77
Basaltic substratum, 475
Baselevel, 176, 178; local or temporary, 179
Basic rocks, rare, 76
Basin and Range Province, 498*, 520, 521*, 523*
Batholith, 63*, 66, 475, 532
Beaches, 373*, 375, 395; cusped, 396*; profile of equilibrium, 395; varieties, 375
Benton seas of North America, 499*
Bergschsund, 281
Biotite, 58
Black Canyon of the Gunnison, 549*
Black Hills, 525, 526*
Blackwelder, Eliot, 128, 235, 249, 254, 522
Bog, 368, 369
Bogoslof Islands, 482
Bolivia, Plateau of, 506
Bolson, 237, 238*, 240*; of Mapimi, 506
Bonneville, Lake, 99, 358
Boothbay, Maine, topographic map, 481*
Boulder dam, 158, 356*, 357
Bowls, 261*

Box canyons, 255
Braided streams, 170, 172*
Breccias, 64
Bretz, J. Harlen, 213, 434
Bridges, National Monument, 203; natural, 203*, 439-440*
British Columbia fiords, 296*, 386*
British Isles, 480
Brooks, C. E. P., 330
Bryce Canyon, 245*
Buttes, 218; lava-capped, 473*

Calcareous rocks, 82, 83
Calcite, 58
Caldera, 355, 469
Calhoun, F. H. H., 159
California, earthquakes, 95, 96; submarine canyons, 410*
Canyons, 181, 182*, 183*; box, 255; filling by dunes, 230*, 231; Grand, 147*, 182, 517*; of arid regions, 255, 256*; recession of walls, 427*; submarine, 408-414, 409*, 410*; Yellowstone, 183*, 184
Carbonaceous rocks, 79, 82
Carbonation, processes of, 121-123
Catastrophe, doctrine of, 7
Cavernous forms, of deserts, 222*, 261*
Caves, 435-439; Carlsbad, 438*, 439; Mammoth, 439; of deserts, 261; sea, 99, 373*; topography of cave regions, 439, 440*, 441*, 442*
Central City, Colorado topographic map, 294
Chain, mountain, 23; volcanic, 460
Chalk, 79, 82
Chamberlin, R. T., 532
Chamberlin, T. C., 17, 329
Champlain, marine stage, 322, 366*
Chemical exfoliation, 127
Chemical precipitates, of caves, 436-438; rocks, 79, 83
Chemical work of the atmosphere, 120; of ground-water, 434, 436*, 437*, 438*
Chesapeake Bay, an estuary, 99
Cirques, 274*, 287, 288*; tandem, 290, 294*
Clastic rocks, 79, 80
Clay, varved, 326, 327*
Clay rocks, 79, 81; in relation to landslides, 423, 431; in relation to mudflows, 234, 235
Cleavage of minerals, 56

Cliffs, sea, 391*; wave-cut, 392*, 393*, 394*
Climate, 43; causes of glacial, 329-333; changes of, 329; classifications, 44; Köppen's, 44-46*, 47; Thornwaite's, 48; Trewartha's, 48; controls, 43; effects on weathering, 132; elements, 43
Climatic zones of North America, 46*
Coal, 79, 83
Coast, 374*, 375*; emerged, 387, 404; line, 374; submergence of, 385
Coast Ranges of the United States, 101
Colorado, epeirogenic movements in, 98; intermontane valleys, 541*, 542*; mountain history, 540-551; mountain structures, 543*, 544*, 545*; National Monument, 117*; Plateau, 508-510; River, 158, 232; River, delta, 209-210
Columbia Plateau, 471-472*
Columnar jointing, 116*
Composite volcanic cones, 461*, 462*
Conglomerate, 79, 80; effect on topography, 108*
Connate water, 417
Continental Drift, hypothesis, 19, 20*, 482
Continental, (epeirogenic) movements, 97; glacial topography, 299-318, 362-367; glaciers, 265, 267*, 278; platforms, 13*, 15, 16, 21; origin of, 17; shelves, 13*, 16, 17, 498*, 500; slopes, 13*, 16
Continents, 16, 21; foundering of, 19; origin, 17-21
Contour, line, 30; interval, 32; maps, 30-32
Coral, 383, 485; atolls, 484, 487-491*; gardens, 485; polyps, 485; seas, 485
Coral reefs, 479, 484, 485*-492; barrier, 484, 487, 488*-491*; characteristics, 486; fringing, 484, 486, 489*, 490*; origin, 487-490*-493
Cordillera, 22
Corrasion, by streams, 166, 252-253; by wind, 221
Cotopaxi, 460
Crater Lake, Oregon, 352*, 353*; origin, 353*-355; relief model of, 354
Craters, 468*; adventive, 469; Aniakchak, 468*; double, 470*; nested, 469*; lakes in, 352
Creep, land, 432
Cretaceous seas, Upper, of North America, 89, 499*
Crete, movements of, 99

Crustal movements, 89
Crystal systems of minerals, 54
Cucamonga, California, topographic map, 211
Cuestas, 154*, 191, 192*
Culture, of topographic maps, 33
Currents, littoral, 379*, 398-402; rip, 379-380*; tidal, 381; topography produced by, 398-402
Cut-offs, 195*
Cycle of development, emerged shore-lines, 403-408; submerged shorelines, 402-403
Cycle of erosion, arid, 236-243; humid, 179-199; interrupted, humid, 199-206
Cyclopean stairs, 289, 292*

Daly, R. A., 320, 412, 470, 490
Dams, 158; list of great, 357
Darwin, Charles, 487
Davis, W. M., 179, 236, 252, 492
Day, length of, at different latitudes, 38
Dead Sea, 109, 177, 337, 349
Deccan, lava plateau, 472
Decken structure, 525, 528*
Deep focus earthquakes, 92
Deeps, ocean, 15
Deflation, 221, 222, 223, 239, 241
de Geer, Baron Gerard, 326
Deltas, 148*, 170, 208-210; Colorado, 209; Hwang-Ho, 209; Mississippi, 148*; passes on Mississippi, 207*; some great, 171*
Dendritic drainage, 155*
Dense rocks, classification of, 76-77
Deserts, 220; erosion in, by streams, 232-233; erosion in, by wind, 220-226; partial list of, 237; pavement, 261*, 262; streams of, 232, 237; topography peculiar to, 243
Devils Tower, Wyoming, 527*
Diagrams to show relief, 28, 29*
Diaphaneity of minerals, 56
Diastrophism, 5, 91, 100*; causes, 101; structures due to, 102; types of, 91
Diatomaceous earth, 79, 83
Dikes, 68*, 69*, 70
Diller, J. S., 353
Diorite, 73, 75
Dip, 102, 103*, 110*
Divides, headward, 176*, 177; lateral, 176, 178; permanent, 176*; shifting of stream, 177*; shifting of glacial, 289

Dolomite, 79, 83
Dolores River, an antecedent stream, 155*; entrenched meanders of, 202*
Domes, volcanic, 463
Drainage, changes, by glaciers, 159*, 160*; dendritic, 155*, 319*; interior, of deserts, 237, 238; trellis, 154*, 539*; through, of deserts, 220, 233
Drift, continental, 19, 20*, 482; glacial, 276*, 277, 323*; structure of, 308*; topography of, 292, 298, 306-313; shore, 400
Driftless area, 318, 319*, 320*
Drowned valleys, 99, 157, 158*
Drumlins, 311*, 312*; erosion of, by waves, 312*, 389*; map showing, 312*; origin, 311
Dunes, 226, 228*, 229*, 230*, 231*; formation, 227; migration, 229; size, 227
Dust, 81; bowl of U. S., 224-225; sources of, 224, 225; storms, 223*, 225; volcanic, 454, 458

Eads, J. B., 165
Earth, age, 9-10; area, 14; a unique planet, 36; changes take place slowly, 7; composition, 1; compression of, lateral, 102; contraction, 10, 101; crust of, 101; materials, 50-61, 62-88; map of earthquake and volcanic regions of, 94; movements, 36, 96; examples of great, 91; types of, 91; place of, in Solar System, 35-36; processes, 4; relief features of, 12-27; sciences, 1-3; stability of, 89; stresses in, 101, 102; structures, 89-91; theories of origin, 17-19; planetesimal, 17-18; liquid earth, 18-19; three essential parts of, 1
Earthflows, 431
Earthquakes, 91; destructiveness, 97; duration, 93; effects on topography, 96; epicenter, 95; focus of shock, 95; frequency, 92; intensity of shocks, 93; intermediate, 92; Italian, 93; Japanese, 93, 96; Plutonic, 92; San Francisco, 97; sea waves due to, 96; tectonic, 92; Tokio, 97; types, 92; volcanic, 92; waves of, 95; zones of, 93, 94*; Helena, 93; Italian, 93; man-made structures in, 97; San Francisco, 93
Echo Cliffs, 509*
Elements, 51; table of common, 52
El Misti, 462*; double crater of, 470*

England, raised beaches of, 99
Epeirogenic (Continental) movements, 91, 97; downward, 98, 99; upward, 98, 99
Eras, 10
Erosion, by streams, 163, 169; by wind, 221-225; cycle of, arid, 236; cycle of, humid, 179; of uptilted sedimentary rocks, 90*; rate, 168
Erosional features of arid regions, minor, 260-262
Eskers, 297*, 298, 313, 314*
Estes Park, 551*
Estuaries ("drowned valleys"), 99, 157, 386
Evaporation, causes of, 41
Everglades, 370
Exfoliation (spalling), 129*; chemical, 127, 233*

Fan, alluvial, 169*, 210, 211*, 247, 248*
Fan-topped pediments, 250
Fault, 91, 92, 107, 109*, 110*; descriptive terms, 110, 111; Bannock overthrust, 524; Helena, 109; Lewis overthrust, 524*; low angle thrust, examples, 112; mountains, 519; normal, 112; relation of, to folds, 108; reverse, 112; San Andreas, 96, 109, 520*; scarps, 110, 112, 113*; slickensides of, 111*, 112; step, 112, 113*; thrust, 112; topographic expression of, 112, 113*; trace, 110*, 111; types, 112; types of movement, 107-108
Fault-line scarps, 113, 114*, 522
Feldspars, 57; weathering of, 122
Felsites, 73, 76
Fenneman, N. M., 530, 536, 537
Fiords, 158, 291, 296*, 302*; shorelines of, 386*
First order relief features, 14
Fissure, flows, 456; eruptions, 471
Flint, 78*, 79, 84
Flint, R. F., 215
Flood-plain, 206; Mississippi, 194*, 195*
Floods, causes, 160; damage by, 161; of arid regions, 234; prevention, 161; topography due to, 162
Folded mountains, 525
Folding, topographic results of, 106*, 154*, 536*
Folds, 103-106*
Foliated rocks, 87
Foot wall, 110*, 111
Fossils, 78

Fracture of minerals, 56
Free, E. E., 345, 348
Freezing water, effect on weathering, 125*, 127*
Fringing reefs, 484, 489*
Fumaroles, 456

Gabbro, 73, 75, 76; weathering of, 123
Geanticline, 103
Geography, branches, defined, 3; scope, 3
Geologic, ages, 10; eras, periods, 10; time table, 10
Geology, branches, defined, 1, 2; relations to geomorphology, 4
Geomorphic cycle, arid regions, 236-243; humid regions, 179-199; shorelines, 402-408
Geomorphic processes, 4; external, 5; internal, 4
Geomorphology, defined, 3; relations to geology, 4; relations to physiography, 3; scope, 4
Geophysics, defined, scope, 2
Geosynclines, 103, 518, 527, 530, 542; Alps, 527; Appalachians, 518, 530; Cretaceous of North America, 542; Rocky Mountain, 519
Geyserite, 83, 452
Geysers, 445, 446*, 447*, 449*, 451*; basins, 446*; causes of eruption, 448-450; heat, 449; nature of eruptions, 446*-450*; New Zealand, 445, 447*, 451*; Norris basin, 446*; Old Faithful, 448, 449*; relations of, to volcanism, 456; storage chambers, 450*; topographic forms made by, 452; tubes, 450*; types of, 446; water supply of, 449; Yellowstone Park, 445, 446, 448*, 449*
Glacial, ages, 263, 322; cirques (see cirques); drift, 276*, 306, 323*; topography of, 306; effects on sea level, 320, 413, 490; loading of continents, 320, 321, 366; moraines (see moraines); topography, 264-328; age of, 328
Glaciation, centers of Pleistocene, in North America, 267*
Glaciers, 264-334; alpine (see valley); Athabaska, 283*; cascading, 266*; characteristics of, modern, 278-285; continental, 264, 265, 278; topography made by, 299-318, 362-367; crevasses,

269*, 280; dimensions, 279; distribution, 264; fluctuations, 279; growth, 268; ice caps, 265, 284; movement, 271-273; New Zealand, 290*; piedmont, 268, 283; stagnation of, 276; surface features, 280; through, 284, 285; types, 265-268; valley, 267, 268*, 269*, 283*, 290*; topography due to, 285-299; wastage, 273; work, 274-278

Glacio-fluvial deposits, 277, 298, 316*; topography of, 313, 314*, 315*, 316*

Gneiss, 86, 87

Gorge, 181; Royal, of the Arkansas, 185

Graben, 112*, 349

Grand Canyon, 147*, 182, 517*

Grand Coulee, 214, 215*

Granite, 72*, 73, 74; weathering of, 120*, 121, 122*

Great Lakes, history of, 362-368

Greenland, fiords, 157; glaciers, 264; Godhavn topographic map, 302*; origin, 482

Gregory, H. E., 260

Gros Ventre landslide, Wyoming, 430*, 431

Ground-water, 416; amount, 416; chemical work, 434-438*; depth of penetration, 417; effect on mass-movements of earth, 421, 422*; mechanical work, 421-434; movements, 418; relations to streams, 152*, 153; sources of, 416; table, 152*, 418, 419*; table, baselevel of arid regions, 243; topography due to, 416-453

Gulliver, F. G., 408

Gully, development of, 174-175

Gumbotil, 324

Gutenberg, B., 92

Gypsum, 79, 84

Hanging valleys, 187*, 287*, 547*

Harrisburg peneplain, 536

Hawaiian Islands, 482; type of eruption, 457; volcanic observatory, 455, 456; volcanoes, 22, 24, 464

Heat, of geysers, 449; of volcanoes, 474, 476

Himalayas, 101, 505

Hogbacks, 154*, 191, 192*

Hooks, 399, 401*

Hope Window, Arizona, 259*

Horst, 112*

Hot Springs, 443; deposits, 444; Iceland, 443; New Zealand, 443; terraces, 444*; Yellowstone, 444

Howe, Ernest, 424

Hudson Bay, geosyncline, 103

Humid regions, classification of, 220; deflation in, 221; dunes of, 229; mudflows of, 235; stream-made topography of, 147-219

Hummocks and kettles, 308*, 315

Humphreys, W. J., 39, 330

Huntington, Ellsworth, 332

Hwang-Ho, delta, 209; floods, 161

Hydration, 124

Hydrology, 2

Hydrosphere, 1, 41

Ice age, causes of, hypotheses, 329; carbon dioxide, 330; continental drift, 330; diastrophism, 331; solar radiation, variable, 332*; wandering poles, 330; volcanic dust, 331

Ice cap, defined, 265, 284

Ice push, 382*, 383

Igneous rocks, chemical composition, 77; classification, 63*, 72*, 73; extrusive, 64, 65*; families, 73; field classification, 76; intrusive, 63*, 64, 66; mineral composition, 73; mode of occurrence, 63*, 64; origin, 62; textures, 71, 72*

Inselberge, 241, 242*

Integrated drainage systems, 240*, 241

Interglacial ages, Pleistocene, 323

Interior basins (bolsons), 237*, 238*

Interior drainage, 237*

Intermediate earthquakes, 92

Intermittent streams, 152*, 153; of arid regions, 220; of deserts, 233-4, 239; relation of, to water table, 152*, 153

Introduction, 1

Intrusive rocks, types, 63*, 66*, 67*, 68*

Islands, 393, 479; Aleutian, 482; British, 480; classification, 479; continental, 479; diastrophic, 480; due to gradation, 483; due to uplifts, 480; Hawaiian, 482; Japanese, 482; life history, 492; origin, 479-484; pelagic, 479; volcanic, 482

Jaggar, T. A., 460, 465, 476, 482

Jetties, 165*

Johnson, D. W., 252, 373, 384, 389, 396, 408

Jointing, 115; causes of, 115; columnar, 116*; due to cooling lava, 116*; due to drying out of rocks, 116, 128*; due to earth movements, 115; due to release of pressure, 115*
Joint patterns, 114-116
Joints, 114; compression, 114; influence on topography, 116, 117*; shear, 114; tension, 114
Jupiter, 35

Kame, 314, 315*; ridges, 315; terraces, 315
Karst topography, 440*, 443
Kettles and hummocks, 292, 308*
Kilauea, lava, 65*, 466*
Knobs and kettles, 308* 309

Labrador ice center, 267*
Labradorite, 54*, 57, 58
Laccoliths, 63*, 66*
Lacustrine plains, 317*, 503
Lagoons, 397*, 405, 406*, 485, 491*
Lake, Algonquin, 365, 366*; Bonneville, 99, 358; Duluth, 365*; Lahontan, 358; Maumee, 363*; Mead, 356; silting of, 158; Nipissing, 367*, 368; Ponchartrain, 344; Whittlesey, 364*
Lake water, sources, 357
Lakes, defined, 335; descriptions of notable, 337; distribution, 336; fate, 359; life history, 359; origin of basins, 338, 357; ox-bow, 194*, 206, 208; playa, 238*, 239, 246*; salt, 358; shore forms and processes of, 372-415
Lakes and swamps, 335-371
Lancaster, topographic map, 319*
Landslides, 422*; causes, 423-425*; topography of, 425*
Lateral divides of streams, 176*, 178; removal of, 177*, 178
Lateral moraines, 282, 293, 297*
Lava, 64, 65*, 454*, 466*, 472*; "aa" type, 467; composition, 474; flows, characteristics of, 64; pahoehoe type, 466*, 467; plains, 466, 472; plateaus, 471; sources of, 475
Lawson, A. C., 251
Levees, natural, 162*
Leverett, Frank, 311, 362
Limestone, 79, 82, 83; decomposition of, 123*; caves, 435-439; influence on topography, 439-442*

Liquid earth theories of earth origin, 18
Lithosphere, defined, 1; materials of, 50-87; rocks of, 62-87; size and shape, 12
Load, of streams, 163*
Loess, 79, 81, 225-226, 324*; topography due to, 226
Loops, 402
Loveland, Colorado, topographic map, 31
Luster, of minerals, 56

Macelwane, J. B., 91
Madagascar, 480; origin, 480, 482
Mammoth Cave, Kentucky, 439; topographic map, 442
Mammoth Hot Springs, 444*
Man, destructive work of, 131
Mantle rock (regolith), 131; movements of, 131
Maps, 28; contour, 30; orientation of, 33; projections, 28; topographic, 30
Marble, 85*, 87
Mars, 36
Marsh, 368; tidal, 369
Mass-movement of the land, 421-434
Matterhorns, 287, 289*
Mauna Loa, 22, 457
Mayon volcano, 454*, 461*
Meanders, 194*, 195*, 207; entrenched, 202*, 204*; widening of, 428
Mechanical weathering, 120, 125; exfoliation, 127, 129*; freezing water, 126; organic agencies, 130, 131
Mercury, 35, 36
Mesas, 216*, 217; lava-capped, 216*, 473*
Metamorphic rocks, 84, 85*; classification of, 86, 87; erosion of, 86
Metamorphism, agents of, 85; contact, 85; regional, 86
Meteoric water, 416
Meteorology, defined, 2
Methods of showing relief, 27
Mexico, Plateau of, 109
Microcline, 58
Middle Park, Colorado, 542*
Milham, W. I., 150
Minerals, associations, 56; crystal systems, 54; defined, 53; distinctions between, 60; groups, 57; physical properties, 54; properties of, 53; table of rock-making, 58
Mississippi, delta, 148*, 209; passes, 207*; sediment carried by, 168

Missouri River, change in course of, 159; regulation of, 158
Models, relief, 27, 28*
Monocline, 103, 104*
Montana, Fort Peck dam, 7*, 158
Monterey, Virginia, topographic map, 539
Monzonite, 73, 76
Moraines, ground, 295, 309*, 310*; lateral, 282, 293, 297*; marginal, 307; structure, 308; topography of, 307-309; medial, 282, 295; recessional, 307; terminal, 282*, 292
Moulton, F. R., 17
Mount Everest, Frontispiece, 16; Mazama, 353*; McKinley, 496*; Rainier, 515*; Whitney, 514
Mountain, 21; chain, 23; cordillera, 22; group, 23; range, 22; system, 22
Mountain growth, periods of, 101
Mountain-making movements, 100
Mountains, age of, 514; Alps, 527-529; Appalachians, 529-540; defined, 22; classification, 22-24, 514-525; diastrophic, 518; fault, 519; folded, 525; history, 529-551; origin, 102, 514-529; plains and plateaus, 495-553; residual, 516; Southern Rockies, 540-551; volcanic, 456, 515
Mozambique channel, 482
Mudflows, 350*, 422; of arid regions, 234*, 235*, 236*; of humid regions, 235; Slumgullion, 350*; volcanic, 235, 467
Muscovite, 57, 58
Muskeg, 368, 369

Nappe structure, 525, 528*
Natural bridges, 203*, 440*
Necks, volcanic, 70*, 71
Neptune, 35
Nevada, Basin Ranges of, 109, 520-523
Névé, 270
New Zealand, geysers, 445, 447*, 451*; glaciers, 290*
Niagara Falls, recession of, 200*, 327
Nip, 404, 405*
Normal faults, 111*, 112
North America, climatic zones of, 46*; paleogeography, 89; Pleistocene glaciation, 267*
Northern Rocky Mountains, 523
Norway, coast of, 157
Novaculite, 79, 84
Nunatak, 289, 290*

Obsidian, 72*, 73, 75
Ocean, area of, 14; basins, 5*, 14-15; depth, 14; origin of, 17; currents, 379; deeps (troughs), 15; waves, 376-379
Ocean City, Delaware-Maryland topographic map, 397*
Offshore bars, 397*, 398*, 404; migration of, 407*
Old Faithful, 448, 449*
Oligoclase, 57, 58
Olivine, 57, 58
Orientation of maps, 33
Orthoclase, 53, 57, 58
Oswego, New York, topographic map, 312*
Outwash plains, 278, 315, 316*
Oxidation, 123

Pahoehoe lava, 65*, 466*
Painted Desert, badlands, 244*
Palatka, Florida, topographic map, 441*
Pan fan, 250*, 251
Paradox Lake, New York, topographic map, 301*
Pedalfers (soils), 145
Pedestals, 260*, 261; ice, 281
Pediments, 241, 248*, 254; dissection of, 258*; fan-topped, 250
Pedocals (soils), 145
Pedology, 135
Pegmatite, 73, 74
Pelée, Mount, dome of, 465*; eruption of, 458, 464; spine of, 465*
Peneplain, 193; Harrisburg, 536; resurrected, 197; Rocky Mountain, uplifted, 196*; Schooley, 196, 535-536; Somerville, 537; Tanganyika, 196; uplifted, 196*, 201*, 202, 502*
Periods, geologic, 10
Permanent streams, of deserts, 232; of humid regions, 152
Peru, Plateau of, 506
Philippine Islands, coral reefs, 487; volcanoes, 454*, 455*, 459, 461*
Physiography, definition of, and scope, 3-4; relations to geomorphology, 3
Physiographic provinces of the U. S., 498*
Pikes Peak, 546*
Pinnacles, 260*, 261
Plagioclase feldspars, 57, 58, 60
Plains, 495; classification of, 495; Coastal Plains Province, 498*, 500; Colorado

Piedmont Section, 498*, 500; defined, 25-26, 495; diastrophic, 497; flood, 206; glaciated, 305, 503; Great Plains Province, 497, 498*, 500; High, 501*; High Plains, Section, 498*, 500; life history of, 503; outwash, 278, 315, 316*; stripped, 198*

Planetesimal hypothesis, 17-18

Planetesimals, 18

Plateaus, 495; Bolivian, 506; border, 507, 508*; classification of, 504-512; Colorado, 508, 509*; Columbia, 213, 471-472; defined, 24; diastrophic, 505; domed, 510; erosional, 511; of Colorado Front Range, 507, 508*; intermontane, 505; lava, 471; life history of, 512; Mexican, 506; Ozark, 510; Piedmont, 507; Quebec, 504*; Tibetan, 505; volcanic, 511; Yampa, 510*

Playa lakes, 238*, 239

Playas, 239, 245, 246*

Pleistocene glacial ages, 323

Pleistocene glacial epoch, duration of, 325

Pleistocene ice, last retreat of, 325

Plugs, 70*, 466, 467

Plutonic earthquakes, 92

Potholes, 167*, 188

Precipitation, 41, 149; amount on land, 41; cycle of, 41; distribution of, 149-150; map of the world, 42*

Profile of equilibrium, beach, 395; stream, 179

Projections, of maps, 29

Pumice, 73, 75

Pyroxene, 58

Pyroxenite, 73, 76

Quarrying by glaciers, 290

Quartz, 58

Quartzites, 86, 87; effects of, on erosion, 182*

Quebec, Plateau of, glaciation of, 303, 304*, 504*

Radioactivity, of minerals, 9; age of earth indicated by, 10

Rainfall map of the world, 42

Ramp, basins, 348; lake basins, 349; valleys, 112*

Range, defined, 22

Rapids, 185

Raton Mesa, 216*, 473

Recessional moraines, 307

Regolith (mantle rock), 131; movements of, 131

Rejuvenation, 199, 548*; in arid regions, 255-259; in humid regions, 199; of streams, 199*; of topography, 199*, 201*, 202*, 205*

Relations of faults to folds, 108

Relic lakes, 347

Relief, methods of showing, 27-33; of the earth, 12; map of the United States, 13; models, photographs of, 27, 28*, 354*, 531*, 541*

Relief features, classification of, 13; first order, 14*-21; second order, 14*, 21-26; third order, 14, 26-27

Reverse fault, 112

Rhyolite, 73, 75

Rift basins, valleys, 348

Rim rocks, 473

Rip tides, 379, 380*

Robinson, C. W., 136

Roches Moutonnées, 291, 296*

Rock fans, 250, 254, 258*

Rock glaciers, 433

Rocks, classification of, 62; defined, 51; effects of wind on, 221; folded, influence of, on topography, 191; groups of, 51; homogeneous, influence of, on topography, 191; igneous, classification of, 63; mode of occurrence, 63*, 64; metamorphic, classification of, 86, 87; erosion of, 86; sedimentary, classification of, 77, 79

Rockslides, 428, 429*

Rocky Mountain peneplain, 508*, 547

Rocky Mountain trench, 349

Rocky Mountains, 89; Northern, 523-526*; Southern, 540-551; structures of, 543*, 544*, 545*

Runoff, 150; factors controlling, 150-151

Russell, I. C., 355, 384

St. Anthony falls, recession of, 328

St. Francis dam, failure of, 165

St. Lawrence River Valley (estuary) 99

Salinas, 246

Salisbury, R. D., 120

Salts, sedimentary rocks, 79, 84

Salt lakes, 358

Salton Sea, 345

San Andreas fault, 95, 96, 109, 520*

Sand, of deserts, 224
Sand blast, effects of, 221
Sandstone, 79, 80; weathering of, 121*, 122*
San Francisco, earthquake, 93, 97
Sangre de Cristo Range, Colorado, 544*, 545*, 547*
Scablands, 213, 214*
Scale, of maps, 30
Scarps, 112-113; fault-line, 113, 114*, 522
Schists, 85*, 87
Schooley peneplain, 535*
Schuchert, Charles, 9, 330
Scotland, raised beaches of, 99
Sea caves, 28, 99, 373*
Sea level, baselevel or stream erosion, 178; changes in, 98, 178; lowering due to glaciation, 320, 490
Seasons, 37
Sea waves due to earthquakes, 96
Second order relief features, 21
Sedimentary rocks, 77; classification of, 79; effects on topography, 108*, 133*, 154*
Seismograph, 93
Semi-arid regions, classification of, 220; mudflows of, 234-236; effects of wind in, 222-223; streams of, 232
Seracs, 281
Serpentine, 58
Serrated ridges, 288
Shale, 79, 81
Sharpe, C. F. Stewart, 423
Sheets, igneous intrusions, 67, 68*
Shepard, F. P., 17, 380, 412, 413
Shield domes, 465
Shore currents, 6, 17, 379, 398
Shore forms, 372-415; processes, 372, 375-384
Shoreline development, 390, 403; accidents in, 408; cycles of, 390-408
Shorelines, 373; classification of, 384; compound, 389; neutral, 389; of emergence, 387, 388, 403-408; of submergence, 385-387, 390-403
Shorelines, warped, 91; uplifted, 394*, 408; wave erosion of, 390, 407
Sierra Nevada, 520
Siliceous rocks, sedimentary, 79, 83
Sills, 67, 68*
Simpson, Sir George, 332
Sinks, 440*, 442*
Slates, 86, 87

Slickensides, 111*, 112
Slopewash, of deserts, 238; of humid regions, 151*
Slumps, 423, 427*
Smith, Warren D., 354
Snow fields, 270
Snow line, 270
Soil, 124, 134; classification of, 136; definitions of soil types, 143; geologic classification, 137; major groups of the United States, 141, 142*; modified Russian classification, 141-145; profile, 142
Soil-creep, 432; topographic effects of, 432
Solar system, 35
Soifatara, 457
Solifluction, 434
Solution, as a weathering process, 122*, 123*, 124*; by streams, 167
Southern Rockies, 540-553; glaciation, 546, 551; history, 540; peneplanation, 546, 547; structures, 543*, 545*; uplifts, 544, 547, 549; volcanism, 545, 547
Spalling, 129*
Spanish Peaks dikes, 68*, 69*
Spheroidal weathering, 127*
Spits, 398*, 399*, 400; recurved, 401*
Springs, 419; deposits of, 444*; hot, 443; mineral, 435; Silver Springs, Florida, 435; terraces of hot, 444*
Stacks, 393, 394*
Stagnant ice, 276
Stalactites, 437, 438*
Stalagmites, 437, 438*
Stocks, 67*
Stone Mountain, Georgia, 119*, 129
Strath, 537; terraces, 537
Stream capture, 157*
Stream meanders, 194*, 195*, 207; entrenched, 202*, 204*
Stream terraces, 203, 204*, 205*; alluvial, 212*
Streams, accidents to, 156; adjustments due to glaciers, 159*, 160*; adjustments of, 156; adjustments due to rock structures, 154*, 157*; anastomosing, 170, 172*; antecedent, 155; braided, 170, 172*, 173*; characteristics of, 151; consequent, 153; deposition by, 169*-173; drowned, 157, 158*; ephemeral, 153; erosion by, in deserts, 237-238; erosion by, in humid regions, 163; graded, 172; in deserts, 237; insequent, 155; inter-

mittent, 153; lateral divides of, 176, 178; removal of, 177*, 178; load, 163*; location and distribution of, 151; obsequent, 154; of arid regions, 232; of humid regions, 149-162; overloaded, 170, 173*; permanent, 152; ponded, 158; profile of equilibrium, 179; sources of, 149; subsequent, 154*; superimposed, 156*; transportation by, 164; transporting power of, 164

Strike, of fault planes, 110*; of folded rocks, 102*; valleys, 192*, 193*

Submarine canyons, 17, 408, 409*, 410*; origin of, 411-414

Subsequent valleys, 154*, 192*, 193

Subsidence, of land, 99

Sun, 35; dominates earth processes, 41

Surf, 377

Suspension of load in streams, 163

Sutherland, Robert A., 356

Swales, 368

Swamps, 335, 368; origin of, 369; topography of, 370

Taal, Philippine volcano, 455*, 469*

Talus, 125*, 126*; cones, 127*; creep, 433

Taylor, F. B., 362

Terminal moraines, 282*, 292, 316

Terraces, 203, 205*, 212

Textures of igneous rocks, 71, 72*

Third order relief features, 26

Thornwaite, C. Warren, 48

Thrust faults, 112

Tibet, Plateau of, 505

Tidal, bore, 382; currents, 381; erosion, 381; inlets, 401, 405, 406*; marshes, 369

Tide, 380-382; height, 381

Till, 277

Tilting of Great Lakes region, 366

Titicaca, Lake, 506

Tokio earthquake, 97

Tombolo, 399, 401

Topographic forms, due to fissure eruptions, 471

Topographic maps, 30; use of, 33

Topographic unconformity, 187, 360*, 391*, 404

Topography, due to glaciers, 264; due to ground-water, 416; due to shore processes, 372; due to streams, 147; Karst, 440*, 443; of arid regions, 220; mature, 239, 240*; old, 241; youthful, 239;

of humid regions, 147; mature, 190*; old, 192; youthful, 181, 183*, 189*; of semi-arid and desert regions, 220; our youthful, 552

Torrential storms of arid regions, 237

Transportation, by currents, 399-401; by glaciers, 276; by streams, 164; by tides, 381; by waves, 394, 395; by wind, 224

Travertine, 79, 83

Treasure Mountain, Colorado, structure and erosion of, 550*

Trewartha, Glenn T., 48

Tuff, 81

Uinta Basin, 347

Undertow, 378

Valley filling in arid regions, 239, 240*

Valley trains, 277, 299

Valleys, development of, 174; drowned, 157, 158*; glaciated, 285, 286*; hanging, 187*, 287*, 547*; intermontane, 540, 541*, 546; limits of, 175, 176*, 177, 178; mature, 179, 190*; old, 179, 193; profiles of, 175*, 179*; subsequent, 193; youthful, 181, 185

Varved clay, 326, 327*

Vegetation, effects on wind erosion, 221

Velocity, of streams, 164, 165

Venus, 36

Vesuvius, 457*

Volcanic, chains, 474; cones, 461*, 462*; cinder, 463*; composite, 461*; spatter, 463, 464*; craters, 468*-470*; domes, 463, 465*; endogenous, 464, 465*; exogenous or shield, 464-466*; dust hypothesis of glaciation, 331; earthquakes, 92; ejecta, dust, etc., 454; eruptions, 454-455; mountains, 459-466, 515; necks, plugs, 70*, 466*; plateaus, 511; spines, 465*

Volcanism, 454, 456; causes, 474; depressed forms due to, 468; elevated forms due to, 461; mudflows due to, 467; origin of gases, 476; sources of heat, 475; types, 456

Volcanoes, central type, definition, 456; classification of, 457; distribution, 94*, 459; number of active, 459

Volcanoes, types of eruption, 454-458; Hawaiian, 457; Peléean, 458; Strombolian, 458; Vulcanian, 458

Waterfalls, 185; causes of, 185*-187; recession, 327; table of great, 189
Water table, 152*, 418, 419*; baselevel of wind erosion, 243
Waters, A. C., 343
Wave action, depth of, 378
Wave-base, 407
Wave-cut cliffs, 392*, 393*; plains, 99, 392; terraces, 392
Wave deposits, 394; topography of, 394-398
Waves, causes of, 376; earthquake, 95; erosion by, 390, 391*; forms, 376-378; height, 377; length, 378; of oscillation, 376; of translation, 378; tidal, 380, 381
Weathering, 119; chemical, 120-124; effects of climate on, 132; mechanical, 125-131; relations of ground-water to, 120; results of, 131; spheroidal, 127*
Wedging by salt crystals, 128*, 129

Wegener, Alfred, 20
Wells, 420
Willis, Bailey, 349, 480
Wind, 39, 43; corrasion, 221; deflation by, 221; deposition, 226-231; gaps, 157, 537*; of arid regions, 236-237; transportation by, 224; work of, 43, 220
Wind Cave National Park, 437*, 439
Windows, desert, 121*, 259*, 260

Yampa Plateau, 510*
Yellowstone, canyon, 183*, 184; falls, 183
Yellowstone National Park, geysers, 445; hot springs, 443
Yosemite Falls, 187*
Youthful streams, 180, 181
Youthful topography, of arid regions, 239; of humid regions, 181; our, 552
Youthful valleys, 180, 185